NEW NATURALIST LIBF

Limpback Reprints

FINCHES

A model of scientific writing for the general reader, this definitive work on the subject describes the ecology of the whole family of European finches. The 18 finches form a fascinating group and include some of Britain's most familiar birds. The Chaffinch is the most common British species, having adapted its mode of life to man-made habitats; the handsome Bullfinch is a pest of orchards and the Greenfinch, Linnet and Goldfinch are common birds of the countryside. Other species range from the upland Twite and the Crossbills of coniferous forests to rare vagrants such as the Scarlet Rosefinch, Arctic Redpoll and Serin.

The author, Dr Ian Newton, for many years with the Nature Conservancy at Edinburgh, has studied finches in the field over a long period and knows all these species both as scientist and birdwatcher. In his balanced, lucid and absorbing text he discusses all aspects of their lives – their status and history, their distribution and varied habitats, their populations, breeding, feeding, flocking, roosting and nesting.

This edition contains unaltered the text and line illustrations of the original publication, and includes a short re-introduction by the author, but the process of manufacture used to achieve an economic price does not, unfortunately, do full justice to all the photographs; and those originally in colour appear in black and white.

Limpback edition 1985
ISBN 0 00 219089 3

New introduction © Ian Newton 1985
Printed and bound by Biddles Ltd, Guildford and King's Lynn

COLLINS
GRAFTON STREET LONDON

Preface to the Limpback Edition

The issuing of this edition has only been possible by keeping the text unchanged but even a completely revised edition would require little amendment. So far as I am aware, none of the ideas mentioned in the first printing in 1972 have been substantially altered by new research, however, on some aspects more information has become available.

The Bullfinch, in particular, has been further studied, as a result of continuing damage in fruit orchards. The extent of bud loss on different pear varieties is now known to be linked to the concentration in the buds of various distasteful toxins (polyphenols). 'Comice' pear, which is normally avoided by Bullfinches, has more polyphenol in its buds than does 'Conference' pear, which is favoured. Similarly, the seeds of ash, which form the major food of Bullfinches, contain another toxin, called fraxinin. The concentration varies between individual trees, and explains why Bullfinches feed selectively, accepting seeds from certain trees, but avoiding the majority. For at least 12 years, ash in south-east England fruited every second year, producing in the 'off' years a biennial pattern in orchard damage. In the 1970s, this biennial pattern was broken, both in the ash crop and in the bud damage. The toxins found in pear and ash provide examples of the chemical defence mechanisms of plants; they are being studied in the hope that they will lead to better means of protecting fruit trees against Bullfinches.

No other finch species in recent years has been subject to such detailed research, but some species have greatly changed their status in Britain since 1972. The Siskin and Crossbill have continued to spread, as more of the new conifer plantations have matured, and both species now have a wide distribution within the country. No major irruptions of Common Crossbills from the continent have occurred since 1963, but a small invasion of Parrot Crossbills in 1982 was followed by the first breeding record of this species in Britain, in Norfolk in 1984. The continuing westward expansion of the Scarlet Rosefinch in northern Europe has led to increasing sightings in Britain, and in 1982 to the first nest, in the Scottish Highlands. On the other hand, the expected spread of the Serin in southern Britain has been slow to get underway, though nests have now been found in at least three counties (Devon, Dorset and Sussex), and sightings continue to increase. Only one species has declined markedly in recent years, namely the Linnet, which depends heavily on seeds of farmland weeds. Its decline is almost certainly due to the growing use of herbicides, which have now greatly depleted the dicotyledonous weed population, and also the bank of weed seeds in the soil on which birds feed in winter.

Such changes in status are perhaps only to be expected in species which are so heavily dependent on habitats and food sources created and continually changed by man. They have presumably been occurring for hundreds of years, long before anyone was interested in recording them.

The finches are delightful birds to study, and I hope that this reprint will stimulate further work on them. It is a pity that high production costs have meant that the original colour plates could only be reproduced in black-and-white. However, the finches have now been so often illustrated in other bird books that the reader should have no difficulty in finding coloured pictures of them.

I. Newton, 1984

Colour plates of Finches by the same artist appear in *The Birds of Britain and Europe* by Herman Heinzel, Richard Fitter and John Parslow (Collins).

THE NEW NATURALIST

FINCHES

I. NEWTON

COLLINS
ST JAMES'S PLACE LONDON

The aim of this series is to interest the general reader
in the wild life of Britain by recapturing the inquiring
spirit of the old naturalists. The editors believe that the
natural pride of the British public in the native fauna
and flora, to which must be added concern for their
conservation, is best fostered by maintaining a high
standard of accuracy combined with clarity of exposition
presenting the results of modern scientific research.

First published 1972
Reprinted 1975
Reprinted 1978
© Ian Newton, 1972

William Collins Sons & Co Ltd
London · Glasgow · Sydney · Auckland
Toronto · Johannesburg

CONTENTS

COLOUR PLATES*

*As explained on the first page, these plates are here reproduced in black and white.

BLACK AND WHITE PLATES

TEXT FIGURES

TABLES

APPENDICES

EDITORS' PREFACE

Several of the New Naturalist special monograph volumes have dealt very successfully with single species of birds, including the ubiquitous House Sparrow and the Wood Pigeon, as well as the more uncommon Redstart, Yellow Wagtail and Hawfinch. We have now, for the first time, been able to produce, in the main New Naturalist series, a volume dealing with a whole group of birds. The eighteen European finches described here include some of the most familiar British birds. Thus the Chaffinch is one of the very commonest, having adapted its mode of life to man-made habitats so that it is well known to every suburban gardener. The Bullfinch is detested as a pest by the fruit farmer, though its handsome appearance endears it to others. The Greenfinch, the Linnet and the Goldfinch are familiar even to the relatively unobservant countryman. Other birds included here range from the Hawfinch, not uncommon locally but seldom seen in many areas, to occasional migrants such as the Scarlet Rosefinch which most of us never expect to be lucky enough to see at all.

Dr Ian Newton shows himself to be the ideal author to pioneer this new development. He combines the rigorous standards of the professional scientist with the fresh approach of the dedicated field observer. He knows all the birds described from personal experience. However, no one scientist could cover the whole of such a wide subject completely, and Dr Newton is sufficiently familiar with the work of others and with the international literature to be able to deal with his vast subject in a critical manner. He has himself contributed substantially to the literature on finches, with many important scientific papers on the Bullfinch and other species. His own work includes both intensive field studies and laboratory experiments to illuminate observations made under natural conditions.

The thing which readers will find most exciting in this book is the way Dr Newton so frequently draws on his own observations to illuminate his text. This he does in such a modest tone that we do not immediately realise what enormous efforts have been expended to produce the relevant information. Thus we are told that, when studying the Linnet, repeated visits were paid to 62 different broods, and full records were made on each occasion. How many of us in a life time of observation have even found anything like 62 Linnet nests, without having made any serious observations on any substantial number of them?

The finches are shown by Dr Newton to be a fascinating group of birds. The whole of their ecology is described, not by a boring catalogue of facts, but in such a way that their reactions to different factors in the environment are discussed, giving a dynamic picture of their relationships to the whole countryside. Obviously full explanations of the successes and failures of all the species cannot be given, but the comparisons between these closely-related birds does begin to show us the way in which we may ultimately understand these processes.

It is impossible today to include the wide range of coloured photographs used in some of the earlier New Naturalist volumes. However, we still endeavour to include illustrations of a high standard. Here, instead of having any colour photographs, we have produced four pages of the superb paintings by Hermann Heinzel, showing all the distinct plumages of the birds considered in the text. These, we believe, are not only of real artistic merit, but also give more accurate representations than could be obtained by any other method.

We believe that Ian Newton's 'Finches' will be warmly welcomed by all those interested in our countryside. Ornithologists and birdwatchers will learn much that is fresh about their particular specialities, and others will increase their general understanding of the interdependence of all forms of wildlife on the changing environment.

AUTHOR'S PREFACE

THIS book is intended for anyone who wants to know more about the European finches, but who has neither the time nor inclination to search through scientific periodicals. Technical terms are kept to a minimum. The first three chapters are mainly factual, and set out to summarise the main characteristics, habits and distribution of the individual species. The remaining fourteen chapters discuss particular aspects of finch-biology, such as feeding, moult or migration, on a comparative basis for the group as a whole. These chapters are unashamedly biased towards those problems which have caught my own interest. Thus, eight are based almost entirely on my own research, while others aim to draw together both personal observations and a scattered literature, and in this sense the resulting syntheses are new. One result of this form of presentation is that the information on each species is scattered through the book, though the index, I hope, will take care of this.

To compile the book, I have searched the literature to 1970 (but had to be highly selective), and the ringing recoveries from 1955 to 1966, or in some species to 1969. Also, to illustrate certain points, I have not hesitated to refer to related finches in other parts of the world, if these species have been studied in more detail than the European ones. For the latter, the nomenclature follows Vaurie (1959).

My own research was carried out mainly during six years at the Edward Grey Institute, in Oxford, and I owe a great debt to the director, Dr David Lack, for stimulation and advice, and for kindly and helpful criticism of parts of the book in draft. While in Oxford, most of my field-work was carried out on Wytham Estate, and I am grateful to the University for permission to work there. I would also like to thank Drs R. S. Bailey, P. R. Evans, D. Jenkins, A. D. Middleton, D. Nethersole-Thompson, C. M. Perrins and P. Ward for helpful comments on the early drafts of particular chapters; Miss J. Coldrey and Dr J. Pinowski for bibliographical help; J. Cudworth, A. Frudd, C. J. Mead, H. Ostroznik, R. S. Scott, and J. G. Young for allowing me to use their unpublished data or for help in other ways; and the British Trust for Ornithology for allowing me to consult their ringing data. Finally, I would like to thank Hermann Heinzel and Robert Gillmor for their delightful illustrations. The former is responsible for the colour plates and figures 3, 8 and 17; and the latter for the pleasing and accurate representations of various displays and postures. Figure 46 was taken from Guy Mountfort's (1956) book on the Hawfinch, and was drawn by Keith Shackleton.

I. NEWTON

INTRODUCTION

To most people, the word 'finch' implies a small, seed-eating bird with a stout bill. But in one part of the world or another, the same word has been applied to at least eleven different groups of birds of varying degrees of affinity, namely the sub-families Fringillinae (chaffinches and allies), Carduelinae (goldfinches and allies), Emberizinae (buntings), Tanagrinae (tanagers), Geospizinae (Galápagos finches), Pyrrhuloxinae (cardinal-grosbeaks), Bubalornithinae (buffalo-weavers), Estrildinae (weaver-finches), Viduinae (whydahs), Ploceinae (weavers), and Passerinae (sparrows). All these birds have the same specialisations for dealing with hard seeds: heavy, conical bills, strong skulls, large jaw muscles and power-ful gizzards. Yet they differ so much in the other details of their anatomy and their behaviour, that they are without doubt derived from several ancestral stocks. They provide an example of convergent evolution – of unrelated animals growing to look like one another because they have the same way of life.

In this book, I shall be concerned with only two of these sub-families, the Fringillinae and the Carduelinae, which most authorities now group to form a single family, the Fringillidae. From now on, I shall use the word 'finch' only for the members of this family. They are distinguished from the various other seed-eating birds by certain details of skull-struc-ture, the presence of nine (instead of ten) large primary feathers in each wing, twelve large tail feathers, and the fact that the hen is responsible for building the cup-shaped nest and for incubating the eggs. Some of these features are shared with other groups, and it is the combination of charac-ters that distinguishes the Fringillidae. Thus defined, the family contains a variety of species, ranging between 10 and 100 grams in weight, some of them richly coloured, and, within the limits imposed by a seed-diet, showing great variation in the shape of their beaks, according to the types of seeds they eat.

The sub-family Fringillinae contains only three species, the Chaffinch and Brambling of Eurasia, and the Blue Chaffinch of the Canary Islands. The Carduelinae is represented naturally in North and South America, Eurasia and Africa (except Madagascar), and by introductions in Austra-lasia. It contains around 122 species, of which sixteen are found in Europe.

The following then, are the subjects of this book:

SUB-FAMILY *Fringillinae*

Fringilla coelebs   Chaffinch
Fringilla montifringilla   Brambling

SUB-FAMILY *Carduelinae*

Coccothraustes coccothraustes   Hawfinch

Carduelis chloris   Greenfinch
Carduelis carduelis   Goldfinch
Carduelis spinus   Siskin

Acanthis cannabina   Linnet
Acanthis flavirostris   Twite
Acanthis flammea   Common Redpoll
Acanthis hornemanni   Arctic Redpoll

Serinus serinus   Serin
Serinus citrinella   Citril Finch

Loxia curvirostra   Common Crossbill
Loxia pytyopsittacus   Parrot Crossbill
Loxia leucoptera   Two-barred Crossbill

Carpodacus erythrinus   Scarlet Rosefinch

Pinicola enucleator   Pine Grosbeak

Pyrrhula pyrrhula   Bullfinch

CHAPTER I

THE CHAFFINCH AND BRAMBLING

THESE two species, with the Blue Chaffinch (*Fringilla teydea*) of the Canary Islands, comprise the sub-family Fringillinae. All three are of similar shape, about six inches (15 cm.) long, with fairly long tails, peaked peads, and prominent shoulder patches and wing-markings. At first glance they show no striking specialisations; they are well proportioned, live in many woody habitats, take a varied diet, and move as well in trees as on the ground. They represent a sort of prototype for other seed-eaters, a link between the insectivorous song-birds and the specialised cardueline finches discussed in the next chapter. From them, the whole finch-family derives its name.

The cock Chaffinch (*F. coelebs*) in winter has a reddish-buff head and nape, passing to buff-chestnut on the back, and thence to olive-green on the rump, and blue-grey on the upper tail-coverts. The cheeks, throat and breast are pinkish-red, merging to creamy-white on the belly. Towards the breeding season, however, as a result of abrasion, the crown and nape become slate-blue and the back a clearer chestnut. The buff tip of each feather is weaker than the rest, and wears down to expose the colour below throughout the year, but mainly after moult, in October/November, and again before breeding in April/May; both are periods of intense activity in Chaffinches. The crown feathers, for example, lose 7% of their length per month at these two times, compared with 1% per month during the rest of the year (Sokolowski 1969). In spring, under hormonal action, the bill also turns from bone-white to blue to match the head; and in these ways the cock dons a special breeding dress without the need to moult. His wings are mainly brownish-black, with white marks, and green leading edges on the flight feathers. Among the tail feathers, the central pair are grey, and the rest mainly black, fringed with green, and with much white on the outer pair, which shows as the bird takes wing.

The hen is slightly smaller than the cock, with silkier feathers, but is less strikingly coloured. Throughout the year, her head and back are light yellow-brown, shading to yellow-green on the rump, and to paler yellow-grey on the breast, and white on the belly. Her wings are browner than those of the cock, but with similar white marks. The juveniles in their first few weeks resemble the hen, except that their plumage is greyer and coarser. Even in the nest the young cocks can be told from the hens by their darker wings. The most conspicuous features of both sex and age groups, however, are the large white shoulder patches and the familiar 'chink' call.

The Chaffinch extends northwards in Europe almost to the limit of the trees, southwards to North Africa and Iran, eastwards into Siberia, and also onto the Canaries, Azores, Madeira and the Cape Verde Islands (Fig. 1). From the northeast of this range nearly all the birds migrate for the winter, and augment those in the southwest, which are resident. The species has also been introduced to South Africa, where it is confined to the vicinity of Cape Town, and to New Zealand, where it now breeds over almost the whole country.

In summer, the territorial behaviour and conspicuous song make Chaffinches easy to count reliably, and in nearly every well-grown wood examined in Europe, they have been found to be by far the most numerous birds, usually comprising between one-fifth and two-fifths of the total bird population. They breed most densely in deciduous woods, less numerously in spruce woods, and still less so in pine, as might be expected if they settled according to the abundance of the insects which form their main food in summer. In each of these woodland types, however, the birds vary greatly in numbers according to the openness of the wood, the amount of undergrowth, the kinds of subsidiary trees present, and whether the wood is on rich or on poor soil. Thus, in Fenno-Scandia, where most studies have been made, Chaffinches have been found in various deciduous woods at 49–145 pairs per square kilometre, in spruce woods at 20–102 pairs, and in pine at 12–29 pairs (Palmgren 1930, Merikallio 1946, Haapanen 1966).

In favoured habitats, moreover, the number of breeding pairs may remain fairly stable from year to year, but in the less good ones the number may fluctuate greatly, as shown by a study in Holland (Glas 1960). Over ten years, the population of a mixed deciduous wood varied only between 66 and 87 pairs per square kilometre (by a factor of 1.3), but in a nearby pine wood, it varied between 12 and 36 pairs (by a factor of 3). Each year the birds occupied the mixed wood first, and the yearlings tended to settle in the pine wood only after being expelled from the mixed. Thus, while the latter was occupied to nearly the same density every year, the pine wood mainly absorbed the overspill, which varied from year to year. But the adults from both woods probably returned to where they had previously bred, so that in no year was the pine wood devoid of birds. During a similar study in Finland, pine woods were more often filled to capacity than were spruce (Haapanen 1966). This was because in spring the snow went from the pine areas first, so that these were occupied before the thicker spruce areas, which then took up the surplus, often to greater density than the pine.

Dividing a given area by the number of pairs present provides an estimate of the mean size of the individual territories. The estimate is maximal, however, because it is hard to be sure that all the ground was occupied. But at the highest densities recorded, the average territory-size of each pair in northern Europe could not have exceeded 6,800 square metres (1.7 acres) in deciduous woods, 10,000 square metres (2.5 acres) in spruce, and 34,500 square metres (8.5 acres) in pine. The equivalent

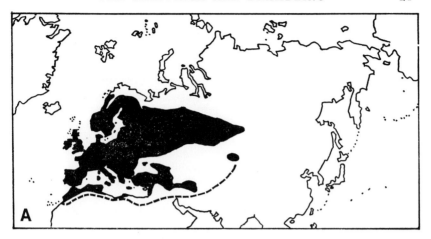

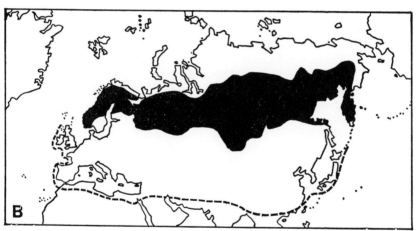

FIG I. The breeding ranges of (A) the Chaffinch and (B) Brambling. The broken line marks the southern edge of the wintering ranges, so far as is known.

figures for Holland were 11,500 square metres (2.9 acres) in the mixed wood and 28,000 square metres (6.9 acres) in the pine. For comparison, the individual territories in various woods near Cambridge, England, as found by watching the movements of 17 pairs, varied between 1,000 and 12,000 square metres (0.25 and 3.0 acres), according to habitat, with a mean of 7,000 (Marler 1956a). Hence, the amount of ground held varies greatly between different Chaffinch pairs, and the small territories in certain deciduous woods owe their smallness partly to the extreme competition there.

Outside woodland, the number of breeding Chaffinches depends mainly on the number of large trees, which provide food and song-posts. In well-timbered parks and gardens, in my experience, the birds may be almost as abundant as in the best woodlands, while in hedgerows they may range from three pairs per kilometre length, where trees are numerous, to none, where trees are lacking. Usually the individual territories are centred where three or four hedges join, or where a hedge adjoins a copse. The Common Bird Census of the British Trust for Ornithology has shown that, on farmland, the Chaffinch typically forms about one-twelfth of the total bird population, is equalled in abundance by the Dunnock (*Prunella modularis*) and excelled only by the Blackbird (*Turdus merula*). In low scrub, with few trees, the Chaffinch is outnumbered by these and other species.

The Chaffinch now breeds in all parts of Britain, except Shetland and the Outer Hebrides. Recent estimates put the area of deciduous woodland in the country at about 8,850 square kilometres, and of coniferous at about 8,500. Now if Chaffinches breed here in the same numbers as on the continent (with 49–145 pairs/sq.km. of deciduous wood and 12–102 of coniferous), then between half a million and two million pairs could nest in Britain in woods alone. Less than one-tenth of Britain is wooded, however, and still too little is known of the Chaffinches in other places to estimate the country's total population. Also the available habitat may no longer be filled to capacity, for many birds have died in recent years from farm chemicals.

It is not only its wide range of habitats that makes the Chaffinch one of the commonest birds in Europe, but also its varied diet. Seeds provide nearly all the food outside the breeding season and, in one region or another, more than 100 species have been recorded as taken. In the few years when the beech (*Fagus silvatica*) crop is good in Britain, Chaffinches feed mainly on the fallen mast, but in other years they forage mainly on open ground, especially farmland. Their feeding is thus greatly influenced by agricultural procedure and, largely for this reason, has been well studied, the earlier work being aimed to assess the species' 'economic importance' (Newstead 1908, Florence 1912–15, Collinge 1924–27, Newton 1967b). The birds evidently eat cereal grains for up to two-thirds of each year, and get them from fields of freshly-sown or ripening corn, from stubbles and from around stacks; they take only the spilled grain from the ground, and neither remove it from seed-heads nor dig it up. The bulk of the food, however, consists of the small seeds of some common weeds, mainly various brassicas (*Sinapis, Brassica*), goosefoots (*Chenopodium*), persicaria (*Polygonum*), and chickweeds (*Stellaria, Cerastium*). These seeds are obtained partly from beneath the plants, but mainly from the surface of freshly-tilled soil. This last supply depends on the fact that many seeds of weeds do not germinate at the first opportunity, but remain viable for years and form a vast reserve in the topsoil, estimated at hundreds of millions of seeds per acre. It is these that attract Chaffinches and other seed-eaters to any newly-turned soil.

In these days the Chaffinch is of course highly vulnerable from agricultural chemicals, and it is probably through eating grain dressed with highly toxic organo-chlorine compounds that the species declined nearly everywhere in Britain around 1960, and especially in heavily farmed areas. The extent of the decline is hard to judge, but the number of nestlings ringed in Britain fell from about 1000 per year around 1950 to 300 around 1964. This coincided with the widespread use of such chemicals, which were also recovered from Chaffinches found dead. In time Chaffinches might also be expected to suffer from the continued use of herbicides, which must have slowed the replenishment of weed-seeds in the soil. Such chemicals have already narrowed the birds' diet in areas where spurrey (*Spergula arvensis*) and other cornfield weeds have been eliminated, for the seeds of these plants were formerly eaten widely.

In the breeding season, the Chaffinch turns from seed-eater to insectivore. It rears its young entirely on animal-matter, mainly caterpillars and other insects from leaves, but also small flies and moths caught on the wing, and other small animals picked off the ground. This last category includes beetles and beetle-larvae, earwigs, spiders and the cocoons of earthworms, all of which are eaten in only small quantities at other times of year.

The breeding habits are discussed in detail later (p. 135–50), so only a few points will be made here. In southern Britain the eggs are laid between late April and mid-June, but chiefly in early May. In consequence, most young are in the nest in the latter half of May and early June, when the small caterpillars on which they are mainly fed, are plentiful. If the eggs or young are lost, one or more repeat clutches may be laid. A few pairs attempt to raise two broods anyway, in which case the second nest is usually started a few days after the young have left the first and, when the hen begins to sit again, the cock alone feeds the first brood (Barrett 1947).

The eggs of the Chaffinch are dark greenish-blue, with purple-brown streaks and spots that have a rim of paler pigment. In Britain the eggs usually number 4–5, sometimes 3 and rarely 6. The mean clutch-size, as determined by the nest-records of the British Trust for Ornithology, remains at around 4 till the end of May, then rapidly falls to 3 (Newton 1964a). This trend is probably adaptive because, by the time the late clutches are hatched, caterpillars have become scarcer than before, so large broods are probably harder to raise. Incubation is by the hen and takes 12–14 days, and the young stay in the nest for a further 12–14 days.

British Chaffinches are remarkably sedentary. Ringing recoveries indicate that nine-tenths move no further than five kilometres from their birthplace, and the rest less than 50. These longer movements are almost all by first-year birds, for once a Chaffinch has bred in an area it tends to remain for life.

The numbers of Chaffinches in Britain are greatly augmented each autumn by immigrants, mostly from Norway and Sweden, but also from Denmark, northern Germany and Finland (Fig. 2). The migrants arrive between mid-September and late November, but chiefly in October, and soon spread widely in southern Britain, from which some pass on to Ireland. Most birds do not cross the North Sea direct from Scandinavia, but move down through Denmark and the Low Countries, and take the narrow crossings, to enter Britain at the southeast corner (p. 207–8). With following easterly winds in Holland, the birds tend to fly high and cross 180 kilometres of sea to Norfolk, but with opposing westerly winds, they fly low and keep down the coast, eventually crossing the 30 kilometres of sea between the Pas de Calais and Kent (Lack 1962). When they leave Britain, between early March and mid-April, a greater proportion than in autumn travel on a broad front across the North Sea, especially the stretch between Norfolk and Holland. It is not known why many birds take a more direct route back, but in contrast to the situation in autumn, all the birds, not just the adults, are returning to an area they already know. Several ringed migrants have returned to the same part of Britain in successive winters. Others, however, have wintered in Britain in one year and at some point along the migration route or near their breeding areas the next, so not all individuals have moved the same distance each year.

To some extent the sexes differ in migratory habits. Linneaus named the Chaffinch 'coelebs' (bachelor) because the few individuals that remained to winter in his homeland (Sweden) were nearly all cocks. Ringing returns have since shown that the hens from Germany and Scandinavia tend to migrate further than the cocks. In consequence, northern cocks outnumber hens in Holland and Britain, as well as in Scandinavia, but in Ireland in winter the hens predominate (Deelder 1949). Also, hens pass through Belgium each autumn a few days earlier, on average, than do cocks, and the reverse is true in spring (Verheyen 1960).

The northern Chaffinches (*F.c. coelebs*) tend to be larger and paler than the British ones (*F.c. gengleri*) and in the hand many can be separated on wing-length. The continentals also behave differently within Britain, for they are found chiefly in large, well-integrated flocks in open fields, and at night they form large communal roosts in woodland or scrub. They tend to concentrate at local abundances of food, and often have rather restricted diets, in which the seeds of a few common weeds predominate. British birds, in contrast, normally remain near their breeding areas for the whole year, and in winter they feed mostly in small groups near woods and hedgerows. The adults usually roost singly within their old territories and the juveniles in groups of 2–3. And because they feed over a restricted area, their diet tends to be more varied than that of the continentals, for they take whatever is available locally and usually cannot specialise. The difference in foraging habits probably reduces competition for food be-

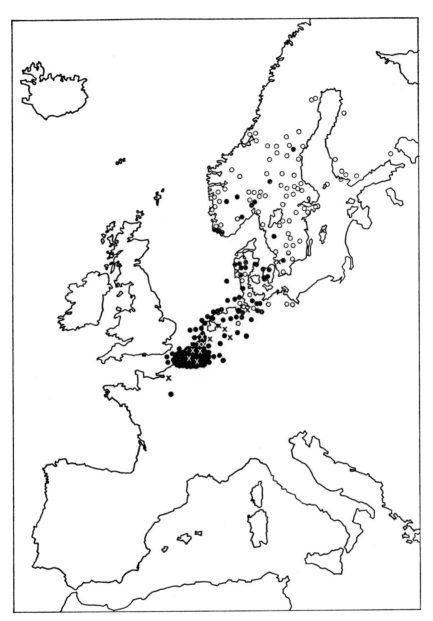

FIG 2. The recoveries abroad of Chaffinches ringed in Britain in winter. Only the distribution of the recoveries is shown, not their number. Filled circles refer to birds recovered in the migration seasons (September-November and March-May), open circles in the breeding season (June-August), and crosses in winter (December-February).

tween the two races, but it is not clear-cut, for residents often join the immigrant flocks, especially in hard weather. Another distinction is that in groups of local birds, both sexes are usually present in about equal numbers, but in the continentals, as mentioned, one or other sex often predominates greatly. Also, on fine mornings in spring, the residents tend to withdraw to their territories, while the immigrants remain in flocks. These various differences were first noted by Marler (1956a) at Cambridge, during a study of a colour-ringed population, and I later confirmed and extended the ecological findings at Oxford, from studies of the wing-lengths, ringing recoveries and diets of birds caught at different feeding and roosting sites (Newton 1967b).

Lastly, a note on longevity. In a large, well-timbered garden in southern Sweden, the local migrant population was studied for four years by Anvén & Enemar (1957). From the high proportion of adults that returned the year after ringing, the authors concluded that few (if any) of the survivors could have moved elsewhere to breed. Fewer of the yearling cocks than of the adult birds came back, and fewer still of the yearling hens. But from the returns of 59 birds of various ages, the annual survival was calculated to be at least 67%, and the mean expectation of life at least 2.5 years. This compares with the estimate of 2.7 years, calculated in the same way for 14 birds in Finland (Bergman 1956). The figure is higher than in most other European song-birds, in which the mean longevity varies between one and two years (Lack 1954), but is in line with the lower reproductive rate of the Chaffinch, in which most successful pairs raise only a single brood each year.

In northern Europe, after a narrow zone in which the two species occur together, the Chaffinch is replaced as a breeding bird by the Brambling (*F. montifringilla*). This species is most numerous near the limits of tree-growth, either at high latitudes or high altitudes (p. 96). It breeds mainly in the subarctic birch woods, but also in the open conifer forests immediately to the south and sometimes in the tall willow scrub on the tundra to the north. Unlike the Chaffinch, which occurs only in the western half of Eurasia, the Brambling extends right across to Kamchatka (Fig. 1). Its total breeding range covers about 23 million square kilometres, compared with about 18 million in the Chaffinch.

To most of Europe, therefore, the Brambling is a winter visitor. It is at once distinguished from the Chaffinch by its white rump, mainly orange-buff colouration, flecked flanks and distinct calls. The cock also has orange shoulder-patches, throat and chest, shading to white on the belly. In winter, the rest of his head and back are mottled buff, but towards the spring these feathers abrade to expose the black below, and at the same time the bill black from yellow (Fig. 3). The axillaries below the wing are bright lemon-yellow, the upper tail-coverts are black with long brown fringes, and the lower ones are pale buff. The hen is at all seasons paler than the cock, a dull orange-brown, with a strongly mottled back and white belly, and a buff-grey head, with a dark stripe round either side. The juveniles are like the hen but paler. The wings and tail are darker and show less white than in the Chaffinch, and the tail is also shorter and more forked. The usual calls include a harsh 'tswark' and a softer 'tchuck', and the latter, repeated rapidly, forms the flight call. No subspecies of the Brambling are recognised, despite the extent of its range, but individual birds tend to be more brightly coloured in the east.

FIG. 3. Variations in the head patterns of cock Bramblings in summer.

In the northern birch woods, the Brambling is usually the commonest bird, except for the Willow Warbler (*Phylloscopus trochilis*), and has been found at densities of up to 52 pairs per square kilometre (Hogstad 1969). In pine forests it has been found at up to 10 pairs per square kilometre and in spruce at up to 13 (Haapanen 1965). The numbers breeding in all these habitats fluctuate greatly from year to year, however, and much more so in the south. This is because in some years when the spring is late, large numbers of Bramblings curtail their northward migration and breed further south than usual, mainly in coniferous areas (Kalela 1938). This is frequent in Fenno-Scandia and occasional in the Baltic region and Denmark. It might have been in one such year that the species bred in Scotland, a nest with seven eggs having been found in Sutherland in 1920 (Hodgkin & Hodgkin 1920).

In the breeding season, the Brambling, like the Chaffinch, is strongly territorial, and where the two species breed in the same area, their territories often overlap, but without any interspecific aggression between the owners (Udvardy 1956). In areas where Bramblings are scarce, the territories of different pairs are often grouped, but the species cannot be considered 'colonial' in the same way as the cardueline finches, discussed in the next chapter. The nest of the Brambling is built in a tree, up to ten metres above the ground, and is made mostly of grasses and bents, with bits of bark and lichens on the outside, and feathers and hair within. It is larger than the Chaffinch's, less well finished, and contains less moss and more feathers. The outside measures 11–12 cm. and the cup 5.5–6 cm., compared with 9.0–9.5 and 5.0–5.5 cm. in the Chaffinch. In the south of the range, laying occurs between mid-May and mid-July, giving time for two broods, with the last fledging in August, but not all birds breed for this long. In the far north, laying begins in June and only one brood is raised. The eggs number 4–8, mostly 6–7, and resemble those of the Chaffinch, but are sometimes paler and greener. They take a fortnight to hatch, and at least in captivity the young stay in the nest for a similar period. As in the Chaffinch, the young are raised on insects, including caterpillars and tipulids, which are picked off leaves, and small moths and flies, which are caught on the wing. (The adults also eat seeds during the breeding season, especially those from the opening cones of conifers.) In some areas, the Brambling falls victim to the Cuckoo (*Cuculus canorus*), which usually lays eggs of almost identical colour, but slightly larger, than those of its host. The Brambling is the only finch that is affected in this way, though the Chaffinch also rears its young on suitable food.

The Brambling is perhaps the most highly migratory of the finches, and is the only species which vacates its European breeding areas completely in autumn and migrates mainly (but not entirely) by night. It winters over almost the whole of Europe south of its breeding range, and usually concentrates in areas of abundant beechmast. In southern Finland, however, up to 20 times more birds are found in winters when the rowan (*Sorbus aucuparia*) crop is good than in winters when it is poor, and among these birds the cocks outnumber hens (Eriksson 1970).

The comparatively small number of Bramblings that visit Britain arrive mainly in the ten weeks from mid-September, and leave in the seven weeks from early March. As might be expected, ringing has shown that the birds come from Fenno-Scandia and that some take the same coastal route through the Low Countries as do Chaffinches in autumn (Fig. 4). The tendency to coast is less marked than in the Chaffinch, however, and at both seasons many Bramblings cross the North Sea direct, including the 400–500 kilometre stretch between Norway and Scotland.

The subsequent recoveries of birds ringed in Britain show a strikingly different pattern from those of the Chaffinch. Instead of lying within a restricted and well-defined route, they are scattered through much of Europe. Birds caught in Britain in one winter have been caught migrating or wintering hundreds of kilometres to the east – in Italy, Germany or Czechoslovakia – the next. Evidently, individuals may take different routes, and winter in widely separated areas, in different years; and in contrast to the Chaffinch, no Bramblings have to my knowledge been recovered in the same place in successive winters. This is because the beechmast that they favour is rarely plentiful in any one area for two years running. In the winter of 1946/47, when southern Sweden and Denmark had a poor beech crop, Switzerland had a good one and millions of Bramblings appeared. One roosting concentration was estimated at 50 million birds and another at 11 millions (Gueniat 1948, Sutter 1948). But the most spectacular assemblage on record was found for a few weeks in the winter of 1951/52 near the Swiss town of Hunibach, around which the woods were full of mast (Mühlethaler 1951, Schifferli 1953). From mid-

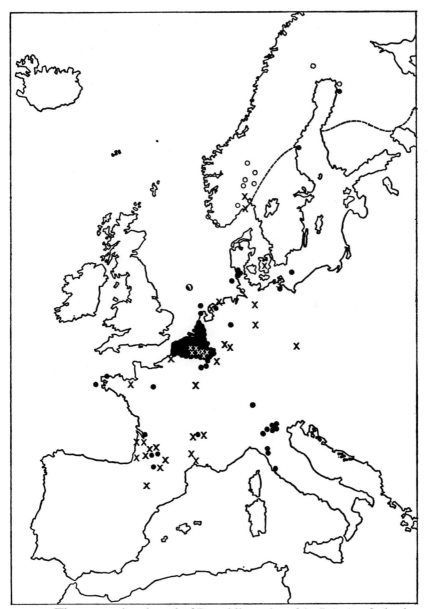

FIG. 4. The recoveries abroad of Bramblings ringed in Britain. Only the distribution of the recoveries is shown, not their number. The broken line marks the southern edge of the breeding range. Filled circles refer to birds recovered in the migration seasons (September-November and March-May), open circles in the breeding season (June-August), and crosses in winter (December-February).

afternoon each day, the Bramblings that had gathered there began to fly towards their roost in some conifers, small parties converged to form small flocks, small flocks to form large ones, so that a few kilometres from the roost they formed continuous streams, which poured non-stop through a small valley for 45–60 minutes each evening. One stream was about 200 metres across and four metres high. The speed of the birds in the wind, as found by car, was 60 kilometres per hour, and the density in these tight flocks was found to be one bird per cubic metre. From these four measurements, this stream was estimated to contain 36 million birds. However, only about half the birds could be seen properly from the observation points, so the total number was probably at least 70 millions.

Besides these birds, another 30–40 millions were found elsewhere in Switzerland at the same time, bringing the total population of the country to at least 100 millions. Further calculation, based on the proportion of young in the flocks, suggested that this number might correspond to at least 26.5 million pairs, and from previous counts in the nesting woods, the total area from which the birds might have come was computed. The conclusion was that this single concentration, the bulk of which roosted within one small valley, could easily have accounted for the entire breeding population between the Norwegian coast and the Urals. Almost certainly, many Bramblings were present elsewhere in Europe during this winter, so perhaps many of the birds came from east of the Urals, though no ringing recoveries came in support. Either way, these observations indicate the extent to which this species will concentrate if food permits.

The tendency to winter wherever beechmast is abundant is probably the main means by which competition with the Chaffinch is avoided in winter (Newton 1967b). Whereas this last species takes beech only if the mast happens to be available locally, the Brambling moves until it finds it, so that the two species come together in large numbers only where their mutual food is plentiful. (The Brambling can also open the nuts more easily than the Chaffinch, for its bill is one-tenth deeper and has sharper edges.) Likewise, whenever the two species take the same seeds from farmland in winter, this is again in my experience only when the seeds concerned are exceptionally numerous.

CHAPTER 2

THE CARDUELINE FINCHES, PART I

PERHAPS more than any other birds, the cardueline finches are specialised to feed on the fruits of higher plants. Not only are they adept at clinging to twigs and stems, but many have specialised bills to deal with particular types of seed-heads, such as cones and pods. They live almost entirely on seeds, and linked with this, show minor differences in skull-structure from the fringilline finches, just discussed, which eat more insects. They feed their young by regurgitation, either on seeds alone or on a mixture of seeds and insects. And instead of defending large feeding territories in summer, most of them nest in loose colonies and forage throughout the year in flocks.

GOLDFINCH-LIKE BIRDS

The genus *Carduelis* (also called *Spinus*), which includes some of the smallest, most colourful and specialised of the carduelines, is represented in both the Old and New Worlds by several species inhabiting open woodlands and wood-edges. Of the three European species, the Green-finch (*C. chloris*) is the largest, at six inches (15 cm.) from bill to tail. Owing mainly to its size, stout build and powerful beak, the species was until recently placed in a distinct genus (*Chloris*), but is connected with the Goldfinch via an intermediate species (*Carduelis sinica*) which lives in similar habitats in eastern Asia. The cock Greenfinch is mainly a dull olive-green, with greenish-yellow on the rump and breast, and lemon-yellow on the wing bars, carpal joints and sides of the tail. The hen is duller, browner and less yellow than the cock; and the juveniles are similar to the hen, but paler and more streaked. In all birds the bill and feet are pinkish-white. The call is distinctive, a loud rapid twitter, 'chichichichichi'; but in the breeding season the cock also utters a wheezy drawn-out 'dwee' note.

The Greenfinch breeds over much of the western half of Eurasia. It extends from about 65°N in Scandinavia and 60°N in Russia southwards to northwest Africa and Israel, and from Ireland east to the Urals, and northern Iran (Fig. 5). Another, isolated, population inhabits the high-lands of Russian Turkestan, the break in range resulting from a belt of steppe and desert, from which the species is absent. It has also been intro-duced successfully into Australia, New Zealand and the Azores (Voous 1951). Over the main range, four races are recognised, according to

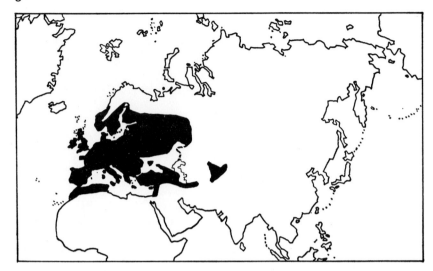

FIG. 5. The breeding range of the Greenfinch. The range extends in winter to the broken line.

colour; and the British population belongs to the most widespread (nominate) race.

In Britain, Greenfinches are widespread and common in lowlands. They are spreading moreover, and have recently colonised some western areas from which they were formerly absent, including some of the Inner Hebrides, the Isles of Scilly and, in Ireland, parts of Mayo and Donegal (Parslow 1968). Reafforestation has helped their spread in what was formerly treeless terrain because these birds nest readily in the young

COLOUR PLATE I

1. Brambling (pp. 26-7): (a) cock, summer (back, head and bill black), (b) cock, winter (back and head buffish, bill mainly yellow), (c) hen, all seasons.

2. Chaffinch (p. 19): (a) cock, summer (nape, crown and bill blue), (b) cock, winter (nape and crown buffish-blue, bill yellowish), (c) hen, all seasons.

3. Hawfinch (p. 61): (a) cock, summer (bill blue), (b) cock, winter (bill yellowish), (c) hen, summer, (d) juvenile.

4. Bullfinch (p. 64): (a) cock, all seasons, (b) hen, all seasons, and juvenile.

5. Trumpeter Bullfinch (p. 70): (a) cock, summer (bill red), (b) hen.

HEINZEL

plantations. Elsewhere they favour large shrubby gardens and church-yards with lots of evergreens, thickets and tall hedges. In tall or extensive woodlands they keep to the fringes and clearings. On farmland, the Common Bird Census of the British Trust for Ornithology has shown that they form only about 3% of the total bird population, ranking eleventh in abundance to other birds. In winter, Greenfinches become more generally distributed, and forage in a variety of habitats from closed woodlands and gardens to open farmland and coastal flats.

The diet is very varied, mainly because the large bill enables the Green-finch to take seeds of a wide size-range (Table 1). Various seeds of wood-land plants, weeds and crops provide the bulk of the food, and are picked directly from the plants or off the ground. From the range of seeds available in woodland, the Greenfinch clearly selects the larger ones: those of dog's mercury (*Mercurialis*) and elm (*Ulmus*) are favoured in summer; those of yew (*Taxus buccata*) and hornbeam (*Carpinus*) in autumn; and those of rose (*Rosa*) and bramble (*Rubus*) in winter. In farmland, the weed-seeds which are eaten regularly are mostly in the families Cruciferae, Poly-gonaceae and Compositae. Particularly popular are those of chickweed (*Stellaria*), dandelion (*Taraxacum*), groundsel (*Senecio*), goatsbeard (*Trago-pogon*), charlock (*Sinapis*) and persicaria (*Polygonum*). The last two provide much of the winter food, being picked from beneath the plants or from freshly tilled soil, where cultivation has turned to the surface seeds buried in previous years. The seeds of burdocks (*Arctium*) are also much sought, and often account for the presence of Greenfinches in autumn and winter on rubbish dumps and along wood-edges.

The crop-plants which are widely eaten include, in one part of the range or another, hemp (*Cannabis*), sunflower (*Helianthus*), flax (*Linum*), hops (*Humulus*) and cereals. In Britain the birds start feeding from standing corn in July, before the grains are ripe, and after harvest, they glean spilled

COLOUR PLATE 2

1. Redpoll (pp. 51-2): (a) cock Mealy (*A.f. flammea*), short-billed form, summer, (b) cock Mealy, long-billed form (*A.f. 'holboellii'*), summer, (c) cock Lesser (*A.f. cabaret* or *disruptes*), summer, (d) first-year cock, or hen first-year or older, (e) cock Lesser, with orange instead of red colouration, (f) juvenile, or adult without red colouration.

2. Arctic Redpoll (pp. 51-2): cock, Hornemann's race.

3. Twite (p. 49): (a) cock, summer (dark bill), (b) cock, winter (yellow bill).

4. Linnet (pp. 43-4): (a) cock, late summer, (b) hen, all seasons.

grains from stubble fields. The seeds of wild grasses are hardly touched, so it is presumably the large size of the cultivated varieties that makes them so attractive. In the past, Greenfinches regularly assembled at stackyards and threshing places during hard weather; but the increased use of the combine harvester has now put an end to this in most areas, and today the birds move mainly into towns and villages at such times. During the great frost of January–March 1963 I caught several hundred Greenfinches at roosts near Oxford and found that they had nearly all been eating peanuts from feeding trays. When the feathers on the birds' necks were blown aside, the nuts could easily be seen in the birds' gullets and they comprised by volume 97% of the total food (Newton 1967b). Since this time, the habit of eating peanuts seems to have caught on over most of Britain, and Greenfinches are now some of the most frequent birds on feeding trays. Murton (1971) has recently drawn attention to the correlation between fluctuations in the British Greenfinch population over 25 years (as deduced from ringing totals) and the number of certain weed-seeds available (as measured in cereal samples). If this relationship was genuine, it is unlikely to be maintained now that the birds are more dependent on householders.

The nest of the Greenfinch is usually placed, just out of arm's reach, in a thick shrub, such as an evergreen, hawthorn or elder. It is rather bulky

Table 1. The main foods of the Greenfinch through the year in southern England. Seeds are listed in order of their appearance in the diet from April onwards. (From Newton 1967b.)

	J	F	M	A	M	J	J	A	S	O	N	D
Chickweed (*Stellaria*)				━	━	━	•	•	•			
Groundsel (*Senecio vulgaris*)				━	━	━	•	•	•	•	━	━
Dandelion (*Taraxacum*)			•	━	━	━	•	•				
Elm (*Ulmus*)				━	━	━	•	•				
Dog's mercury (*Mercurialis perennis*)				━	━	━	•					
Charlock (*Sinapis*) & other brassicas	━	━	━	━	•			•	━	━	━	━
Goatsbeard (*Tragopogon*)							━	━	━			
Cultivated cereals	━	━	━	━		•	━	━	━	━	━	━
Persicaria (*Polygonum*)	━	━	━	━	•		•	━	━	━	━	━
Burdock (*Arctium*)	━	━	━	━	•				•	━	━	━
Bramble (*Rubus*)	•	•	•	•	•				•	•	•	•
Thistles (*Carduus* & *Cirsium*)							━	━	•			
Yew (*Taxus*)										━	━	•
Hornbeam (*Carpinus*)	•	•	•	•	•					•	━	━
Rose (*Rosa*)	━	━	━	━	•					•	━	━

and made of twigs, dried grass, moss, and wool, and is lined with fine roots and hair. The eggs, which number 4–6, are whitish, with red-brown spots. Incubation lasts 12–14 days, and the young usually stay in the nest for 13–16 days (p. 177–9). The breeding season is long. In southern Britain, clutches may be laid any time between mid-April and mid-August, so that the last young fledge around mid-September. In these five months each pair could raise four broods, but probably few (if any) breed for the full season, and the output of most pairs is reduced by the heavy predation on the eggs and young (p. 181–3). In late summer, in my experience, the proportion of young to adults is usually around 3:1.

At the time of writing, 240,000 Greenfinches have been ringed in Britain and 5,000 have been recovered. At 2%, this is a higher recovery rate than in any other British finch, reflecting the fact that the Greenfinch spends so much time near people. In an earlier analysis, Boyd (1931) established that birds began to disperse within a few weeks after they had left the nest; that they more often moved long distances in their first-year than later in life; and that, having once bred in an area, they tended to remain there, though they might move away for short periods in winter. Most of the birds recovered had moved less than five kilometres, suggesting that normally a Greenfinch lives in the same area throughout its life. Nevertheless, the local movement is considerable, for it is possible to catch and ring in a few winter months several hundred birds in the same place and still have fresh ones arriving daily. (A radius of five kilometres comprehends nearly 80 square kilometres.) Some Greenfinches move further, however, up to several hundred kilometres. More than forty birds have been recovered on the nearest parts of the continent, one in west Germany and another in Spain, whose movement at 1,100 kilometres (700 miles), is the longest recorded for a British Greenfinch. There have been three recoveries from Ireland. Long-distance movements take place in all directions but, at least at the coasts, are mainly southerly in autumn and northerly in spring. As yet, however, ringing has provided no evidence that any British Greenfinches migrate between regular breeding and wintering grounds. Likewise, the influx of birds into eastern Britain each autumn probably results from a general dispersal of continental birds at this season, rather than a regular westward migration. Six such ringed birds have been recovered in Britain, all from northern France.

The second European *Carduelis*, the Goldfinch (*C. carduelis*), is one of the most colourful, and measures nearly five inches (12 cm.) from bill to tail. The bird is predominantly buff or chestnut on the back and flanks, and whitish on the belly, with a red face-mask, white cheeks, black crown and side-stripes. Its wings are black, with a broad yellow bar, and white tips on each feather; the tail is also black, with white tips on the upperside of each feather and broad white patches on the underside of the two outer pairs. The long, narrow beak is whitish and in winter has a black tip.

The hen is smaller and duller than the cock with a less expansive red 'blaze' on the face. In both sexes the feathers of the blaze are particularly short and stiff and probably help to resist the prickles and spines when the bird pushes its beak into the heads of its various food plants. After the moult in autumn, these feathers appear orange, and in many hens they remain so, but in cocks they redden within a few weeks. The juveniles have the wings and tail coloured like those of adults, but bodies a streaky greyish-brown, in which plumage they are sometimes called 'grey-pates'. The call of the species is an unmistakable liquid twitter 'switt-witt-switt'.

Goldfinches breed over much of the western two-thirds of Eurasia, from southern Fenno-Scandia southwards into North Africa, the Azores and the Canaries (Fig. 6). They fall into two groups: a western (*carduelis*) form, in which the crown is black, and an eastern (*caniceps*) form in which the crown is grey and merges in colour with the back. Where the two forms meet, they interbreed to form two main hybrid zones, one south-east of the Caspian and another in Siberia. The eastern *caniceps* are found predominantly on mountains, around openings in mixed and coniferous forests. The western *carduelis* are found mainly in cultivated landscapes, nesting in parks, gardens and villages. These birds are much the commonest in the south of their range, and the most northerly breeding areas are largely vacated in winter, when many birds move south and west. At this season enormous numbers of Goldfinches concentrate in the Mediterranean basin, where the mild damp winters ensure the almost continuous growth and seeding of their herbaceous food-plants. In Iberia, the Goldfinch is probably the most numerous bird in winter, the abundant local population being augmented at this season by others from at least seven countries to the north and east.

Because of its popularity, the Goldfinch has been introduced into Australia, Tasmania, New Zealand, Argentina, Bermuda and North America, in most of which it has flourished and increased to become a common bird of town and garden. In parts of New Zealand it is treated as a pest, because it pecks out the seeds from ripening strawberries, causing the fruits to rot. But in North America it never became well established, though a colony persisted for many years on Long Island, New York, until the habitat was built over in the nineteen-fifties (Austin 1968). The species is probably now extinct on that continent, and its failure there may be partly through competition with the closely-allied American Goldfinch (*Spinus tristis*), which has similar feeding habits.

Over its whole natural range, the Goldfinch has long been a common cage-bird, and the rise and fall of commercial bird-catching in Britain is often held responsible for the general decline of the species here in the nineteenth century and for its recovery in the first half of the present one. In 1860, it was alleged that 132,000 were being caught each year near Worthing in Sussex, which is on a main migration route; and a record exists of twelve dozen being caught in a single morning on the site now occupied by Paddington Station. The newly-formed Society for the Protection of Birds made saving the Goldfinch one of its first tasks, but it is not certain how much a spread of thistles also helped the recovery. Nowadays, the Goldfinch is common in southern Britain, but becomes scarcer and more local from the Midlands north, though still increasing. It does not breed in northern Scotland and in the northern and western-most Isles but nests regularly on Arran, Bute and Islay. In Ireland it breeds in every county, but is everywhere thin on the ground, perhaps because until recently bird-catching was still legal there.

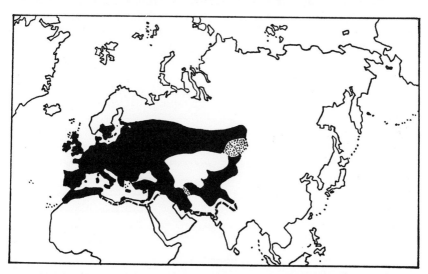

FIG. 6. The breeding range of the Goldfinch, showing, so far as is known, the hybrid zone (dotted) between black-headed birds, which occupy the bulk of the range, and grey-headed birds, which occupy the south-east. The broken line shows the southern edge of the wintering range.

In summer, it is found in much the same places as the Greenfinch, but unlike the latter, which needs bushes for nesting, the Goldfinch also breeds among scattered trees in open country. The nest is usually placed high on a swaying bough, 4–10 metres above the ground; it is neat and compact, made of moss, roots and lichens, wool and spider silk and lined with the down of thistles and other plants; and its unusual depth helps to retain the contents in windy weather. The eggs number 4–6 and are whitish, with red-brown speckles. Incubation takes 11–13 days and the young stay in the nest for 13–16 days. As in the Greenfinch, breeding is prolonged. In most years in southern England, eggs are laid from mid-May to early August, but in some years laying begins in late April, and in others con-tinues into September, depending chiefly on the weather (p. 191). This would give time for 2–4 broods, but it is doubtful that any raise more than three successfully. Young are usually most numerous after warm, dry summers.

After breeding, Goldfinches become more widespread, foraging on waste land, overgrown rubbish dumps, neglected allotments, and rough pastures, or indeed anywhere where their food-plants grow. They specialise on seeds of plants in the family Compositae, especially thistles (*Carduus* and *Cirsium*), dandelions (*Taraxacum*), groundsels and ragworts (*Senecio*), hardheads (*Centauria*), and burdocks (*Arctium*), which they extract with the help of their long sharp beaks (Table 2). Around Oxford, thistles pro-

Table 2. The main foods of the Goldfinch through the year in southern England. Seeds are listed in order of their appearance in the diet from April onwards. (From Newton 1967b.)

Seed	J	F	M	A	M	J	J	A	S	O	N	D
Chickweed *(Stellaria)*					▬▬▬····							
Groundsel *(Senecio vulgaris)*					▬▬▬▬		···· ▬▬ ····					
Dandelion *(Taraxacum)*				···▬▬▬▬		·······················						
Elm *(Ulmus)*				▬▬▬▬···								
Ragwort *(Senecio)*					▬▬▬▬▬▬▬▬▬▬▬········							
Sowthistle *(Sonchus)*					▬▬▬▬▬▬▬▬▬▬····							
Thistles *(Carduus & Cirsium)*	▬▬▬▬·					▬▬▬▬▬▬▬▬▬▬▬▬▬▬						
Hardhead *(Centauria)*	··					▬▬▬▬▬▬··········						
Teasel *(Dipsacus)*	▬▬▬·					········· ·······▬						
Meadowsweet *(Filipendula)*						····▬▬··					
Burdock *(Arctium)*	▬▬▬·					·····▬▬▬						
Birch *(Betula)*						···········					
Alder *(Alnus)*	▬▬▬····					·········						
Pine *(Pinus)*	···▬▬··											

vide a third of the annual diet and their seeds are taken from mid-summer, as soon as they become available, throughout the autumn and winter (Newton 1967b). In some years, only few heads keep their seeds, but in wet summers many more fail to open, and food for Goldfinches is consequently much more plentiful in the following months. During the winter, many dead seed-heads fall and disintegrate, and at this stage Goldfinches prefer to take them from the ground, where they are easier to work. This incidentally results in heads on the plant being left till later, so that they are often accessible at times of snow, when heads on the ground are covered. Fallen burdock heads are likewise preferred to those on the plant. When their favourite foods are scarce, Goldfinches also feed in winter from teasels (*Dipsacus*), birches (*Betula*) and alders (*Alnus*), and in spring from the opening cones of pine (*Pinus*) trees and on insects from developing larch buds. Small parties of birds may travel many kilometres in the course of a day's feeding, and are often at particular places at the same time on successive days.

The number of Goldfinches that remain to winter in Britain are few compared to those that leave. The local population around Oxford falls by four-fifths between mid-September and late October each year, this being the main migration season. The numerous autumn recoveries from Belgium show that many birds leave Britain through the southeast corner, using the shortest sea-crossing, but this number is increased, perhaps, by the official bird-catching season in that country, which lasts for six weeks from 1 October. Subsequent recoveries on the continent all lie west of a line which runs south-southwest through the Low Countries, France and Iberia (Fig. 7). The longest recorded movements span more than 2,000 kilometres, but even in mid-winter, recoveries have come from all stages along the migration route, including Britain, implying that individuals vary greatly in the distance they move. Ringing has further shown that some birds might reach the continent in one year, and remain in Britain the next, or vice versa. Also, to judge from the sex ratio in Britain in winter, more hens than cocks migrate. The spring passage is both smaller (because of winter mortality) and less protracted than in autumn, most birds entering Britain between mid-April and early May. As already indicated, Goldfinches from other parts of Europe also winter in Iberia, some in the west like the British, and others in the east.

Other Goldfinch movements around Britain need to be clarified by further ringing. First, some British birds winter in Ireland, as shown by the westward movements which are seen annually over the island of Saltee in the Irish Sea and by one ringing recovery. This suggests two directional tendencies in the British population, most birds initially flying south-southeast in autumn and others west. Second, some birds are seen to move southward within Britain during hard weather in winter, but it is not yet known whether they take the same route as the autumn migrants. Third, Goldfinches also arrive on the east coast of England in some autumns, but ringing has not yet confirmed that any birds wintering in Britain are of continental origin. These latter birds (*C.c. carduelis*) are paler, on average, with whiter cheeks than British birds (*C.c. britannica*), but could not be distinguished in the field.

The third European *Carduelis*, the Siskin (*C. spinus*), is one of the smallest, at four and a half inches (11 cm.) long. It has a longish narrow bill and a short forked tail. The cock is mainly a streaky yellow-green, but paler and unstreaked below, with a blackish bib and crown, and yellow rump, wing bars, sides of tail and lores. The amount of black on the head varies greatly between individuals and some lack the bib (Fig. 8). The hen is

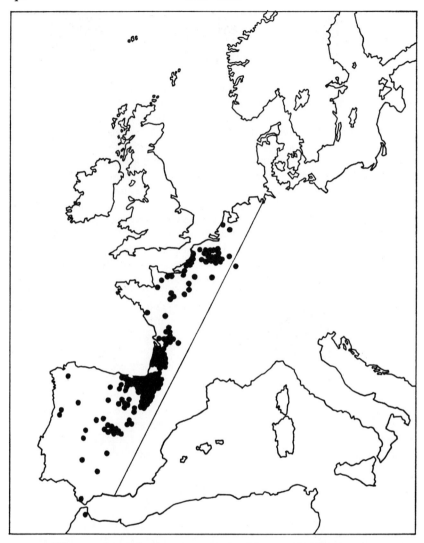

FIG. 7. The continental wintering areas of British Goldfinches as shown
by ringing recoveries. Line shows eastern limits of wintering range. Only
the distribution of the recoveries is shown, not their number.

paler, greyer and more streaked than the cock, and lacks the black on the
head. The usual note sounds like 'tsu-tsu-tsu', and the flight-note is a
squeaky drawn out 'tzee' or 'tzee-zee'.

The Siskin breeds in conifer forests. Its main range comprises two

FIG. 8. Variations in the head patterns of cock Siskins.

separate areas: one extending over much of Europe and part of the Soviet Union as far as Omsk at 75°E, and the other in the Far East; between them only a few isolated populations exist though not through lack of habitat (Fig. 9). Despite this discontinuity, no subspecies have been described.

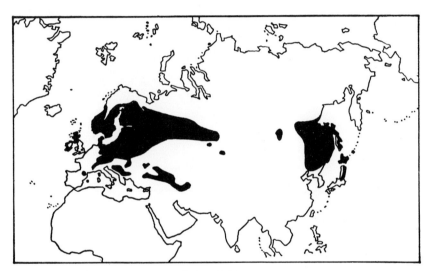

FIG. 9. The breeding range of the Siskin.

In the west the breeding range extends from just below the Arctic Circle in Scandinavia and Russia southwards to central Europe and then locally on mountains to the Pyrenees, Sardinia, Italy, Yugoslavia, Bulgaria, Asia Minor, the Caucasus and southern Caspian. Some birds remain in their breeding areas throughout the year, but most move southwest in autumn, spreading over most of Europe, northwest Africa and parts of Egypt, Iraq and Iran. In Britain their breeding stronghold has long been in the old pine forests of northeast Scotland, but they have spread with the planting of conifers, and now nest regularly in southern Scotland, northern England, northern and southwest Ireland, parts of Wales, and occasionally elsewhere (p. 90). They are still extremely local, however, and everywhere their numbers fluctuate greatly from year to year.

Over much of the range, the seeds of spruce (*Picea abies*) form the main food in early summer and, on returning from winter quarters, Siskins settle most densely in areas where the crop that year is good (p. 222). In northern Europe they may begin nesting in early April, and raise their first brood on seeds from the opening cones. Later broods are reared on seeds from pine cones (which open later than those of spruce), on insects and on the seeds of other plants. In years when spruce seeds are scarce, moreover, breeding does not begin till late May or June, and only the later broods are raised (Haapanen 1966). In these years the birds forage largely outside the forests, in fields and hedgerows. There the seeds of elms (*Ulmus*), dandelions (*Taraxacum*), dock (*Rumex sanguinea*), hardheads (*Centauria*), thistles, and meadowsweet (*Filipendula*) are favoured (Table 3). As expected, the birds start breeding earlier in central than in northern Europe, in February in good spruce years and in April in others, as found in the Alps.

Table 3. The main foods of the Siskin through the year in northern Britain. Seeds are listed in order of their appearance in the diet from April onwards. (Partly from MacDonald 1968.)

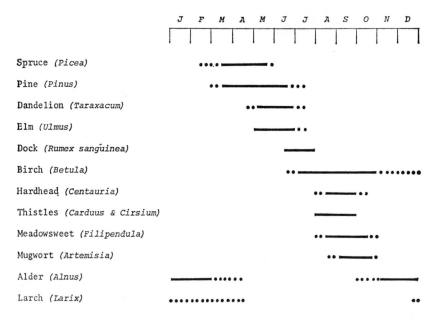

Siskins build high in conifers, usually out on a branch; their tiny compact nests are made of moss, lichens and grasses, and lined with hair and feathers. The eggs number 3–5 and are bluish-white, with pale reddish spots and streaks. Incubation takes 11–13 days, and the young stay in the nest for 13–17 days.

By the time the cones have emptied in July and August, conifer forests hold little food for Siskins, and the majority of birds then move into birches where they feed on the seeds until the time of their autumn migration. In winter they feed primarily from alder (*Alnus*), getting the seeds first from the cones, and in late winter from the ground below. In spring the birds move back into conifers, except at the extreme south of the wintering range, where they eat the seeds of acacias instead. Also, in the mid 1960s, Siskins in several localities in southern Britain fed on fat put out in gardens for tits, a habit long known in the closely-related North American Pine Siskin (*Spinus pinus*). Since then European Siskins have been seen many times at nut-bags put out for birds in gardens.

To most of Britain, the Siskin is still a winter visitor only. The majority of birds which breed in northern Britain probably move south in autumn, though this has not been confirmed by ringing. But they are then greatly outnumbered by continental birds which arrive mainly between late September and late October and depart between mid-March and mid-May. Ringing recoveries show that some of the immigrants come from Fenno-Scandia, and others from the mountains of central and eastern Europe (Fig. 10). Six recoveries are of birds which appear to have wintered in widely separated areas in different years, for in one winter they were caught in Britain and in another in Holland (1), Belgium (1), France (1), Spain (2) and Austria (1) respectively. Other examples of the same thing may be found among the ringing reports of other countries (p. 227).

LINNET-LIKE BIRDS

The scrub-dwelling *Acanthis* finches are mostly streaked brownish or greyish in colour, with longish forked tails, short broad bills, and pink or red patches in the plumage. In the Linnet (*A. cannabina*) the red is on the crown and breast, in the Twite (*A. flavirostris*) on the rump, and in the Redpolls (*A. flammea* and *A. hornemanni*) on the crown, breast and rump. In the first two species the red is restricted to the cocks. In all four, however, the colour is enhanced in summer when the dull tips to the feathers wear off to expose the red below, and these birds, like the fringilline finches, can thereby acquire a special breeding dress without the need to moult. The Linnet and Twite are found only in the Old World; but the Redpolls in the New World too.

The Linnet measures just over five inches (13 cm.) from head to tail, and as well as the red forehead and breast, the cock has a streaked chestnut-brown back and dark brown wings and tail, with white edges to some of the flight and tail feathers; the head is greyish-brown and the underparts are buff, finely streaked with dark brown. The hen lacks the crimson and

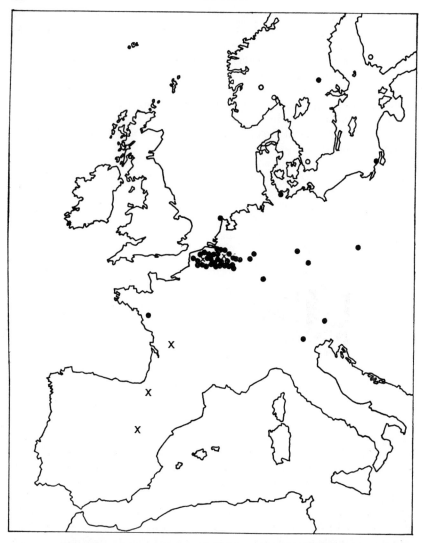

FIG. 10. The recoveries abroad of Siskins ringed in Britain in winter. Filled circles refer to birds recovered in the migration seasons (September–November and March–May), open circles in the breeding season (June–August), and crosses in winter (December–February).

is more heavily streaked; and the juveniles are similar but paler, even more heavily streaked, and show less contrast between the back and the underside. The usual note is a slightly metallic 'kekekekeke'.

Linnets breed from a few degrees below the arctic circle southward to

the desert fringes of northwest Africa, Asia Minor, Israel and Iran, and
east into Kazakhstan at 90°E (Fig. 11). Their Asiatic range is broken by a
broad belt of desert and steppe from which they are absent. The birds
winter mainly in the southern parts of their breeding range, but also
reach parts of Egypt, Iraq and across to northwest India, where they do
not nest. Two subspecies are recognised in the main range, with the
nominate *A.c. cannabina* occupying most of the range including Britain
and *A.c. bella* that part lying south and east of the desert–steppe belt.
Another fairly distinct race occurs on Madeira and two others on the
Canary Islands.

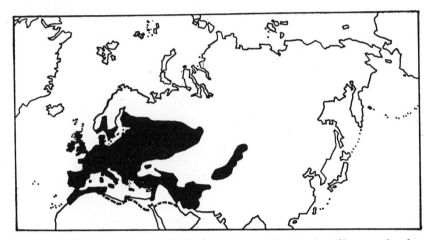

FIG. 11. The breeding range of the Linnet. The broken line marks the
southern edge of the wintering range.

The numbers of Linnets in Britain are thought to have declined during
the nineteenth century, but to have recovered to some extent early in the
present one; this coincided with the fluctuations in the Goldfinch and is
likewise linked with the rise and fall of commercial bird-catching. Nowadays, Linnets are widespread and common in most of Britain and Ireland,
but are absent or local in northwest Scotland, partly through shortage of
suitable habitat, and have disappeared recently from the Outer Hebrides
and Shetland. They nest mostly in gorse-grown commons, on rough
ground and beside railways, in shrubs and other low vegetation, and also
in hedges in farmland. In this last habitat the Common Bird Census of
the British Trust for Ornithology indicates that they form about 3% of the
total breeding birds and rank tenth in abundance to other species.
Occasionally they nest in gardens adjoining open country or in large
parks, but not in suburban gardens. In winter Linnets are found in open
country, including agricultural and waste land, salt marshes and coastal

mud-flats. In summer they feed directly from herbaceous plants, by clinging to the stems, and in winter from the ground.

Although the Linnet's latin name denotes its fondness for hemp (*Cannabis*) seeds, which are eaten widely abroad, more than any other finch the bird depends on the weeds of cultivation. The distribution and abundance of its food is thus determined largely by agricultural procedure; each harvest reduces the seeds available and each cultivation brings fresh ones to the soil surface. Plants in the families Cruciferae, Polygonaceae, Chenopodiaceae and Compositae are favoured (Table 4). Over the year as a whole near Oxford, the seeds of charlock and other brassicas form a third of the total food; those of persicaria, fat-hen (*Chenopodium*) and chickweed are also available over long periods and bulk large in the diet, while those of dandelions and thistles are important for short periods. On the other hand, Linnets eat fewer tree-seeds than other finches and avoid berries and other fleshy fruits. With a diet like this, their numbers might have been expected to decline over the last few decades with the increased use of herbicides; but the evidence is difficult to assess because the removal of scrub and hedgerows has also changed their local distribution.

Table 4. The main foods of the Linnet through the year in southern England. Seeds are listed in order of their appearance in the diet from April onwards. (From Newton 1967b.)

	J	F	M	A	M	J	J	A	S	O	N	D
Chickweed (*Stellaria*)				━	━	━	━					
Meadowgrass (*Poa*)				━	━							
Dandelion (*Taraxacum*)				·	━	━	·	·	·	·	·	
Elm (*Ulmus*)					━	━						
Jack-by-the-hedge (*Alliaria*)						━	━	·				
Sorrel (*Rumex*)						━	━	·				
Buttercup (*Ranunculus*)						━	━	·				
Catsear (*Hypochoeris*)						·	━	━	·	·	·	·
Brassicas (esp. *Sinapis* arvensis)	━	━	━	·				━	━	━	━	━
Thistles (*Carduus* & *Cirsium*)							·	━	━	·		
Persicaria (*Polygonum*)	━	━	━	·				·	━	━	━	━
Fat-hen (*Chenopodium*)	━	━	━	·				·	━	━	━	━
Mugwort (*Artemisia*)	·	·	·					·	━	━	·	·
Meadowsweet (*Filipendula*)								·	━	━	·	

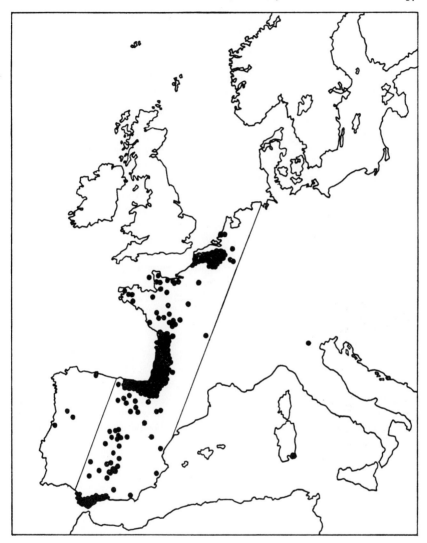

FIG. 12. The continental wintering areas of British Linnets as shown by ringing recoveries. The lines enclose the principal wintering range. Only the distribution of the recoveries is shown, not their number.

The Linnet is one of the first finches to start nesting in spring, and in southern England lays eggs from mid-April, about the time that fresh seeds first become available. Laying continues into early August, so that a pair breeding to maximum capacity would have time to raise four broods. Placed in low bushes or tussocks, the nests are made of dry grass, bents, moss, thin twigs and roots, and lined with hair or wool. Since the earliest birds start breeding while deciduous shrubs are still bare, they build mostly in gorse and other evergreens, or in brambles that have retained their dead leaves, whereas most later nests are placed in deciduous shrubs, such as hawthorn or elder (Appendix 1). The eggs of the Linnet, which number 4–6, are bluish-white with spots and streaks of purplish-red. The incubation and nestling periods each last 11–12 days.

While some Linnets remain near their breeding areas throughout the year, most do not. The migrants from Britain take roughly the same route as Goldfinches, but start both migrations a few weeks earlier. They leave mainly in the eleven weeks between late August and mid-November, and return in the seven weeks between mid-March and early May. Almost all the recoveries on the continent lie in a narrow band, about 500 kilometres wide, running south-southwest through the Low Countries, France and Iberia (Fig. 12). The longest recorded movements span more than 2,200 kilometres, but throughout the winter recoveries have come from all points along the migration route, suggesting that individuals vary greatly in the distance they move. They show further that some birds might remain in Britain in one winter and leave the next, or vice versa. Also, two birds were recovered well off the main route, in Italy and Sardinia.

Linnets are also seen each autumn moving west towards Ireland, and at the same time others leave the south coasts of Ireland, presumably destined for France or Spain, but neither movement has been confirmed by ringing. In addition, some move south within Britain during hard weather in winter, but again it is not known whether they follow the same route as the autumn migrants. Lastly, some continental Linnets

COLOUR PLATE 3

1. Goldfinch (pp. 35-6): (a) cock, all seasons, (b) juvenile.

2. Siskin (pp. 39-40): (a) cock, all seasons, (b) hen, all seasons.

3. Greenfinch (p. 31): (a) cock, all seasons, (b) hen, all seasons, (c) juvenile.

4. Serin (p. 57): (a) cock, all seasons, (b) hen, all seasons, (c) juvenile.

5. Citril Finch (pp. 58 & 60): (a) cock, all seasons, (b) hen, all seasons, (c) juvenile, (d) cock, Corsican form (brown back).

HEINZEL

HEINZEL

move into Britain each autumn, and the two recoveries were of birds ringed as nestlings in Norway and Holland.

The Twite can be distinguished from the Linnet by its more slender build, darker upper-parts, orange-buff throat, and longer, more forked tail; and from the redpolls by the lack of a black chin and red cap. The bird is just over five inches (13 cm.) long. It is predominantly warm-buff in colour, streaked with blackish and brown on the upper-parts, and lighter below, shading to orange-buff on the throat and lores. The dark brown primaries and tail feathers are edged with white, though less distinctly than in the Linnet, and in summer the cock has a rosy-pink rump. The young resemble the hen, but are paler and more streaked on the throat and breast, and slightly greyer on the crown and nape. The song and flight-note are Linnet-like, distinguishable only to the practised ear, but in addition the Twite has a characteristic harsh 'chweet' call, which is also incorporated into the song. British birds (*A.f. pipilans*) tend to be slightly darker than continental ones (*A.f. flavirostris*).

The Twite breeds· in rather barren, open, windswept environments, including arctic and alpine tundras. Its main range covers the cold steppes and stony mountain areas of central and southwest Asia (Fig. 13). In Afghanistan, it breeds above the tree-line up to 3,400 metres (11,500 feet), and in eastern Tibet up to 4,400 metres (14,400 feet), descending to lower levels for the winter. Another population breeds near the northwest seaboard of Europe, from Britain, along the Norwegian coast, and at scattered localities on mountains throughout Lapland to the Kola peninsula. These birds winter mainly around the coasts of the Baltic and North Seas. More than 2,700 kilometres separate the breeding areas of the two populations and some 1,200 kilometres their winter ranges. Within each area, two or more subspecies are recognised.

COLOUR PLATE 4

1. Common Crossbill (pp. 73-4): (a) cock, all seasons, (b) hen, all seasons, (c) juvenile (bill uncrossed), (d) cock, Scottish race.

2. Two-barred Crossbill (p. 80): (a) cock, all seasons, (b) hen, all seasons.

3. Parrot Crossbill (p. 80): cock, all seasons.

4. Pine Grosbeak (p. 68): (a) cock, all seasons, (b) hen, all seasons.

5. Scarlet Rosefinch (p. 71): (a) cock, second year, with full red, (b) hen.

In all these species, the amount of red is very variable, and may sometimes be replaced by orange or yellow.

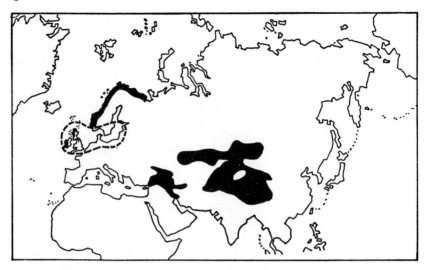

FIG. 13. The breeding range of the Twite. The broken line encloses the main wintering area of the European population, though one ringing recovery has also come from northern Italy.

In Britain the present strongholds of the species are on the coasts of northwest Scotland, Shetland, Fair Isle, Orkney and the Hebrides, and the northwest coast of Ireland and its offshore islands. On the Scottish Islands, the Twite is one of the commonest birds and benefits greatly from cultivation. It is most conspicuous in winter, as the flocks work over weedy ground, stubble fields, corn stacks, gardens and poultry runs for seeds; but in summer, it becomes more widespread, as many birds take to the hills and moors to breed. Elsewhere in Britain, the bird breeds locally on hills south into Staffordshire, with a stronghold in the southern Pennines. Here it nests on heather moors and bracken-growth slopes, and forages on the lower pastures, areas of burnt *Molinia* grass being especially important in spring. Past deforestation must have greatly extended the range of the Twite in Britain, because most of its present breeding areas lie well below the natural tree-line. The inland range is now contracting, however, and since 1900 the species has for unknown reasons gone from much of Scotland, most of the Lake District, parts of Yorkshire and the northern Pennines, and the Isle of Man. The Lancashire and Cheshire mosses on which it bred have since been reclaimed and are no longer suitable. In Britain, as on the continent, many Twites move to estuaries and salt marshes for the winter, the Wash being a favoured area.

The birds return to their breeding areas from March onwards. They begin egg-laying between late April and mid-May, according to locality, and continue into August. This would give time for three or four broods, but it is unlikely that many raise this number. The nest is usually built in tall heather or in other rank vegetation, among stones on the ground or in a wall, in a cliff face, peat stack, or under an upturned sod. It is made of thin twigs, grasses, stalks, and moss, and lined with hair, wool and feathers. The eggs number 4–6, and are bluish-white, with sparse red-brown spots. The incubation and nestling periods each last 11–12 days.

In feeding habits the Twite resembles the Linnet: the weeds of pasture and of cultivated land provide much of the food in summer, dandelions (*Taraxacum*), charlock (*Sinapis*), wild radish (*Raphanus*), thistles and hardheads (*Centauria*) being favoured. Saxby (1874) examined some birds that had been killed at oat stacks on Shetland and found that they contained mostly weed seeds from the butts of the sheaves. Probably little corn is eaten, except immediately after harvest, though the Twite on Fair Isle have much decreased since the importation of seed-corn dressed with mercurial compounds, birds having been found dead or dying after eating it. On the coasts in winter, sea-aster (*Aster*), marsh samphire (*Salicornia*), sea-rocket (*Cakile*), cord grass (*Spartina*), thrift (*Armeria*) and seablite (*Suaeda*) seeds form the main foods. But inland at this season, those Compositae that have very small seeds are favoured, notably golden rod (*Solidago*), milfoil (*Achillea*), mayweeds (*Anthemis*), marigolds (*Chrysanthemum*) and mugworts (*Artemisia*) (Bub 1969).

While the migrations of continental Twite are well known as a result of a recent massive ringing campaign (Bernhoft-Osa 1965), those of British Twite are not. It is clear, however, that some birds move regularly between different Scottish Islands. On Fair Isle, the bird formerly wintered in thousands, but is now mainly a summer visitor, leaving between late August and November, and returning between late February and early May. One ringed bird was recovered in winter on Westray, Orkney, and another in autumn on board ship in the North Sea. Of birds ringed elsewhere in Britain, one was recovered the following winter in Essex, and four on the continent, on the coasts of Holland, Belgium and France, and inland in northern Italy. In addition, Twite are also seen to arrive from overseas on the east coasts of Britain in autumn and to leave in spring. These are presumed to be mainly continental birds, but none has been found by ringing.

The Redpolls vary more in size and colour than most other bird-species; and while some taxonomists (e.g. Salomonsen 1928) prefer to group them all in a single enormously variable species, most prefer to distinguish two 'species': a large pale form (*C. hornemanni*) with much white in the plumage, which breeds mainly on the high arctic tundras, and a smaller greyish or brown form (*C. flammea*) which breeds mainly in the open birch and conifer forests to the south. No clear line separates the two forms, and in the zone of overlap their respective proportions may change greatly from year to year. In some places in the contact zone the two forms hybridise to produce populations of great variability, but over most of the range the majority of individuals can easily be classed as belonging to one form or the other. The main field character is the whitish unstreaked rump of *hornemanni* and the darker streaked rump of *flammea*. In addition, typical *hornemanni* have a shorter and deeper bill, greyer (less brown) plumage, with little or no streaking on the breast, abdomen and under tail-coverts; and the cocks are pinkish on the breast and rump instead of red as in *flammea*. There are also physiological differences linked with the fact that *hornemanni* lives further north and in colder climates than *flammea* (p. 252). Textbooks subdivide the two forms into the following subspecies:

		Body Length (cm.)	Wing Length (mm.)		Breeding area
			Cocks	Hens	
Mealy Redpoll	A. flammea flammea	12.5	72–78	69–76	N. America, N. Europe Siberia
Greenland Redpoll	A.f. rostrata	14	78–85	75–81	Greenland Baffin Island
Iceland Redpoll	A.f. islandica	12.5	74–82	72–81	Iceland
Lesser Redpoll	A.f. cabaret	11.5	67–73	63–69	Central Europe
Lesser Redpoll	A.f. disruptes	11.5	67–73	63–69	British Isles
Hornemann's Redpoll	A. hornemanni hornemanni	14	82–88	79–85	Greenland
Hoary or Coue's Redpoll	A.h. exilipes	12.5	73–79	69–76	N. America, N. Europe Siberia

The differences between subspecies are much as one would expect, with the smallest and darkest birds in the southern parts of the range, and the largest and palest further north. Also, Mealy Redpolls from Finland eastwards (formerly called *A.c. holboellii*), which spend more of their lives in coniferous areas, tend to have longer bills than the western birds, which eat more birch.

Redpolls of all races can best be identified by their call, a loud metallic 'chi chi chi chi . . .'; by their bounding song-flight over the breeding grounds; and at close quarters by the combination of a red forehead and black chin. Within each race, the amount and intensity of the red on the head and breast varies greatly between individuals. In the cocks the cap is usually bright red, but in the hens it is dull red, orange, yellow or brown. In *flammea*, the cocks range from some with almost pure white breasts to others with the whole throat and chest a brilliant rosy colour; and older cocks usually show more red than yearlings. In *hornemanni*, pale-breasted cocks predominate, and even the majority of old ones carry little pink on the chest.

Although redpolls as a group breed mainly in the open northern forests and tundras, migrating south in winter, in Europe isolated populations also breed in Britain, the Alps, the Bohemian Forest, the Carpathians and at scattered localities elsewhere (Fig. 14). The numbers, movements and breeding of all these European birds is closely dependent on the abundance of birch seeds which form their main food. However, the dark form has also been introduced from Europe on to certain islands in the southern hemisphere, on all of which it has been remarkably successful, despite the absence of birch. In New Zealand, for example, the Redpoll is now one of the commonest birds, and on South Island is found in most habitats from the mountain tundras to the lowland farms, and has become a pest through destroying the blossoms of fruit trees (Stenhouse 1960, 1962).

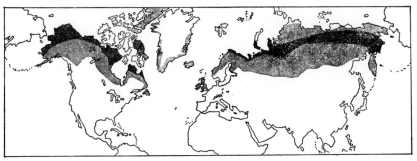

FIG. 14. The breeding range of the Redpolls, showing the overlap between the Arctic Redpoll (*A. hornemanni*) in the north and the Common Redpoll (*A. flammea*) in the south.

The British 'Lesser Redpolls' are smaller, darker and less variable than redpolls elsewhere. In the breeding season they are common and widespread in the north of the country, fluctuating considerably from year to year, but in the south and in Ireland, they are local and more or less restricted to hilly country. They breed mainly in birch scrub but also in thickets of alder, sallow and hawthorn, and in rough straggling hedgerows. In recent years they have taken to nesting in young conifer plantations with trees up to six metres high, and have spread considerably since 1950 as a result of increased afforestation (p. 90).

Typically the nest of the Lesser Redpoll is placed in a tall bush, 2–4 metres above the ground, and is surprisingly large and untidy for so small a bird, being built of grasses, moss, old flower-heads and roots, and lined with plant-down, hair and feathers. Egg-laying begins between late April and late May, according to latitude, and continues at least until mid-July, giving time for two or three broods. The eggs, which number 4–6, are bluish-white, without gloss, and spotted and streaked with light brown. Incubation takes 10–11 days and the young stay in the nest for 11–12 days.

The main foods of Lesser Redpolls in spring are the flowers and seeds of sallow (*Salix*) and insects from the opening buds of Larch (*Larix*) and other trees. In early summer, the seeds of grasses, sorrel (*Rumex*), dandelions (*Taraxacum*) and other Compositae are favoured (Table 5). When birch seeds ripen in July, however, these form the mainstay as long as they last; but the seeds of meadowsweet (*Filipendula*) and willowherbs (*Epilobium*) are also eaten in late summer and autumn, and those of alder (*Alnus*), tansy (*Tanacetum*), mugwort (*Artemisia*) and fat-hen (*Chenopodium*) in winter. At this season the birds become more generally distributed, but concentrate in areas where birch seeds are plentiful. If these seeds are scarce, the birds forage instead mainly on waste land and along railway embankments.

Table 5. The main foods of the Lesser Redpoll through the year in northern Britain. Seeds are inferred except where otherwise stated. Items are listed in order of their appearance in the diet from April onwards.

	J	F	M	A	M	J	J	A	S	O	N	D
Sallow (*Salix*) flowers and seeds				●● ▬▬▬ ●●								
Insects from opening tree-buds				●● ▬ ●●								
Chickweed (*Stellaria*)				● ▬ ●●								
Dandelion (*Taraxacum*)				●● ▬▬								
Grasses (*Gramineae*)					●●●● ▬▬ ●●							
Sorrel (*Rumex*)					●● ▬▬ ●●							
Birch (*Betula*)	▬▬▬ ●					●●● ▬▬▬▬▬▬▬▬						
Meadowsweet (*Filipendula*)							●● ▬▬▬▬ ●●●					
Willowherbs (*Chamaenerion* and *Epilobium*)	●●●●●●●●●						●●● ▬▬ ●●●●●					
Fat-hen (*Chenopodium*)	●●●●●●●●								●● ●●●●●●			
Alder (*Alnus*)	▬▬▬ ●●●								●● ▬▬▬			
Mugwort (*Artemisia*)	●●●●●●●●●								●●●●●●●●			
Tansy (*Tanacetum*)	▬▬▬ ●●●								●● ▬			

Although some Lesser Redpolls remain to winter in northern Britain, most move into southern England in late September and October, and some then cross into Holland, Belgium, France and western Germany (Fig. 15). More birds remain in England in winters when the birch crop here is good than in winters when it is poor. This is reflected in the ringing

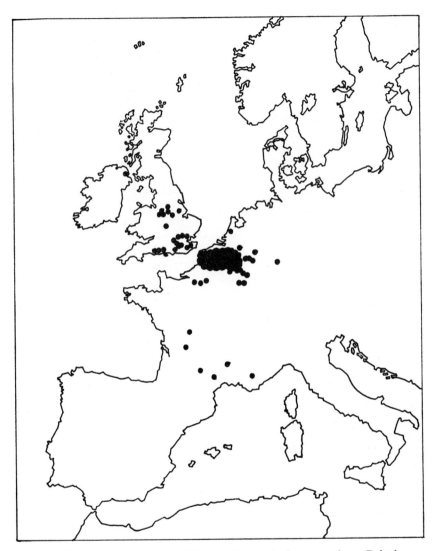

FIG. 15. The wintering areas of Lesser Redpolls from northern Britain, as shown by ringing recoveries. Only the distribution of the recoveries is shown, not their number. The mass in Belgium compared with elsewhere results chiefly from the official bird-catching season, which lasts for six weeks from 1 October.

recoveries, which tend to be most numerous in Belgium in years when birch seeds in England are scarce (Evans 1969). Evidently the distance the birds migrate is influenced by how much food they find on the way, for they tend to stop in areas of abundant food, and move on if they do not find them. In consequence the Redpolls found in particular localities vary greatly in number from year to year, according to the size of the birch crop, and many individuals winter in widely separated areas in different years. At least six ringed birds were found in Britain in one winter and in Belgium another; but on the other hand, at least two visited the same part of Germany in consecutive winters (Mohr 1967). Also the six Lesser Redpolls caught in successive summers in Britain had all returned to the same locality to breed or moult, but at this season they are less dependent on birch seeds.

Exceptionally large numbers of Redpolls left Britain in the autumns of 1959 and 1964. In the first year they reached Iberia (observations only), where they do not normally winter, and in the second southern France (Erard 1966). After both years, moreover, some birds bred on the Frisian Islands, Holland; and one bird caught there in July 1965 had been ringed in Britain the preceding autumn as a juvenile. Previous records of breeding in Holland were in 1942 and 1954. The two tendencies, to move much further in some years than in others and to breed outside the normal range in years following large emigrations, are typical of so-called 'irruptive migrants' (p. 219–28).

Mealy Redpolls also arrive each autumn on the east coasts of Britain, but in greatly varying numbers. At least eight large invasions occurred in the last century and one in the present century, in 1910 (Evans 1911). Since most migration out of Fenno-Scandia is southeasterly, these large influxes are puzzling, but as some birds come every year, their numbers could be swollen accordingly in years of exceptional emigration. One Mealy Redpoll ringed in Hampshire in March 1960 was later recovered in Sweden. Greenland Redpolls also appear annually on the northern Isles and northwest Scotland, though even in good years their numbers are small. More than usual appeared on Fair Isle in 1925, 1955 and 1959 (Williamson 1963). Such birds are probably drifted migrants, which have missed Iceland, the normal wintering area for this population. In addition, white-rumped Redpolls are occasionally seen in Britain. It is not possible to ascertain their race in the field, but both Coue's and Hornemann's were collected on several occasions in the last years of the nineteenth century and in the first years of the present one.

SERINS

The last genus in this chapter, *Serinus*, is one of the largest, but its stronghold is in Africa and only two species, the Serin and the Citril Finch, breed in Europe. In appearance and habits, the Serin *S. serinus* is a typical representative, a small streaky green bird, about four and a half inches (11.5 cm.) long, with a stumpy bill and a short forked tail. In the cock the forehead, eye-stripe, nape, breast and rump are yellow, the back and sides are greenish-brown with grey-brown stripes, and the belly is whitish. The hen is duller, more streaked and less yellow than the cock; while the young are similar to the hen but paler and even more streaked. In all birds, the wing and tail feathers are mainly blackish-brown, with white tips on the inner secondaries. The call-note is a canary-like 'tsooeet', and the flight-note sounds like 'si-twi-twi-twi'.

Many people associate the Serin with Mediterranean towns and villages, where it can be seen pouring forth its monotonous jingling song from a tree or overhead wire. And indeed it is commonest in the southern half of its range, from Iberia east to the Balkans and Asia Minor, and south to the Moroccan Atlas. But for at least two hundred years, it has been spreading, and now breeds to the tip of southern Sweden, through Germany and Poland, to the Baltic States and Western Ukraine (Fig. 27, p. 91). To most of these newly colonised areas, it is a summer visitor, withdrawing south in autumn. The bird first bred in southern England in 1967, when young were reared in at least one locality and possibly in two (Ferguson-Lees 1968). This was preceded by a steady increase in the number of vagrant individuals recorded.

In its natural habitat, Mediterranean woodland, the Serin is found around openings and along the fringes. But it now lives mainly in cultivated land, nesting in vineyards, orchards, hedgerows and tree-lined avenues, around villages and in town parks and gardens. The small seeds of various weeds and grasses form the bulk of the food, but buds are eaten in spring and insects in summer. A study in Germany showed that elm (*Ulmus*) buds, birch (*Betula*) catkins and dandelion (*Taraxacum*) seeds were important in spring, shepherd's purse (*Capsella*), brassica and persicaria (*Polygonum*) seeds in summer and autumn, and mugwort (*Artemisia vulgaris*) seeds in winter (Eber 1956).

In the south of the range, eggs are laid from late February to August, but it is not known how many broods are raised by each pair. Further north, the birds lay between mid-May and July and thus have time for only two broods. In woodland, the nest is often placed on the spreading bough of an oak or pine, usually within seven metres of the ground; but in cultivated land it is placed in an orchard tree or a thick bush, usually within two metres of the ground. Either way, the structure is small, compact and well concealed, made of grass, lichens, roots and moss, bound with spider silk, and thickly lined with hair and feathers. The eggs number 3–5 and are bluish-white, with purple-brown spots and streaks. Incubation takes 12–14 days, and the young stay in the nest for 14–16 days.

A close relative of the European Serin, the drab green *S. canaria*, from the Canary Islands, the Azores and Madeira, was the ancestor of all domestic canaries. The wild bird was brought to Europe in the sixteenth

Domestic 'Border' canary on nest-pan.

century, and all the modern yellow canaries have been developed by care-
ful breeding from chance mutations. During domestication the difference
in appearance between the sexes was also lost, and now the only way of
distinguishing them is by the song of the cock, which is also more elaborate
than in the ancestral form. So keen has been the interest in canary breeding that in Britain alone, a dozen varieties now exist, which differ in size,
shape, colour and song. The 'Norwich' variety, for example, is a large,
almost spherical bird, with a great broad head and copious plumage,
while the 'Yorkshire' is tall and slim, with tight sleek plumage. The
'Border' is the small, well-rounded variety, closest to most peoples' idea
of a canary, but still other varieties have crests on their heads or long
frilly feathers on their flanks. By tradition the birds are fed mainly on the
seed of the grass *Phalaris canariensis*, which is grown commercially in
Mediterranean countries, and are given hard-boiled egg or other protein
food to rear their young. But despite their long domestication, canaries of
all sorts still behave essentially like the wild serin from which they were
derived.

In contrast to the Serin, the Citril Finch *S. citrinella* has a limited distribution, being confined to the mountains of central and southern Europe,
with another race on the Balearics, Corsica and Sardinia (Fig. 16). It is
nearly five inches (12.5 cm.) long. The adults of the mainland form are
distinguished by their predominantly yellow-green plumage, shading to
slate-grey on the nape and sides of the neck, greenish-yellow rump and
unstreaked underparts. The wings and tail are blackish, and the former
carry two dull-green bars. The hen is dingier and more streaked than the
cock. The juveniles lack all trace of green, but are mainly brown above
and greyish-brown below, and are well streaked; with buff wing-bars
instead of green ones. In the field the Citril Finch is distinguished from
the Siskin and the Serin by the grey in the plumage, the uniform streaked
underparts and generally duller appearance. The usual call-note is a
plaintive 'tsi-ew' and the flight note is a metallic 'tweek' or 'tweek-eek-
eek'.

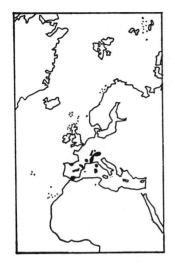

FIG. 16. The breeding range of the Citril Finch.

The mainland form breeds among conifers in northeast and southeast Spain (chiefly Pyrenees, and the Sierras de Guadarama and Nevada), southern France (Massif Central, Pyrenees, Vosges, Jura, Alps), southern Germany (Black Forest), southern Austria (Tyrol), Switzerland (Alps), and northern Italy (Alps and Apennines). In most of these areas it is local and breeds mainly above 1,400 metres (4,500 feet), but in the Black Forest, down to 600 metres (2,000 feet) (Ferguson-Lees 1956). Originally restricted in the breeding season to the vicinity of alpine meadows near the tree-line, the species has spread downhill to some extent since the forests were opened by man. In forest it eats conifer seeds directly from the cones, and in open areas, it feeds from grasses, dandelions (*Taraxacum*), thistles and other Compositae, clinging to the stems to get the seeds or picking them off the ground. The nest, which is placed high in a tree, is a small, fairly neat structure, of grasses, roots and lichens, lined thickly with thistle down, fine roots and feathers. The eggs number 3–5 and are bluish-white with red-brown streaks and spots. Incubation lasts 12–14 days, and the young stay in the nest for 17–18 days, longer than most other finches (Lang 1948). Egg-laying usually begins between mid-April and early May, according to altitude, and continues at least until late June, giving time for up to three broods. But in years of good spruce crops, the birds may lay in late February or March and raise an earlier brood on seeds from the opening cones. In this respect, the Citril Finch resembles the Siskin, discussed earlier.

In the Alps, a few Citril Finches remain all year near their breeding areas, some move lower in autumn, but most migrate to southern France. This migration covers 200–300 kilometres each way, but at least one ringed bird moved more than 600 kilometres into Spain (de Crousaz & Lebreton

1963). Citril Finches also winter on low ground in central and southern Italy, along the Mediterranean coast, and various parts of southern Spain. In some such areas they feed in birches and alders along with Redpolls and Siskins. The solitary British record is of an adult female caught at Yarmouth on 29 January 1904.

The Citril Finches inhabiting the mountains of Corsica and Sardinia (*S.c. corsicana*) differ in both colour and habits from the mainland birds. The mantle is warm brown instead of green, and more strongly streaked, and the underparts are a paler yellow, especially in the cock, while the hen is also more streaked on the sides. Here the birds live in dry scrub-covered rocky ground. Sometimes they are found in areas with a scattering of conifers, but also breed far above the present tree-line, at least to 1,650 metres (5,500 feet) (Armitage 1937). These birds nest in low tree-heaths or genista bushes, usually less than a metre above the ground. In some places on the islands they breed in the maquis scrub almost down to sea-level, and most move lower in winter, when they become one of the commonest birds around the coasts.

CHAPTER 3

THE CARDUELINE FINCHES, PART 2

THIS chapter deals with the less typical carduelines, most of which are not particularly closely-related to one another. It is convenient to start with the Hawfinch *Coccothraustes coccothraustes*, which has already formed the subject of a monograph in this series (Mountfort 1957). The species is the only member of its genus and, at seven inches long (18 cm.) and 50–60 grams in weight, is the second largest of the European finches. The massive head and bill, bull-neck and short tail combine to give the bird a stocky, top-heavy appearance. The general colouration appears orange-brown, with mainly blackish wings and large white shoulder patches. In the cock the head is chestnut, the nape pale-grey, and the back a rich brown, while the underparts are pinkish-brown shading to white beneath the tail, except for a large black bib the size of a thumb-nail. A thin black line runs from either side of the bib up around the bill, and the bill itself is blue in summer and pale-horn in winter. The flight feathers shine with iridescent purple and green, and in the hand the four inner primaries and the secondaries are seen to be notched and curled at the ends (for use in courtship), a feature shown by no other finch (Fig. 17). In the tail, the two central feathers are brown and the rest are mainly black with white tips

FIG. 17. The modified flight feathers of the Hawfinch. *Left*, a single feather; *right*, appearance in the closed wing.

and rufous fringes. The hen Hawfinch is paler and greyer than the cock, and in summer has less blue on the beak. The juveniles lack the black bib and are more yellow than the adults, with narrow black bars across the breast, instead of streaks like the young of other finches. Young cocks can be distinguished from young hens by the presence of black round the bill and by their darker underparts. The usual note of the species is an explosive 'tzik'; the contact note, used as the birds move among the branches, is a thin 'zee'; and the flight note sounds like 'tzik-ic'.

The Hawfinch is perhaps best known for its ability to break open the extremely hard fruits of cherries and other trees, its whole head being enlarged and specialised accordingly. The inside of the bill is equipped with striated pads for gripping such stones, the skull is strengthened and

modified to accommodate powerful muscles, with large areas of attachment, and the individual muscles are unusually tendinous (p. 103).
These muscles form bulges on either side of the head and make the bird
in life look swollen-cheeked.

In summer Hawfinches feed mainly in trees, and in autumn and winter,
when the fruits have fallen, on the ground below. In trees, the birds are
difficult to pick out among the leaves, and on the ground they are extremely
wary, taking flight at the least alarm and disappearing like rockets into
the tree-tops. They reappear only after a long interval and drop one by
one in cautious stages through the branches, pausing between each move
and slowly turning their great heads from side to side to look around. A
feeding flock can nonetheless be located at a distance by the constant
sound of cracking stones. In fact the presence of split stones of holly (*Ilex*)
or cherry beneath the trees is a sure sign of these birds for, if food holds out,
they return daily to the same place. The birds are usually found in parties
of less than a dozen, though flocks of several hundreds are seen from time
to time.

Hawfinches extend from Britain across Europe and part of the North
African coast through Palaearctic Asia to Japan, reaching 60°N in Europe
and 55°N in Asia (Fig. 18). Over most of this area they are found in
mature broad-leaved woodland, and are especially numerous in the beech
and hornbeam forests of central and eastern Europe. In the north, they
inhabit the deciduous trees bordering the rivers that run through an
otherwise coniferous landscape, and in the south the steppe-woodlands
and thorn-thickets of desert-fringes. Where they are common, they also
breed in orchards, large gardens or parks, including those in some towns
and cities. From west to east across the range, the birds become gradually
paler; and five subspecies are recognised, the nominate form occupying
most of the range, including Britain.

The Hawfinch was not proved to breed in Britain until about 1830,
when several nests were found in the Epping Forest and at other localities
in the southeast, but the bird was certainly present before then. In
Norfolk, Sir Thomas Browne (1605-82) wrote that it was '*chiefly seen in
summer time about cherrietime*'. Today, it does not breed in Cornwall, western
Wales, most of Scotland, and the whole of Ireland, despite the abundance
in some of these areas of suitable habitat (Parslow 1968). Its present strongholds lie in southeast England, the Severn Valley and the Bristol District,
parts of the Midlands, the Lake District, and at scattered localities elsewhere. These are all areas with extensive deciduous woodlands or of woodlands and orchards. The 21,000 acres of cherry orchards in England are
particularly favoured haunts. The fallen fruits are eaten from mid-summer
to the following spring, while buds, blossom and ripe fruits are also taken in
season, though to a much smaller extent. Apples and pears rotted on the
ground also provide food, the birds balancing on the top to tear out the
flesh and reach the pips. In some areas the birds also visit kitchen gardens

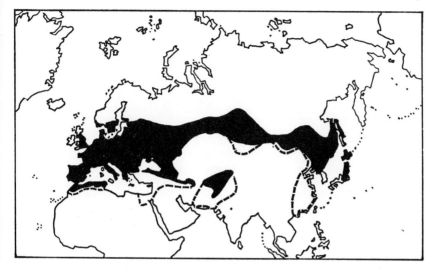

FIG. 18. The breeding range of the Hawfinch. The broken line marks the southern edge of the wintering range.

for peas, usually in the early mornings, and leave characteristically shredded pods behind.

Hawfinches live chiefly, however, on the large fruits of woodland trees, including those of wych elm (*Ulmus*), hornbeam (*Carpinus*), beech (*Fagus*), sycamore and maple (*Acer*), which are eaten from the time they are formed in summer as long as they last into winter. The birds then search hedgerows for hips (*Rosa*), haws (*Crataegus*), and other fruits, and finally in late winter return to woodlands for the buds of oak (*Quercus*) and other trees, and the terminal shoots of yew (*Taxus*) (not the tips, but the new stem behind). In early summer, Hawfinches also eat a lot of caterpillars, such as those of *Operophthera brumata* and *Tortrix viridana*, from leaves, and catch large beetles, such as cockchafers (*Melonantha*), on the wing. The young are raised on a mixture of seeds and insects (p. 167).

The nest is usually in a wood or orchard, built near the main stem of a sapling or on the horizontal branch of a taller tree, rarely less than three metres above the ground. It is untidy and flimsy, consisting of a saucer of twigs, lined with roots, grasses and lichens. The eggs number 4–5, rarely 3, 6 or 7, and are buff, grey-green or pale bluish, marked irregularly with spots and squiggles of purple-brown and pale grey. The incubation period lasts 11–13 days and nestling period 12–14 days. In southern England, the eggs may be laid from early May at least until mid-July, so that the last young fledge in August. This would give time for three broods, but probably most pairs raise fewer. However, one captive pair raised three and attempted a fourth in this time; and in Germany a nest with young was found in the wild as late as 30 August (in Mountfort 1957).

Over the range as a whole, the most northern populations of Hawfinches are migratory and the southern are resident. The general direction of migration in Europe is northeast–southwest, as in most other finches, and movements exceeding 500 kilometres have been recorded by ringing. At the time of writing, only 360 individuals have been ringed in Britain, and the recoveries have provided no indication that the British stock migrates, though from time to time birds of unknown origin have been taken at lighthouses around the coasts.

BULLFINCH *Pyrrhula pyrrhula*

The Bullfinch is the only European representative of a small, mainly Asiatic, genus of forest-dwelling birds. It is about six inches (15 cm.) long, with a short rounded bill, a longish square-ended tail, and soft silky plumage which shows no hint of streaking. In both sexes the wings, tail, cap and bib are glossy black, the rump and ventral regions are white, and the secondary coverts are grey, forming a bar across the wings. The cock also has a pinkish-red breast and a blue-grey back, but in the hen both these regions are brownish-grey, darker on the upper than on the under-side. In both sexes the bill is black and the legs are black or brown. The juveniles lack the black on the head, and are browner than the hen, with yellow-brown secondary coverts and bill. The familiar call is a loud piping whistle held on a steady monotone; it is given mainly by isolated birds wishing to rejoin a group, and such birds will readily come to a human imitation of the call. Once together, the birds keep in touch with a faint pipping note. The soft creaky song is uttered by both sexes, but carries only a few metres so is seldom heard. In autumn and winter Bullfinches are met mainly in groups of less than a dozen, and during the rest of the year in pairs.

The species extends from Ireland, across Europe and Asia to Japan (Fig. 19). In general, individual birds become larger and brighter towards the north of the range and towards the tops of mountains. The British birds are given subspecific rank (*P.p. pileata*) because they are smaller than *P.p. pyrrhula* from northern Europe and Siberia, and darker and duller than all the continental forms. Over most of their range, the birds breed in forests dominated by coniferous trees, but usually at low densities. They have been found at up to 15 pairs per square kilometre in spruce forests in Finland (Palmgren 1930, Haapanen 1966), but only by observation which is none too reliable on this species. In western Europe, where they extend south into pure deciduous areas, they reach densities exceeding 50 pairs per square kilometre, as I have found near Oxford and elsewhere by the more reliable method of catching and ringing.

Bullfinches are common and widespread over most of Britain, breeding in woodland undergrowth, thickets, shrubberies and straggling hedge-

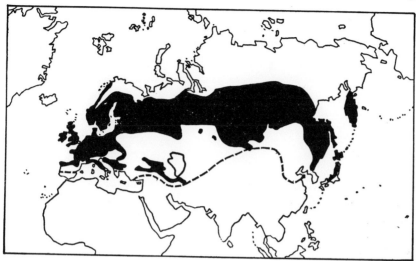

FIG. 19. The breeding range of the Bullfinch. The broken line marks the southern edge of the wintering range.

rows, but are absent from the Isle of Man (despite much suitable habitat) and from northernmost Scotland, the Outer Hebrides and the northern Isles (where suitable habitat is sparse). Since the mid-nineteen-fifties the birds have increased in the south, especially in the parks and gardens of towns, and their depredations on fruit buds have become serious in commercial orchards (p. 116). This problem results because Bullfinches prefer the buds of such trees to their main natural foods in spring, namely the buds of hawthorn (*Crataegus*) and other native trees and the flowers of sallow (*Salix*) and oak (*Quercus*). For the rest of the year the birds eat a great variety of seeds (Table 6). In a mixed deciduous wood near Oxford I found that at least four-fifths of the tree-species and half the herbaceous plants present provided food at one time or another. But these foods were not taken in proportion to their abundance and some of the least common plants yielded a substantial part of the food. From May onwards the most important seeds were dog's mercury (*Mercurialis perennis*), wych elm (*Ulmus glabra*), birch (*Betula*), bramble (*Rubus*), nettle (*Urtica*), docks (*Rumex*) and ash (*Fraxinus*). On nearby cultivated land the birds ate mainly the seeds of various weeds, such as chickweed (*Stellaria*), dandelion (*Taraxacum*), buttercups (*Ranunculus*), sorrel (*Rumex acetosa*), sowthistle (*Sonchus*), and fat-hen (*Chenopodium*). In upland areas, heather (*Calluna*) seeds are eaten extensively, and on the continent, rowan (*Sorbus*) fruits are important in autumn and maple (*Acer*) seeds in winter (Eber 1956, Erkamo 1948).

Bullfinches prefer to feed directly from their food-plants (rather than

Table 6. The main foods of the Bullfinch through the year in southern England. Items are listed in order of their appearance in the diet from April onwards. (From Newton 1967d.)

	J	F	M	A	M	J	J	A	S	O	N	D
SEEDS												
Chickweed (*Stellaria*)				••	━━	━	•	••				
Dandelion (*Taraxacum*)				•	━━	━	•	••	•			
Elm (*Ulmus*)					•	━━	━	••				
Dog's mercury (*Mercurialis perennis*)					━━	━	━	••				
Jack-by-the-hedge (*Alliaria petiolata*)					•	━	━					
Buttercups (*Ranunculus*)					•	━	━	•				
Sowthistle (*Sonchus*)							••	━━	━	••	••	••
Charlock (*Sinapis*)							••••	━━	━	••••	••••	•
Birch (*Betula*)	••••	•						•••	━━	━		••
Dock (*Rumex*)	━━	•	•••					•••	━━	━	━	
Fat-hen (*Chenopodium*)							••	━━	━	•	••••	
Meadowsweet (*Filipendula*)								━━	━	•••		
Bramble (*Rubus*)	━━	•••••						••	━━	━	━	━
Nettle (*Urtica dioica*)	••••								••••	━━	━	━
Ash (*Fraxinus*)	━━	•••••								••••	••	━
BUDS AND FLOWERS												
Crab-apple (*Malus sylvestris*)	━━	••	••••	••••								
Hawthorn (*Crataegus*)	••	━━	━									
Elm (*Ulmus*)	••	━	━	••								
Blackthorn (*Prunus spinosa*)			•••••	━	•							
Sallow (*Salix*)			━	••••								
Oak (*Quercus*)			•	━	━	•						

off the ground), under cover of wood or hedgerow, and move into the open only when food is short. Compared to other finches, they eat many more tree-flowers, buds, berries and other soft fruits, to which their short rounded bills are ideally suited (p. 106). They raise their young on a mixture of seeds and invertebrates, including caterpillars, spiders and small snails, the latter being de-shelled in the bill like seeds.

In the breeding season, the adults develop in the floor of their mouths special pouches in which food for their young is retained (Fig. 20). These pouches open, one on each side of the tongue and, when full, extend back under the jaw as far as the neck, when they together hold about one cubic centimetre of food. A bird with full sacs shows a bulging throat, over which

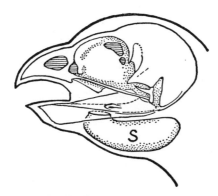

FIG. 20. The food sacs (s) of the Bullfinch.

the feathers stand nearly erect. Each time the sacs are emptied they shrink and their walls fold. I have been unable to find them in Bullfinches in winter, so probably they are formed each spring by the proliferation of tissue on the mouth floor. Similar pouches have been noted in the Pine Grosbeak (*Pinicola*), in the Trumpeter Finches (*Rhodopechys*), and in one of the North American rosy finches (*Leucosticte tephrocotis*), perhaps implying a close relationship between these genera (French 1954, Niethammer 1966, Miller 1941). Other cardueline finches carry food for their young in their gullets.

The nest of the Bullfinch is usually placed in a thick shrub, 1–2 metres above the ground. It is easily recognised, consisting of a shallow base of thin twigs, lined with a pad of rootlets. The eggs number 3–6, and are greenish-white, with red-brown spots. Incubation takes 12–14 days and, in the absence of disturbance, the young stay in the nest for 15–17 days. In most years in southern Britain, laying occurs between early May and late July, so that the last young fledge in August, but in some years laying continues to mid-September, so that the last young fledge in October. This would allow each pair to raise three broods in a short season and four in a long one, but few (if any) pairs can raise this number, because of the heavy predation on the eggs and nestlings (p. 181–3). In my experience near Oxford, the ratio of young to adults after a short season is usually around 3:1 and after a long one 5:1.

British Bullfinches are remarkably sedentary. At the time of writing, over 40,000 have been ringed and nearly 900 recovered. About 85% of these had moved less than five kilometres, suggesting that the average Bullfinch remains in the same locality throughout its life. Most other movements recorded by ringing were less than 25 kilometres, and only two exceeded 200. Cross-channel movement is evidently negligible, for there are only two recoveries, one from Holland to Essex and one from Kent to France. Northern Bullfinches, however, migrate regularly, and in most autumns some reach Shetland and Fair Isle. There are few authentic records of this subspecies further south, though in January 1964 I caught a cock near Oxford. Movements from the northern conifer forests southwards are said to be most pronounced every third or fourth year, and from the mountains to the plains of central Europe every second year, but so far these movements have not been linked with the fluctuations of any particular fruit-crop.

PINE GROSBEAK *Pinicola enucleator*

A bird of the northern forests, the Pine Grosbeak is the largest of the European finches, eight inches long (20 cm.) and around 60 grams in weight. It is heavily built, with a longish slighty-forked tail, a swollen bill, and a conspicuous double white wing-bar. Typically the cock has the head and body suffused with rose-red on a background of blue-grey, which may show through anywhere, but especially on the flanks and belly. The wings and tail are mainly brown, but the primaries are faintly fringed with red, and some of the secondaries and all the tertials are fringed with white; the white wing-bars are formed by the tips of the median and greater coverts. The bill and legs are blackish. In the hen the red is replaced by a bronze or greenish colour, brighter on the crown and rump, and shading to grey on the back. The juveniles are similar to the hen, but more grey-green. Whatever the sex and age, however, the individual variation is great, and after a moult in captivity all cocks turn yellowish. The species is adept at clinging to branches, but moves slowly and deliberately in trees and spends long periods feeding or sitting in the same position, hence its Canadian nickname 'mope'. To the delight of photographers, the bird is often amazingly tame and can sometimes almost be touched. It is generally seen in parties of 5–15, and in the open its flight is more undulating than that of other finches. Four subspecies are recognised in Eurasia and eight in North America.

Although classed in a genus by itself, the Pine Grosbeak is undoubtedly close to the Bullfinches. This is shown by its general shape, with plump body and longish tail, its copious soft plumage devoid of streaks, its long rictal bristles round the bill, and the same throat pouches for holding food for the young. It also behaves similarly, is generally quiet and unobtrusive, flicks up its wings and tail when uneasy, and puffs out its breast feathers during display. The call, which sounds like 'tee-tee' or 'tee-tee-teu' on descending scale, is like the pipe of the Bullfinch,* but with each note shorter and higher pitched; the contact note sounds nearly the same; and the song (again uttered by both sexes) is similar, but louder and more musical. The species also resembles the Bullfinch in its forest-habitat, its

---

* In North America the call varies so much between some races that they can easily be distinguished by it, and individuals of certain races will not respond to the calls of others (C. Adkisson, *in litt.*).

PLATE I. The Chaffinch (cock, *above*) is the most numerous and wide-spread finch in Europe; it breeds almost anywhere where there are trees.

PLATE 2. Bramblings at their nest in a birch in Swedish Lapland. The cock carries food for the young in his bill, a feature that distinguishes the fringilline from the cardueline finches, which feed their young by regurgitation.

diet rich in buds, shoots and soft fruits, and its habit of fly-catching on the
wing, for which the rictal bristles help.

In northern Europe, the Pine Grosbeak breeds sparsely in a narrow
belt straddling the arctic circle between 65°N and 70°N, but further east
it becomes progressively more numerous and widespread, extending south
in Siberia to the latitude of Paris (Fig. 21). Rather light open forests,
pine-clad hillsides and subarctic birch woods are where it nests. In the
New World, it also extends southwards from the northern forests in
conifers on the Rocky and Cascade Mountains into Colorado and California. In both the Old and New Worlds, the northern birds move south
in autumn, and often enter towns to feed, but those which live on the
American mountains stay there through the year.

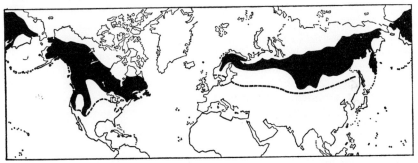

FIG. 21. The breeding range of the Pine Grosbeak. The broken line
marks the southern edge of the invasion areas, so far as it is known.

The Pine Grosbeak takes much the same foods in Eurasia and North
America. At one season or another it eats the buds and fruits of almost all
the northern woody plants, and when these are scarce, it takes the seeds
of numerous herbaceous plants. In spring the buds of various conifers,
willow (*Salix*), birch (*Betula*) and aspen (*Populus*) predominate in the
food; in summer the young staminate cones of conifers and the fruits of
Vaccinium, Empetrum, Rubus, Juniperus and other plants of the forest undergrowth; in autumn rowan (*Sorbus*) and other succulent tree-fruits; and in
winter these and the drier fruits of maple (*Acer*), ash (*Fraxinus*) and other
trees. Almost certainly buds form a larger part of the winter diet in years
when tree-fruits are scarce. Young Grosbeaks are raised on a mixture of
seeds and invertebrates, including tipulids, caterpillars, beetles and grass-
hoppers. The species has many foods in common with the Bullfinch, but
its larger body and bill enable it to deal with larger items, and in most
winters the Grosbeak remains north of the Bullfinch, its fluffier plumage
giving better protection against the cold.

In Europe, Pine Grosbeaks lay their eggs between late May and early
July, but mostly in the first half of June. Some pairs would thus have time

for two broods, but probably the majority raise only one, most late clutches being repeats after the loss of an earlier one. Nests in conifers are usually near the trunk or near the end of a splayed branch, 2–7 metres above the ground, but nests in birches or shrubs are usually less than two metres above the ground. The nest is like the Bullfinch's, but larger and deeper, with an outer layer of twigs and bents, and a lining of thinner grass, lichens and rootlets. The eggs number 3–4, rarely 2 or 5, and are usually deep greenish-blue, blotched and spotted with blackish or dark purple-brown, with violet marks. Incubation takes 13–14 days, but the nestling period is known from only one nest in captivity at which it was 13–14 days (Bernhoft-Osa 1960).

In Fenno-Scandia, some Pine Grosbeaks remain all year on their breeding areas, but most move south or southwest to the central districts in October and return at the end of March. Their local movements at Kemi, in Finland, have been correlated with the rowan crop, many Grosbeaks coming in winters when berries were numerous, but few or none when they were scarce. When the available berries had been consumed each year, the birds grew restless and soon moved on (Grenquist 1947). The extent of the movements varies greatly, however, and in some years, large numbers of hungry birds move further than usual, to the south of Fenno-Scandia and the Baltic Provinces, or sometimes through central Europe into northern Italy, Switzerland, France and rarely to Britain. The population of Fenno-Scandia is probably too small to give rise to these large invasions, and in recent years observations have confirmed that they originate further east. In the last 100 years movements to the south and west of the usual winter-range occurred in 1890/91, 1913/14*, 1918/19, 1938/39*, 1942/43, 1952/53, 1954/55 and 1956/57 (Faxén 1945, Malmberg 1949, Karvik et al. 1953, Markgren 1955, Markgren & Lundberg 1959). Those marked with an asterisk were mainly into the southern Baltic region, and the rest mainly into Fenno-Scandia. The various records (few authenticated) of the species in Britain were mostly from the eastern counties between October and March, as one might expect, but surprisingly the species has only twice been recorded in Scotland, latterly on the Isle of May, the same year (1954) as an invasion on the continent (Flower, Weir & Scott 1955).

TRUMPETER FINCH *Rhodopechys githaginea*

Mention can conveniently be included at this point of the Trumpeter Finch, which is a rare vagrant to Mediterranean countries, but otherwise has no claim to inclusion in this book. The species inhabits open, arid areas in the Canary Islands, North Africa and southwest Asia, where its distribution is governed by the presence of water. It is pale buff in colour, with mainly blackish wings and tail, though the cock also has a pink flush on the body feathers. The species feeds on the buds, leaves and seeds of various desert plants, and over most of its range, nests from March to early June. It gets its name from its call.

SCARLET ROSEFINCH *Carpodacus erythrinus*

The Scarlet Rosefinch is the only member of a large genus to extend into Europe. It is six inches (15 cm.) long, with a heavy, brown bill, a dumpy stance with head sunk between shoulders, and two pale wing-bars. The cocks come in two main colour phases. In some the body is mostly dull crimson or pink, brighter on the head, upper breast and rump, and mixed with brown on the back and sides, with a white belly and ventral region. The wings and tail are brown. Other cocks, supposedly in their first-year (but capable of breeding), lack all red and are mainly greyish-brown. A few are intermediate, however, and after a moult in captivity, even the reddest cocks turn dull yellow or brown. The hens are pale olive-brown, streaked with darker brown; and the juveniles are similar, but darker and more streaked. Both hens and juveniles are rather nondescript, however, and are best distinguished by the combination of a regularly streaked breast, a very rounded crown, the pale bars rather high on the wing, and the forked tail. In the hand, the plumage of both sex and age-groups appears hard and coarse.

In contrast to most *Carpodacus* finches, which live in scrub on high mountains and have extremely restricted ranges, the Scarlet Rosefinch extends into lowlands and occurs over more of the Palaearctic than any other finch (Fig. 22). It breeds over almost the whole of Asia, between latitudes 25 and 68°N, and in parts of Europe, excluding Britain. The species is divided into a northern lowland form (*C.e. erythrinus*) and a southern mountain one (*C.e. roseatus*), largely separated by tracts of steppe and desert from which the species is absent. Since about 1930, the northern form has been spreading westwards, and now breeds at scattered localities in Poland, eastern Germany, Finland and southern Sweden. (A similar spread was recorded at the beginning of the century, but later contracted.) Over most of its range, the lowland form is wholly migratory, wintering in the southernmost parts of Asia from Iran through India and Burma to China. The mountain form breeds in the Himalayas and other parts of southern Asia between 8,500 and 14,500 feet, and descends in winter.

In Europe, Scarlet Rosefinches breed in thickets of willows, alders or poplars. They prefer areas in which most bushes are 3–4 metres high, with a few taller ones for song-posts (Czarnecki 1961, 1962) and in these habitats breed either in forests or in otherwise open country. In their strongholds further east, they also breed in drier places, in gardens, and in briar and scrub patches in farmland. Most of their food in summer is obtained directly from plants (rather than the ground) and in Europe consists of the buds and young leaves of birch (*Betula*), wild cherry

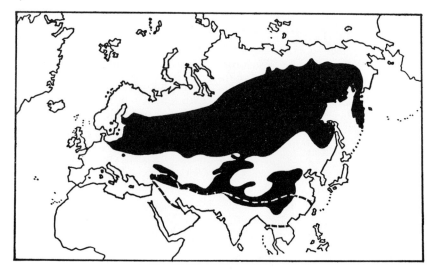

FIG. 22. The breeding range of the Scarlet Rosefinch. The broken line encloses the wintering range, so far as it is known.

(*Prunus*), wild apple (*Malus*), lilac (*Syringa*), rowan (*Sorbus*) and sallow (*Salix*), and the seeds of sallow, grasses, dandelions (*Taraxacum*) and other Compositae, berries and various insects (Sokolowski 1958, Risberg 1970).

The species spends only a short time on its European breeding grounds, arrives in the latter half of May and leaves in August, so has time for only one or two broods. The nest is placed low in cover, often at the base of a bush and surrounded by dense grass and reeds. It is loosely made of grass and roots, and lined with plant-down and hair. The eggs number 4–6 and are very distinctive: a deep vivid blue with a few dark spots and streaks. Incubation lasts 11–12 days and the young stay in the nest for 10–11 days (Reinikainen 1939, Risberg 1970).

The bird migrates in August, as mentioned, and is the only European finch which postpones its moult until it reaches winter quarters. Birds from unknown breeding areas arrive on the northern plains of India in September, and start moulting when they reach the south in November. They here mingle with the resident *C.e. roseatus*, which descends to the plains in autumn, and are generally encountered in large flocks in open country, gardens and villages, feeding on weed seeds from the ground among undergrowth or in millet and other crops (Whistler 1941).

The Scarlet Rosefinch was first collected in Britain in 1869, but has been recorded with increasing frequency since then, and is now seen annually on the northern isles. On Fair Isle, it appears mostly in September, with up to ten in a single year. All the birds so far seen have been brown ones.

CROSSBILLS

To their diet of conifer seeds, the crossbills are superbly adapted, using their large feet to hold the cones they have plucked and their crossed mandibles to open them. The upper part of the bill curves downward, and the lower curves upward and at the same time twists to the right or left of the upper. The birds are adept at climbing among the branches, using feet and bill to pull themselves along in parrot-fashion, and often hang upside down while feeding. They are otherwise distinguished by their large heads, short forked tails, call-notes and colouration. In all three species the cocks are mainly reddish and the hens and young are greenish-grey. They are all about 6½ inches (16 cm.) long. The species differ chiefly in body-weight, bill-size and preferred food, each specialising on different types of cones (Lack 1944). All three are noted for their erratic behaviour, because they appear in particular localities only at irregular intervals and at least two of the species will breed in any month.

To understand their behaviour, it will help first to say something about their food-plants, to the fruiting of which the lives of crossbills are geared. The seeds of all conifers form in late summer, and then remain on the tree until the cones open, 3–22 months later, according to species. Crossbills can extract the seeds from cones at any stage of ripeness, but most easily from those which have begun to open naturally. Hence, the seeds of different species of conifers become most accessible at different seasons. Of the European trees that are important, spruce (*Picea abies*) retains its seeds for nine months until the following spring, pine (*Pinus sylvestris*) for 22 months until the spring of the second year (but only in the last year are they much use to crossbills), and fir (*Abies alba*) and larch (*Larix decidua*) for three months until the first autumn. The cones of this last tree stand erect, however, so keep some seeds for months after most have been shed. Once the seeds of these various conifers have fallen, they are effectively lost to crossbills, which cannot easily pick them off the ground.

In the northern forests, good cone crops are sporadic. In any one year, the productive areas, extending perhaps over hundreds or thousands of square kilometres, may be separated from one another by terrain in which that year the crop is poor. The following year the crops may be good in different areas. Crossbills therefore move every summer when the new crops are forming, leaving areas where they are poor and settling where they are good. If the seeds hold out, the birds then remain in these areas until the next summer, moulting and breeding in the meantime, when again they move in search of regions rich in seeds. Crossbills in Europe thus differ from other birds in making only one major movement each year, in mid-summer, from one area rich in cones to another, and in this way they cope with both regional and annual variations in their food-supply. In some areas, however, there is also a minor movement in the autumn, when larch and fir shed their seeds, but as these trees usually

grow together with other conifers to which the birds then turn, this movement tends to be less marked than the summer one, and in areas where
these trees are lacking, it is absent altogether. But local movements can,
of course, occur in any month, as in other finches, at least partly in response
to changes in food.

These various movements occur every year in the northern forests, but
crossbills are best known for another, less frequent, movement, in which
they leave their regular range in enormous numbers for other regions,
often where conifers are lacking. These massive eruptions have often been
attributed to the widespread failure of the cone-crops or to over-population
on the usual range. Many of the emigrants perish and others live as best
they can and return to their home range in a later year. These movements
are discussed fully in Chapter 15, however, so the following deals only
with the main features, habits and distribution of the three species.

COMMON CROSSBILL *Loxia curvirostra*

In the Common Crossbill, most cocks are brick-red in colour, brighter on
the rump, with dark brown wings and tail, and greyish undertail-coverts.
In some, however, the red is replaced by yellow or orange, or by a mixture
of red and yellow feathers. This is not related consistently to age, but
young cocks from winter broods tend more often to be yellow in their
first 'adult' dress than do other cocks (p. 203). The hens are greyish-green,
shading to yellow-green on the rump and pale grey on the abdomen and
under tail-coverts, sometimes with a hint of streaking throughout. The
juveniles resemble the hens, but are paler and much more streaked on the
head and body. In all birds the beak is pale brown and the legs are dark
brown.

The Common Crossbill breeds in conifers over much of Europe, Asia
and North America (Fig. 23). The typical form, which in Eurasia feeds
mainly from spruce, occupies most of the range, but 12 isolated subspecies,
which differ slightly in colour, size, bill-shape and food from the nominate
form, are found in the Old World on certain mountains and islands outside
the main range, namely Scotland, Corsica, the Balearic Islands, North
Africa, Cyprus, the Crimea, the Altai, the Tien Shan, the Himalayas to
the mountains of western China, the Far East and Japan, northern Luzon
and southern Annam (p. 86). Thus, the Scottish Crossbill *L.c. scotica*,
which is resident in the pine forests of northeast Scotland, is here classed
as a race of the Common Crossbill which has developed a larger bill
through long association with pine. In body and bill-size it is intermediate
between the Common and the Parrot Crossbill, described below, and
breeds in eight countries, wandering elsewhere occasionally (Fig. 24).
Some would prefer to call this form a race of the Parrot, but until the
other large-billed forms have been considered, little can be gained by
changing the name of this one.

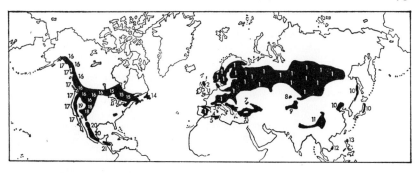

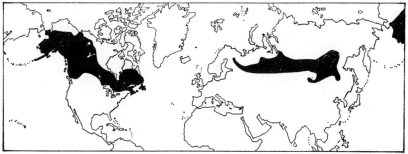

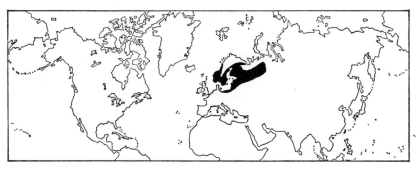

FIG. 23. The breeding ranges of the Common (*top*), Two-barred (*middle*), and Parrot (*bottom*) Crossbills.

1, *L.c. curvirostra*; 2, *scotica*; 3, *corsicana*; 4, *balearica*; 5, *poliogyna*; 6, *guille-mardi*; 7, *mariae*; 8, *altaiensis*; 9, *tianschanica*; 10, *japonica*; 11, *himalayensis*; 12, *meridionalis*; 13, *luzonensis*; 14, *neogaea*; 15, *pusilla*; 16, *minor*; 17, *bendirei*; 18, *benti*; 19, *grinnelli*; 20, *stricklandi*; 21, *mesamericana*.

The typical form of the Common Crossbill also breeds in Britain, chiefly in plantations. In the Brecklands of East Anglia and in the New Forest it breeds every year, in some other parts of southern England, Northumberland, southern Scotland and Ireland in most years, and elsewhere chiefly after invasions. In fact, the numbers of Common Crossbills in Britain expand greatly after each irruption from the continent, and then contract steadily again until the next. Reafforestation with conifers has provided much new habitat, though most of the plantations are still too young, the birds preferring mature forests for breeding, with the trees tall and well-spaced. It is at this stage that they yield most cones.

FIG. 24. Heads of nestling Common, adult Common (*L.c. curvirostra*), adult Scottish (*L.c. scotica*), and adult Parrot Crossbills (*L. pytyopsittacus*).

Although, over the range as a whole, the Common Crossbill has been found to breed in every month, in any one area the nesting season depends on the species of conifers available. In the European spruce forests, breeding may begin in August, soon after the cones have formed, and continue until the following April or May, when the seeds have fallen. Such prolonged breeding is apparently usual in northern Russia (Formosov 1960), and was also recorded in southern Scotland in 1967/68, when occupied nests or freshly-fledged young were seen in each of the nine months from August (Ostroznik & Smith *in litt.*, pers. obs.). In general, records of nests in spruce areas are most numerous in spring (February–April), less so in autumn (August-November), and least numerous in winter (December–January), though this may be partly through a dearth of field-work in the colder months. Only in these forests, however, is breeding known to span the whole period for which seeds are available in the cones.

In pine forests, nesting does not normally begin until late winter or spring, perhaps because, before this time, the birds cannot extract the seeds from these hard cones fast enough to permit them to raise young. The breeding season given in most British text-books is based on what happens in the planted pine woods of southeast England, where eggs have been found between December and June, but mainly from February to April (Fig. 25). In any one year, there is less spread in laying than the diagram would suggest; the season is anyway shorter and later than in spruce forests, and in no other forest-type in which the Crossbill has been studied does it breed only in these months.

In the mixed spruce/pine forests of northern Europe, breeding lasts longer than in planted forests which contain only one of these trees. This is because pine cones open later than spruce, and shed their seeds more slowly. Crossbills can then breed in the spruce areas from August to May,

PLATE 3. Cock Brambling in winter plumage. Towards summer, the buff edges of the head and back feathers will wear off to expose the black below, and at the same time the bill will darken (compare with Plate 2).

PLATE 4. In winter, the Brambling (hen, *above*) can be seen in most parts of Europe, but usually concentrates in areas rich in beechmast.

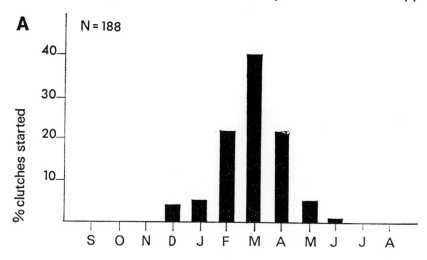

FIG. 25. The laying season of the Common Crossbill. *Above*, in English pine plantations. Compiled mainly from records published over the years in 'Zoologist' and 'British Birds'. *Below*, the annual cycle in mixed spruce/pine forests.

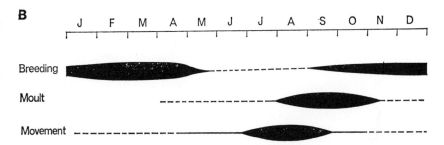

and in the pine areas from May to early July, a total of nearly a year (Haapanen 1966). I am not aware that anyone has actually observed a season of this length, however, though records are available for every month from different years.

In the mixed larch/pine forests of the southern Urals, crossbills eat mainly pine seeds in spring, and mainly larch seeds at other times. When both trees fruit well, the birds breed twice, first in April–May, when the pine cones open, and again in August–September, when the larch cones open. In years when only pine fruits well, the birds nest only in spring, and in years when neither tree does well, the few birds that remain fail to breed at all (Kirikov 1952).

Another pattern occurs on the Tien Shan mountains of central Asia, where some slopes support the spruce *P. shrenkiana*, which keeps its cones for only four months. Here the local Crossbills nest only in late summer and early autumn, while the seeds are readily available. In the Rocky Mountains of Colorado, the birds begin to breed on the foothills in December, and move up during the ensuing months, to exploit the later seed-fall on higher ground. They also use the different conifer-species growing at different levels. They breed from December to June in the low hills, but continue into September on the high tops, a total of at least ten months (Bailey, Niedrach & Baily 1953).

The breeding season of the Common Crossbill thus varies in different regions. In general, the birds can breed for up to three months each year in larch areas, up to seven in pine, up to nine in spruce, and even longer in mixed forests, where the cones of two conifer species open at different seasons. This variation in breeding schedule cannot be due to inherent differences between the Crossbill populations involved, for not only does the season vary from year to year in the same forest-type, but the same birds may breed in different forest-types in successive years. The birds which nest in English pine plantations in one year, for example, might have bred in the European spruce/pine forests in the preceding one. Rather the irregular breeding results because the birds are stimulated to nest by an abundance of food, whenever and wherever this might arise (p. 189). In adaptation to a sporadic food-supply, their nesting has become independent of the changes in daylength which help to bring other finches into breeding condition at an appropriate date each year.

Although breeding is often in progress in a forest for more than nine months, individuals probably do not breed for this long. Thus, flocks of non-breeding (paired and unpaired) birds are nearly always present and, in years poor in seeds, only a fraction of the total birds may nest (Svärdson 1955). None the less, some pairs raise at least two broods in swift succession (Bailey, Niedrach & Baily 1953), and some captive ones bred twice in one year with a long interval between (p. 190).

Unlike other finches, Common Crossbills sometimes nest while they are moulting (p. 202). Not only does the moulting season of the population as a whole (late summer and autumn) lie completely within the potential breeding season, but occasional individuals in heavy moult have been shot off nests, or with their gonads well developed. The birds have also been found to breed in juvenile plumage, and hence within a few months of leaving the nest. In British Columbia, two young cocks were shot with enlarged testes on 3 and 13 August 1931, and two hens with eggs in their oviducts on 19 and 20 August (McCabe & McCabe 1933). All four were probably from spring broods, but whether the young reared in autumn ever breed the next spring, as is sometimes stated, has not been proved.

The nest of the Crossbill is placed high in a tree, usually on the south side, amid thick foliage. It is made of grass, moss, lichens and bark-shreds, on a base of thin twigs, and is warmly lined with lichens, moss, hair and feathers. The nests tend to be bulkier and more thickly lined in winter than in summer. The eggs, which are pale bluish-green, spotted with brown and violet, usually number 3-4, occasionally 2 or 5, and the average clutch-size is smaller than in other European finches. Of 34 clutches in Finland, 31 consisted of 3 eggs, with one each of 2, 4, and 5, and a mean of 3.1 (Suormala 1938).

The eggs take 13-16 days to hatch. In my experience, they are sometimes laid at daily intervals and, at least in cold weather, are covered by the hen from the start, so are not allowed to freeze. They thus begin to develop immediately and hatch over several days, so that the young often vary greatly in size, the first hatched being the largest. This also gives the various young different chances of survival and, if food becomes scarce, the smallest dies quickly, and the brood is rapidly trimmed to a new level. If the young were all of the same size, competition between them would be less decisive, much food would be wasted on young that would die anyway, and the survival of the whole brood might be jeopardised. Asynchronous hatching and its consequences have long been known in owls and other birds that depend on an unpredictable food-supply (Lack 1954), but seems not previously to have been noted in Crossbills.

The growth of the young, both in the nest and out, takes about half as long again as does that of other finches, and is also more variable (p. 181). Most broods spend 18-22 days in the nest, but periods of 16-25 days have been recorded, according presumably to the amount of food they get (Ptusenko & Inozentzev 1968, Robertson 1954, Voroblev 1955). Perhaps helped by their slow and variable development, the young can easily survive temperatures that would kill the young of other finches. At one nest near Moscow, the air-temperature on the day the eggs hatched fell to $-35°C$. On the third day, when it was $-18°C$, a thermometer in the nest registered $+38°C$ while the hen brooded, $56°C$ more than the outside world. Even at these extremes the young were left for long periods, while their parents collected food. When the adults returned, the young were often torpid, but after a few minutes' brooding, were able to lift their heads again for food (Ternovskij 1954). At most times of year the young are raised entirely on conifer seeds, but in early summer they may get insects as well. Also, at one nest in Minnesota, the young were raised on sunflower seeds from a feeding tray (Johnson 1969).

The crossing of the bill involves only the horny surface layer, not the underlying bone. Usually the upper mandible begins to lengthen on the 14th day, but when the young leave the nest, around the 20th, their bills are still uncrossed. By the 27th day, when the upper mandible is well grown, the lower begins to bend to one side, and by the 30th protrudes above the upper. From then on, the young begin to practise on cones, and insert their bills between the opening scales; by the 38th day they can pull out the seeds, but not until the 45th can they feed themselves effectively (Ternovskij 1954). The young are apparently subsidised by their parents till an even greater age, however, and if nests follow in swift succession, the care of the first brood may largely overlap the second.

PARROT CROSSBILL *Loxia pytyopsittacus*

This species is larger than the Common Crossbill, with a larger head and more massive, more arched, bill. In the hand, the hens tend to be greyer about the head, and the cocks have whitish tips to the greater coverts, but neither feature shows in the field. In a mixed flock, Parrot Crossbills are more sluggish and tame than Common, but are still difficult to pick out, except by call, a deep emphatic 'quop quop', compared with the higher pitched 'quip quip' of the Common. The call is the only sure way of distinguishing juveniles of the two species, even in the hand, because for several weeks after fledging, their bills and other measurements overlap (Appendix 2).

The Parrot Crossbill is associated mainly with Scots Pine. It breeds regularly in Fenno-Scandia, northern Russia east to the Urals, and sporadically in the Baltic provinces, Poland and eastern Germany (Fig. 23). Its whole range lies within that of the Common Crossbill, and overlaps that of the Two-barred. Its irruptions usually coincide with those of the Common Crossbill, so might often be overlooked, but they seem to be less frequent and extend less far, reaching Denmark and western Germany regularly, but elsewhere rarely (p. 229). In 1962 many birds appeared in Britain, 36 being caught on Fair Isle and a few elsewhere, and in the next year a pair probably bred in Surrey (Davis 1964).

On the regular range, eggs have been found from December to June, but mostly from mid-March to mid-April. The nest is said to be bulkier than that of the Common, and the eggs are slightly larger with bolder spots. Incubation takes 14–16 days. In one study (seven nests) the young left the nest at 15–17 days, and in another (two nests) at 25 days, again implying great variation in the rate the young develop (Valeur, in Bannerman 1953, Olsson 1962, 1964).

TWO-BARRED CROSSBILL *Loxia leucoptera*

The double white wing-bars, formed by the white tips of the median and greater coverts, distinguish this species. It is also more lightly-built, brighter in colour, with a more mottled back, darker scapulars, wings and tail, and a more slender bill than other crossbills, and in addition, has white tips on its tertials. The Two-barred was formerly regarded in Fenno-Scandia as a hybrid between the Common Crossbill and the Chaffinch, which aptly fits its appearance. Its call, a dry 'chiff-chiff', is harsher and more rapid than that of the Common, and is interspersed with musical 'peet' notes. A flock at a distance sounds like a flock of Redpolls, except for the inclusion of this last note.

In both the Old and the New Worlds, the Two-barred Crossbill inhabits colder regions and extends further north than the Common, though in both areas the breeding ranges overlap (p. 97, Fig. 23). At any one place in the zone of overlap, however, the two species rarely seem to be plentiful in the same years, and either one or the other predominates greatly. In the Old World, the Two-barred breeds mainly in northern Asia, in forests dominated by Siberian Larch (*Larix sibirica*) or Dahurian Larch (*L. dahurica*), which form the main food-plants. The invasions regularly reach Finland and Sweden, and occasionally west into Norway, Denmark, Holland and Belgium, and south into Poland, Roumania, Yugoslavia and northern Italy. Only stragglers reach Britain, and are mostly seen in parties of Common Crossbills. After invasions, the Two-barred has occasionally bred in Fenno-Scandia, often in plantations of larch (which does not grow naturally in this region). Otherwise in these countries, it eats chiefly rowan fruits. Its breeding has not been studied in detail, but in Canada it is known to nest in every month, mainly in spring and autumn (Taber, in Austin 1968). The incubation and nestling periods are not known.

With such peculiar adaptations, one might think that the crossbills were far removed in the evolutionary tree from the other cardueline finches. But this is not so, for their courtship displays and general breeding behaviour resemble closely those of the *Carduelis/Acanthis/Serinus* finches, discussed in the previous chapter. Moreover, hybrids between the Common Crossbill and the Greenfinch have several times been bred in captivity, again suggesting a close affinity between these groups. The hybrids had uncrossed bills.

CHAPTER 4

DISTRIBUTION, HABITATS AND HISTORY

THE present distribution of birds in Europe is difficult to understand because of the profound effects that man has had on the native vegetation. In little over 3,000 years he has transformed the forested landscape of primeval Europe into a mainly open, cultivated one. Some birds now breed only in the patches of natural and semi-natural habitat which remain, but others have colonised cultivated land, or are in process of doing so, and are thereby extending their range. The main aim of this chapter is to discuss some changes in the ranges and ecology of the various finches due to man, but this first entails an attempt to reconstruct the status of these birds in primeval Europe.

Under natural conditions, climate and soil encourage the growth at different latitudes of distinct types of vegetation, often some form of forest (Polunin 1960, Eyre 1968). Fig. 26 shows the major vegetation-types as they existed in Europe some 3,500 years ago, and as they would presumably now be, but for man, since the climate is essentially the same. The Mediterranean woodland, which formerly covered most of southern Europe, is rather open, with low trees, and an abundant growth of herbs and shrubs below. It is dominated in most areas by the evergreen oaks *Quercus ilex* and *Q. suber* and in others by Aleppo and Stone Pines (*Pinus halepensis* and *P. pinea*). On dry or rocky ground, the trees give way to scrub of various types, which is often dense and impenetrable. To the north, where the climate is cooler and wetter, Mediterranean vegetation is replaced by deciduous forest, which formerly covered much of middle Europe. The trees grow taller and closer than in Mediterranean woodlands, and are dominated in most areas by the oaks *Q. robur* and *Q. petraea*, with an understory of hazel (*Corylus avellana*) and other shrubs. The damper ground supports mainly alder (*Alnus*), with various coarse herbs below, and the calcareous and other well-drained soils support beech (*Fagus sylvatica*), with few, if any, plants below.

Further north, where the winters are cold and snowbound and the summers are short, coniferous trees take over. The boreal forest extends over northern Europe and Siberia, reappears in Alaska, and sweeps southeast across Canada. Many animals of this type of forest are found in both the Old and the New Worlds, including among the finches the two redpolls, two of the crossbills and the Pine Grosbeak. In northern Europe the boreal forest is dominated by spruce (*Picea abies*) on heavy soils and by Scots Pine (*Pinus sylvestris*) on dry or rocky ground, with

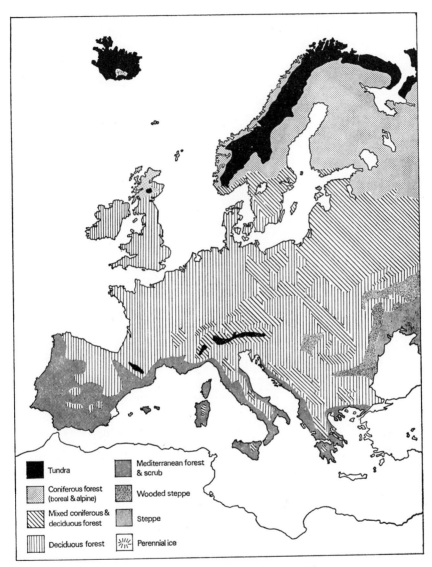

FIG. 26. The climax vegetation of Europe, as it existed some 3-4,000 years ago, before man altered it. The map shows the vegetation that would be found over much of the area if it were naturally well-drained, of only gentle gradient, and completely undisturbed by man. But in each vegetation-type, tremendous variation can occur over short distances.

birches (*Betula*) and sallows (*Salix*) around the numerous lakes and rivers. Its southern margin interdigitates with the deciduous forest to form in eastern Europe a vast area in which deciduous and coniferous communities intermix. Its northern margin gives way first to a broad belt of open birch woodland, and thence to open tundra. The latter is a mainly sedge-, heath-, and lichen-covered landscape, with dwarf birches and willows in the sheltered hollows, but the terrain becomes more barren and the vegetation sparser towards the arctic ocean.

While the three types of forest and the tundra comprise the main natural vegetation belts of western Europe, further east the hot dry summers and cold winters favour the development of grassland, which covers vast areas from eastern Europe to eastern Asia. These steppe-lands are separated from the forest to the north by a broad intermediate zone, the wooded steppe, which comprises clumps of trees and shrubs in an otherwise open landscape and tongues of forest which follow the rivers. The miles of contact between forest and steppe probably provided the most extensive wood-edge habitat that existed in primeval Europe. Equivalent habitats elsewhere were probably found only at the transition between forest and tundra or where forest confronted open water, marsh or rocky ground, or areas cleared by fire, wind or landslide. (The separation of woodland-edge is important because it harbours many birds which are absent from the closed forest.)

A similar zonation of the vegetation, as exists in western Europe, from broad-leaved, through coniferous forest to tundra, exists up mountain-sides, as the climate becomes harsher towards the tops, the equivalent zones being higher on southern than on northern ranges. These montane habitats are in part floristically different from their equivalents further north, but they look much the same.

In addition to these major formations, various marsh, bog and coastal habitats would have existed in primeval Europe in more or less their present form. Also, the diversity of all the forests was increased by succession, burnt or cleared ground being colonised first by herbaceous plants, then by shrubs and finally trees.

The important point, however, is that apart from the steppes and the tundras of arctic and alpine regions, almost the whole of Europe was formerly under forest or scrub, broken in the lowlands only where the ground was too wet or too sterile for trees. Until man changed them, these same habitats and their bird communities had existed for many thousands of years, but were continually moving south then north in Europe, as the ice of successive glaciations advanced and retreated. In little over 3,000 years, however, under the influence of axe and plough, almost all the original Mediterranean and deciduous woodland, some parts of the boreal forest, and almost all the European steppe have gone. Only the tundra remains in a mainly natural state, except where overgrazed by domestic reindeer.

Table 7. The natural habitats of European finches in the breeding season.

	Mediterranean		Deciduous		Boreal		Montane coniferous		Wooded steppe	Tundra		Barren rocky mountain tops & north-west sea-coasts	Sand-dunes
	Forest	Forest-edge and scrub	Forest	Forest-edge and scrub	Forest	Forest-edge and scrub	Forest	Forest-edge and scrub		Arctic	Alpine		
Chaffinch	●	●	●	●	●	●	●	●					
Brambling					●	●			●				
Hawfinch	●		●										
Greenfinch		●		●		●		●	●				
Goldfinch		●		●		●			●				
Siskin			●		●		●						
Linnet		●		●		●		●	●				●
Twite										●	●	●	
Redpoll					●	●		●		●			
Arctic Redpoll										●			
Citril Finch								●					
Serin		●											
Bullfinch				●		●		●					
Pine Grosbeak					●	●							
Common Crossbill					●		●						
Parrot Crossbill					●								
Two-barred Crossbill					●								
Scarlet Rosefinch						●		●					
Totals	6		7		13		9		4	3	1	1	1

Finches in natural habitats

Table 7 lists the finches which breed in each major vegetation-type, as shown by the vestiges. It thus presumably shows all the habitats occupied by each species before man created others. The number of species found in natural forest increases from south to north, with only six and seven in the Mediterranean and deciduous forest, but 13 in the boreal. This is surprising, both because it reverses the overall trend in animals and because the boreal contains fewer plant-species than other forests, with a reduced range of suitable seeds. Linked with this, most of the boreal finches are highly specialised. The three crossbills and the redpolls subsist for long periods on the seeds of one or two tree-species, which in turn is possible only because the seeds concerned remain available for most of the year. Within the boreal region, the Brambling, Redpoll and Pine Grosbeak breed primarily in the open forest below the tundra, and the Chaffinch, Siskin and Crossbills further south.

Whatever the type of forest, more species breed on the edge or in scrub than under a closed canopy, but some, like the Chaffinch, are found in all three situations. The Chaffinch in fact is naturally the most widespread species in Europe and breeds in all types of forest, except the most northern birch and conifer areas, where, after a narrow zone of overlap, it is replaced by the Brambling (p. 96). The remaining species which inhabit a forest interior breed in only one or two forest-types, the Siskin and the Common Crossbill in conifers, both boreal and montane, and the Hawfinch in broad-leaved woods, both Mediterranean and deciduous. In the boreal forest, the Common Crossbill (*L.c. curvirostra*) is associated primarily with spruce, the Parrot Crossbill (*L. pytyopsittacus*) with pine, and the Two-barred (*L. leucoptera*) with larch, which is the commonest tree over large parts of Siberia. Despite the huge areas of larch that exist naturally in the Alps and other parts of Europe, the Two-barred Crossbill does not breed south of the boreal belt (p. 75). In fact, all the montane forests of central Europe, whether of spruce, fir or larch, are inhabited by Common Crossbills. But further south, where some form of pine predominates, larger-billed crossbills occur, adapted to deal with the harder cones (p. 108). Local races exist in Scotland (*L.c. scotica*), Corsica (*L.c. corsicana*), the Balearics (*L.c. balearica*), North Africa (*L.c. poliogyna*), Cyprus (*L.c. guillemardi*), the southwest Crimea (*L.c. mariae*), and on several Asiatic mountain ranges (p. 74). All these forms are presumed to have been derived from the Common Crossbill by being isolated in pine areas and developing heavier bills in adaptation to the harder cones. The Scottish Crossbill has evolved in association with pine alone because the post-glacial isolation of Britain prevented the re-entry of spruce, which was native here in pre-glacial times.

Although these large-billed races live outside the regular range of the

Common Crossbill, contact occurs during invasions of the Common from the north. Yet the southern populations retain their distinctness, suggesting that they interbreed little, if at all, with their supposed parent-form. They present a difficult case in taxonomy, being part way between subspecies and full species. Less of a problem exists with the Parrot Crossbill because its entire breeding range, which extends into Fenno-Scandia, northern Russia, the Baltic Provinces and Poland, lies permanently within that of the Common, yet the two forms apparently do not interbreed, so are best considered separate species. They are of course segregated ecologically because of the Parrot Crossbill's greater dependence on pine. The range of the Parrot Crossbill is surprisingly restricted, however, considering that its main food-plant grows over more than six times the area occupied by the bird itself.

The mountain forests of central Europe share two other finches, both edge species, with the boreal forest to the north. The Redpoll is found in the scrub above the tree-line, which in Scandinavia and Britain is mainly of birch, and in central Europe of stunted conifers; and the Bullfinch is found mainly among young trees and shrubs at points of regeneration within the forests. On the other hand, the Two-barred and Parrot Crossbills, the Pine Grosbeak and the Brambling breed only in the boreal region, and the Citril Finch breeds only on mountains. This last species is the only bird endemic to the mountains of Europe. It occurs near the tree-line on the Alps and on all suitable ranges to the west and south, but it is unaccountably absent from equivalent habitat on the Carpathians and other eastern ranges.

The species which inhabit forest-edge or scrub breed in more vegetation types than do those which inhabit the closed forests. The Scarlet Grosbeak breeds over more of Eurasia than any other finch, mainly in swampy thickets, but in southern Asia in drier mountain scrub, up to 13,000 feet. Also, the Greenfinch, Goldfinch and Linnet breed on the edges of all forest-types, and hence over most of Europe, but they do not extend far into the boreal zone. The Goldfinch, which needs trees for nesting and open areas for foraging, occurs naturally in the wooded steppe, and wherever forest adjoins marshland, coasts or other open ground. The Greenfinch occurs in similar habitats, but depends more on shrubs for nesting, and less on open ground for feeding. The Linnet breeds on any open ground with low scattered bushes, typically on the scree slopes of mountainsides, among sand-dunes, or again, where forest gives way to open country. At least seven 'edge-species' are found near the tree-line on mountains, yet to my knowledge no one area holds more than four. The Chaffinch occurs in this habitat almost throughout its range, the Greenfinch mainly in eastern Europe, the Linnet in southwest Asia, the Redpoll in central and northern Europe, the Citril Finch in central and southwest Europe, the Bullfinch in central Europe, and the Scarlet Rosefinch in southern Asia.

Lastly, the Twite is the only European finch which inhabits windswept seacoasts and barren grasslands. One population breeds on the mountain tundras and high steppes of southwest and central Asia and another on the northwest seaboard and arctic tundras of Europe. The discontinuity is presumed to have arisen since the retreat of the last Ice Age, before which the Twite probably ranged right across the Eurasian tundras (Voous 1960). The occurrence today of the species in the maritime environments is just as puzzling as is its absence from the alpine tundras of central Europe. The tundra habitats of the species would have existed in primeval Europe in more or less their present form, as would the main winter haunts, coastal flats and salt-marshes.

Finches in man-made habitats

Man the hunter did little to the natural vegetation of Europe except to increase the number of fires. It was the wholesale destruction of forest for cultivation that had the greatest impact, opening up the landscape and increasing the wood-edge habitats at the expense of closed forest. The destruction of the Mediterranean forests began around 4,000 years ago, but even in late Roman times considerable tracts remained. The deciduous forest was cleared more recently, and only a thousand years ago four-fifths was still standing (Darby 1956), while large parts of the boreal forest remain even today. In Britain deforestation began more than 2,500 years ago and affected first the beech forest on the chalk downs. Subsequent clearance was neither continuous nor sustained, but is now nearly complete, though some virgin forest remained in England until the eighteenth century and in Scotland at least until the nineteenth (Tansley 1949). Hence, man-made habitats have not existed anywhere in Europe for more than about 4,000 years, and on any scale in middle Europe for more than 2,000. They are thus very recent in the evolutionary history of the birds that now live in them. These new habitats include all those that have replaced the natural, such as farmland, gardens and orchards, parks and playing fields, towns and villages, roads and railways, and industrial wasteland. It need scarcely be added that those woodlands remaining in the southern two-thirds of Europe have usually been so modified that they bear little resemblance to virgin forest. The selective felling of certain trees, the deliberate planting of others, the removal of dead timber, the slowing of natural regeneration through grazing by domestic stock, all affect the structure of modern woodland; while the present practice in Britain of growing dense monocultures of exotic conifers is producing habitats as artificial as any other crop.

Those finch-species which still live primarily in natural forest in the north will also breed in modified forest, and some in adjoining gardens and villages. Common Crossbills and Siskins regularly nest in such places, and both have spread into new areas where conifers have been planted by man.

Table 8. The man-made habitats of European finches (b = breeds; w = winters).

| Species | Conifer plantations | RURAL | | URBAN | | | Visits feeding stations in gardens |
		Farmlands and orchards	Villages	Parks, gardens and cemeteries	Industrial waste land and allotments	Inner London[4]	
Chaffinch	b	bw	bw	bw	bw	bw	+
Brambling		w	w(rare)		w(rare)		+(rare)
Hawfinch		bw	bw	bw		bw	+(on continent)
Greenfinch	b[3]	bw	bw	bw	bw	bw	+
Goldfinch	w	bw	bw	b	bw	bw	
Siskin	bw		w[2]				+2
Linnet	b[3]	bw	b	b(rare)	bw		
Twite		w			w(mainly on continent)		
Redpoll	b[3]w	w			w		
Serin		bw	bw	bw	bw		
Bullfinch	b[3]	bw	bw	bw	bw	bw	+(on continent)
Common Crossbill	bw						
Scarlet Rosefinch		bw(Asia only)	bw(Asia only)				

Notes: 1. Data from Homes (1964), Cramp & Tomlins (1966).
2. From the mid-1960's visited gardens in parts of southern Britain to feed from fat, and later from nut-bags put out for birds.
3. Young plantations only.
4. Inner London is mentioned as the ultimate in suburban living by birds.

Thus the Crossbill has established itself in southern Britain, in the pines oɪ
Breckland and of the New Forest, and after invasions has bred in the
newer plantations elsewhere. In the last 30 years the Siskin has also nested
in most English counties and now breeds regularly in many from which
it was formerly absent (Parslow 1968). But even more spectacular has
been the increase of the Lesser Redpoll, which early this century took to
nesting in plantations of young conifers, 2–6 metres high, and in this
habitat spread over most of Britain in ten years from 1950. This was most
marked in the southwest, and the species is now fairly common in Devon,
where before 1953 it is known to have bred only once. It has also colonised
the same habitat on the sandy coasts of Holland and Denmark (Hald-
Mortensen 1970). Around 1965, moreover, the species began destroying
fruit buds in Kent, a habit which began about fifteen years earlier in
New Zealand, where the bird was introduced in the last century (Stenhouse 1962, Newton 1967c).

The finches vary in the extent to which they have colonised the more
open habitats created by man and, as expected, those species which inhabit
forest-edge or scrub have been more successful than have those typical of
closed forest. The only true forest species which has spread elsewhere is the
Hawfinch, which now breeds commonly in some city parks on the continent. The species has never become well established in such places in
Britain, though it breeds in a few towns and winters in others. The Chaffinch,
originally a bird of both forest and forest-edge, is now found throughout
cultivated land, breeding anywhere with tall trees, including the parks
and gardens of towns. Its habit of feeding mainly on open land in winter
is probably recent, however, for in primeval Europe the amount of
suitable open land would have been negligible.

The position summarised in Table 8 is by no means stable, for in
recent years the status of several finches has changed in Europe, as they
have spread from natural to man-made habitats, or from countryside to
town. The Greenfinch and Goldfinch now breed in rural and urban areas
throughout their range and in these habitats are spreading north. But the
Greenfinch occupied towns only recently, at least in central and eastern
Europe, where last century it was found only in remote rural areas, even
in winter (Sokolowski 1958). The spread to towns is probably also recent
in Britain, where the bird 'is widely reported as having become much
commoner in urban and suburban areas' (Parslow 1968). It is breeding
increasingly in Inner London, for example, but at the start of the century
was present only in winter, a trend helped perhaps by the increased
feeding of birds by householders. The Bullfinch has also colonised towns
and spread further into farmland in the last 30 years, especially in southern
England, hence the increased damage in orchards (Newton 1967d). It
likewise began by visiting towns in winter, returning to woods to breed,
as it still does in parts of the continent. In central and northern Europe,
the species also visits feeding trays, for hemp and sunflower seeds and

fat, but this habit has not yet caught on in Britain (Doerbeck 1963).

A spread to a new habitat may lead not only to an increase in numbers, but also to a big extension in range (Fig. 27). The best documented case is that of the Serin, which occurs naturally in open Mediterranean woodland, but which, more than a century ago, found suitable breeding places, similar in appearance to open forest, in parks and gardens with

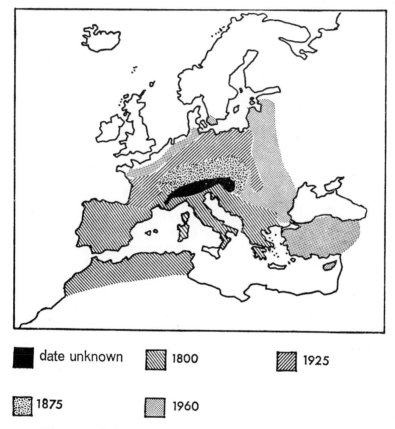

date unknown   1800   1925

1875   1960

FIG. 27. The spread of the Serin in Europe. (Based partly on Mayr 1926.)

scattered trees. In this new habitat it spread north into much of central Europe during the nineteenth century (Mayr 1926), and further in the present century, breeding for the first time in Britain in 1967 (p. 57). To most of these newly colonised areas the Serin is a summer visitor, withdrawing south in autumn.

One finch to expand its wintering range in recent years is the Twite, which at the same time has also adopted novel feeding and roosting habits.

The coast of the southern Baltic has long been an important wintering area, but increasing numbers of birds are now wintering inland, as far as Hungary and Czechoslovakia (Tomialójč 1967). In the main inland areas, in Poland, the birds feed chiefly from vast beds of Golden Rod (*Solidago serotina* and *S. canadensis*). These plants were introduced from America at the beginning of the last century, have since spread widely, and might have encouraged the Twite to spread, for their seeds are available at times of snow when other foods are covered. Just after the war, moreover, large numbers of Twite fed from the weeds which sprang up in bombed cities, including Warsaw and Berlin, a food-supply which no other finch exploited to any extent. The re-building of the cities has now put an end to this, but in the meantime the birds had started to roost in towns. They still regularly use high buildings in the busy streets of Berlin and Hamburg, feeding in fields by day, and have also used those of Magdeburg since 1963 (Dien 1965, Hilprecht 1964, Lange 1960, Bruch & Löschau 1960).

Not all attempts by finches to exploit new habitats have been successful. The Linnet has twice colonised man-made habitats in northern Europe, but mainly different ones each time (Tast 1968). In the first third of this century, the bird was widespread in southern Finland, nesting in small shrubs around meadows and feeding from weeds, much as it does in Britain. In the nineteen-thirties and forties, however, the species disappeared from most such localities and became rare in others. This coincided with changes in farming practice, which reduced weeds, and in two districts where the old methods were retained, the Linnets remained. The birds began to return to the rest of the country in the late forties, but in different habitats, and have since re-occupied much of their former ground. They now nest mainly within small towns and villages, in parks, gardens and industrial wasteland, around railways and woodyards. Thus at first they lived mainly in rural areas in Finland, and now mainly in urban ones. Similar changes occurred in Sweden (Durango 1947), but in Britain Linnets still do not nest regularly in suburban gardens, only in large parks within easy reach of fields.

The main changes recorded in the habitats and distribution of European finches during the last 150 years are summarised in Table 9. Of the 15 changes described only two have taken place within a natural habitat, the spread of the Scarlet Rosefinch from Asia into Europe and the northward shift of the boundary between the Chaffinch and Brambling (p. 71 and p. 96). The remaining 13 changes, involving eight species, have all occurred into or within man-made habitats, though some have been only temporary. In the best documented cases, the species involved spread to a new habitat first in winter, and only later remained to breed; they also colonised rural areas before urban ones. Some species have occupied new habitats which bear little resemblance to their original ones. Thus, no one who knew the Redpoll only from young conifer plantations in southern England could have guessed that it was originally a bird of northern

Table 9.   Some recent changes in the habitats and ranges of European finches.

Chaffinch and Brambling	A northward shift in the zone of overlap between the breeding ranges of the two species.
Greenfinch	A spread from countryside to town throughout middle Europe and Britain, and a northward expansion of range in cultivated land in Fenno-Scandia, mainly this century.
Goldfinch	A northward expansion of range in cultivated land in Fenno-Scandia, mainly this century.
Siskin	Occupation of new conifer plantations in Britain and consequent expansion of range, mainly since 1940.
Linnet	(a) A withdrawal from rural areas in Fenno-Scandia during the 1930's and 1940's. (b) A re-occupation of much of Fenno-Scandia, but in urban habitats, in the 1950's and 1960's.
Lesser Redpoll	(a) A withdrawal from rough hedgerows, alder and sallow thickets in southern Britain, mainly between 1910 and 1920. (b) A re-occupation of much of southern Britain, but in young conifer plantations, mainly since 1950.
Twite	(a) Increased wintering inland in river valleys and farm-land in eastern and central Europe, mainly since 1905. (b) A temporary exploitation of weeds that sprang up over bombed cities in eastern and central Europe, between mid-1940's and mid-1950's. (c) The habit of roosting on high buildings in large towns, which started in the mid-1950's and is spreading.
Serin	A spread from open woodland to cultivated land, towns and villages, and a northward expansion of range in Europe. Began mid-19th century, and still spreading.
Bullfinch	An increase in cultivated land, and a spread from country-side to towns in southern Britain, mainly from mid-1940's.
Common Crossbill	An occupation of the new conifer plantations in Britain and a consequent expansion of range, mainly this century.
Scarlet Rosefinch	A westward spread from Asia into Europe, in alder and sallow thickets, in the early 20th century, followed by a partial retreat, and another spread around mid-century.

Note: Details from Bruch and Löschau 1960, Dien 1965, Durango 1947, Ferguson-Lees 1968, Hilprecht 1964, Kalela 1952, Mayr 1926, Merikallio 1958, Newton 1967d, Parslow 1968, Sokolowski 1958, Tast 1968, Tomialojc 1967, Voous 1960.

birch scrub. Nor could it have been predicted that, of all the finches, it would be the Twite which most thoroughly exploited the weeds of bombed cities.

Once started, the occupation of a new habitat has often been rapid. It has taken only a century for the Serin to spread over half of Europe, and only a decade for the Bullfinch to colonise suburban parks and gardens and for the Redpoll to spread through southern Britain. This last species spread soon after suitable habitat became available, but for the other two the habitat had long been available before it was occupied. This raises the question of why such changes occurred when they did and, while there is little information, it seems that most were associated with an increase in the numbers of the bird. It is never certain, however, whether a prior increase in the original habitat forced the surplus birds into other places or whether the acceptance of the new habitat occurred first and the population explosion followed. Either way, the spread to a new habitat has often been followed by an expansion of range.

Habitat selection

If the spread of a species to a new habitat entails a broadening in the range of habitats it finds acceptable, how might this change occur? The means by which birds recognise their habitats seem to be partly inherited and partly learnt. Probably each bird has an innate preference for country with certain characteristics, and responds to such general features as the type, height and spacing of the dominant plants. On top of this is a tendency for the bird to prefer that habitat in which it was itself raised. Direct evidence for these views so far comes from birds other than finches. In some areas the American Chipping Sparrow (*Spizella passerina*), for example, normally occurs only in pine. Birds trapped in the wild and given the choice in an aviary of sitting among pine or oak branches strongly preferred pine. Likewise, some hand-raised young, which had never before seen any foliage and were given the same choice, spent two-thirds of their time in pine, suggesting that they had an innate preference for it. However, when other hand-raised young were at first provided only with oak branches, and later given the choice of oak or pine, they spent less than half of their time in pine, so their innate preference was modified, but not eliminated, by experience (Klopfer 1963). Observations on wild Reed Buntings (*Emberiza schoeniclus*) in England are to similar effect (Bell 1968). These birds usually nest in marshes, but occasionally on drier ground. Bell ringed large numbers of nestlings and then noted the habitat in which they subsequently bred. A higher proportion of young from nests on marshy than drier ground selected their natal habitat for breeding, and a lower proportion changed to the other situation. As in the Chipping Sparrow, the choice of habitat was influenced both by heredity and by experience. On the basis of this knowledge, the occupation of new habitats by finches probably represents a break with tradition, rather than a genetic change, and the subsequent spread of the behaviour results because the young raised in the new habitats find them more acceptable than did earlier generations. But the chances that a species will succeed in a new habitat should also change with time, as land-use and environmental conditions change, which might explain why some habitats were not occupied as soon as they became available.

Introductions

Man has also directly extended the ranges of some finches by introducing them to parts of the world that they would not be expected to reach naturally. Four species (Greenfinch, Goldfinch, Redpoll and Chaffinch) were introduced into New Zealand around 1865, and in 30 years had not only occupied the whole of that country, but had also reached several other islands in the Australasian seas, up to 800 kilometres away (Williams 1953). About the same date the Greenfinch and Goldfinch were introduced into southeast Australia, and a little later the Goldfinch to Bermuda and Argentina, and the Chaffinch to South Africa. It is not certain whether the Greenfinch and Goldfinch were also released on to certain Atlantic Islands, or whether they found their own way there, but they now breed commonly in both the Azores and the Canaries.

Not all the introductions were as successful as in New Zealand. Thus in South Africa the Chaffinch flourishes only in a restricted part of Cape Town and its suburbs, not larger than about 25 square kilometres, and has never spread further (Broekhuysen, in Thorpe 1961). In Australia, the Goldfinch is restricted to the temperate southeast corner and to the south-western towns of Perth and Albany, where it feeds almost wholly from introduced plants (Middleton 1970). Attempts to establish the European Goldfinch in North America have failed, though until recently a few bred annually on Long Island, New York (p. 36). In addition, the Linnet and Bullfinch bred for a time in New Zealand, and the Chaffinch and Siskin in Australia, but all have since died out.

Of the successful introductions, only two species have colonised a natural habitat: in New Zealand the Chaffinch breeds, among other places, in the native forests, and the Redpoll in the scrub above them and in the tundra-like vegetation of some neighbouring islands. But the fauna of all these islands is notoriously poor in species, and these finches might not have become established in natural habitats elsewhere in the world. The remaining introduced finches, in all their new homes, live entirely in towns and cultivated land.

Climate and distribution

The fact that several finches have extended their range where suitable habitat has been provided by man suggests that they were formerly restricted by lack of habitat, rather than by climate or other factors. In at least three groups, however, climate seems to be important, not in itself, but in influencing the boundary between closely-related species, which for the most part occupy different geographical areas. The replacement of the Chaffinch by the Brambling in the north of the boreal forest is a case in point. The zone of overlap has shifted north in the last 50 years by about 110 kilometres in the west of Finland and 260 kilometres in the east, corresponding to an amelioration in climate (Merikallio 1951). Some other southern species have extended north in the same period (Kalela 1949, 1952), but since the advance of the Chaffinch has been accompanied by a corresponding retreat in the Brambling, the position of the zone of overlap is probably determined by competition, the Brambling being superior solely in the extreme conditions of the far north. Both species share common wintering areas, but have other means of avoiding competition there (p. 30).

The summer distribution of the two forms of redpolls presents parallels, but is complicated by interbreeding. Throughout the northern hemisphere, only the dark form (*C. flammea*) breeds in forest scrub in the boreal zone; both forms breed around the tree-line and in the low tundra with patches of tall scrub; and only the pale, white-rumped form (*C. hornemanni*) breeds on the high tundra with short scrub. The latter occurs alone in parts of north and northeast Greenland, far northern Siberia and some of the Canadian polar islands. In some regions where the two forms meet, such as eastern North America and Greenland, hybridisation is extremely rare; but in others, such as northern Europe, hybridisation is so common that the intermediates outnumber either parent-type (Harris, Norman & McColl 1965).

The situation in the hybrid zone of Alaska has been clarified by Baldwin (1961), who examined a series of birds collected in the breeding season at selected localities. The proportion of pale birds increased from southeast to northwest across the state as the climate became colder. And while all the samples contained intermediates, indicating some interbreeding, in no area did the intermediates outnumber either parent-type, indicating that some degree of segregation was also maintained.

The scarcity of interbreeding in some regions may not be because the birds have evolved special behavioural or other means of preventing it, but a chance result of a difference in migratory habits. *C. hornemanni* migrates less far and returns and pairs earlier than does *C. flammea*, so mixed pairs have little chance to form (Wynne-Edwards 1952). But the existence of these two redpolls, which in some regions interbreed and produce fertile hybrids, raises the question of how they evolved into different forms from what must originally have been a common stock. Salomonsen (1928, 1951) thinks that *hornemanni* is simply a mutant of *flammea* with a selective advantage in the high arctic. An alternative view is that the two forms evolved their differences in isolation, and when they

PLATE 5. Bramblings sometimes gather into roosts containing many millions of birds. From mid-afternoon each day, they assemble in bare tree-tops (*above*), then near dusk they swarm in impressive wheeling flights over the roost before descending for the night (*left*).

PLATE 6. The shy and elusive Hawfinch breeds mainly in deciduous woodlands, but also in large gardens and orchards. It has a massive powerful bill able to break open cherry stones and other large tree-fruits.

subsequently re-met, were sufficiently distinct to behave as separate species in some areas but not in others.

In their regions of overlap, except for migratory habits, the two forms appear identical in their ecology. Yet nowhere does *hornemanni* breed regularly in the forest and nowhere does *flammea* extend far into the high arctic; hence some factor must be preventing one or both forms from spreading through the range of the other. The most likely is climate, the pale form being favoured in the north and the dark in the south. In Greenland, moreover, where the two forms behave as separate species, the zone of overlap has advanced northwards this century, too rapidly for a marked change in the vegetation, but corresponding to an improvement in climate (Salomonsen 1951).

The third group in which climate seems to influence the boundary between two species is the crossbills. Their ranges overlap more in Eurasia than in North America, but in both areas the Two-barred inhabits colder regions and extends further north than the Common (Fig. 23). Thus the former breeds in places with the July isotherms between 55 and 60°F, and the latter between 59 and 71°F (Voous 1960). The two species differ in bill-size presumably through adapting to the prevalent tree-species in their particular ranges: on both continents pine is more numerous in the range of the Common Crossbill.

In the Old World, the main centre of the Two-barred lies in Siberia, where the forests are dominated by the larches *Larix sibirica* and *L. dahurica*. The Common Crossbill lives mainly to the south and west, where most of the forests are dominated by spruce or pine. However, the distribution of neither crossbill corresponds exactly with any particular forest-type or tree-species, and in the southern Urals and central Europe the larch forests, as mentioned, are occupied by the Common Crossbill. In the New World the same principle applies, the Two-barred being found mainly in the northern boreal forest, and the Common mainly in the southern boreal forest, in the western mountains and in the eastern Lake Forests. Probably, therefore, climate determines which species shall be present in any particular area, the Two-barred being superior in competition with the Common only in the cold forests of the extreme north of America and the extreme north and northeast of Eurasia. Following invasions westward, the Two-barred Crossbill has often bred in Fenno-Scandia, but has not become established there, probably because in this climate it cannot long hold its own against the Common. In support of this view, the only place where the Two-barred has become naturally established in a warmer climate is on the tropical island of Hispaniola, where the Common Crossbill is absent. This is also the only place where the Two-barred inhabits pine forests, in which it has developed a larger bill than the parental form in North America, from an invasion of which the island form is presumed to have been derived.

The three pairs considered each concern two closely-related species which breed in mainly different areas. In two pairs, the Chaffinch/ Brambling and Common/Arctic Redpolls, the boundary has shifted in recent years, with change in climate; while in the third pair, the cold-dwelling species has established itself in a relatively warm climate only where its congener is absent. Climate may also help to set the boundary between the Linnet and Twite in Europe, the latter breeding in areas that are colder and more barren, but of this situation more study is needed.

To summarise this chapter, some finches still breed only in natural or semi-natural habitats, but others have successfully colonised cultivated land, or are in process of doing so. Those species which under natural conditions inhabit forest-edge or scrub have been more successful colonists of man-made habitats than have those which inhabit closed forest. The Siskin, Redpoll and Common Crossbill, which still breed mainly in natural habitats, have extended their range in Britain because of the increased planting of conifers. In the last 150 years the Serin has spread from natural to cultivated habitats, and the Greenfinch, Bullfinch and Linnet (Fenno-Scandia only) have spread from countryside to town. In cultivated land, the Greenfinch, Goldfinch and Serin have spread north in recent years, while the Twite has extended its wintering range and adopted new feeding and roosting habits. The availability of habitat has been proved to be the main factor delimiting the ranges of most finches, but climate probably influences the boundary between certain pairs of closely-related species, which occupy similar habitats but breed in mainly different areas.

In view of these known changes, it is reasonable to speculate that many other changes in the habitats and ranges of European birds occurred as a result of man's activities before there were ornithologists to record them. Hence, the present distribution of birds was probably established recently, and some of the most familiar birds of today may have been extremely rare or localised in primeval Europe. This is the main lesson to be drawn from the changes we see today.

CHAPTER 5

FEEDING ECOLOGY

SOME finches, like the Chaffinch, regularly eat a great variety of foods, including many types of seeds, insects and other invertebrates. Others, like the crossbills, are extremely specialised, obtaining almost all their food from a single plant-species. But most finches fall between these extremes, concentrating on a few items and taking many others occasionally. The Linnet, for instance, eats the seeds of more than 50 plant-species, but obtains the bulk of its food from only six. Any one species may of course vary its diet with season, year and locality, and also give special foods to its young (p. 178–9).

The food of finches can be studied either by analyses of gut-contents or by observations in the field. The first method gives an unbiased picture of what is eaten only if the analysis is restricted to the gullet, where the food is stored unaltered. In this position, the latest meal can be seen through the skin if the feathers on the neck are blown aside, so there is no need to kill the bird to study its diet. Further down the gut, hard materials figure too prominently in the food, because they take longer to digest than do soft ones; hence analyses of this kind not only entail killing the bird, but are also less valuable. Observations of feeding birds are useful mainly in showing how and where the food is got. I used both these methods, combined with anatomical studies, to assess the feeding habits of finches around Oxford (Newton 1967b, d). Some aspects of the subject had previously been studied by Dr Janet Kear (1962), and this chapter is a synthesis of our joint findings.

In Britain most of the seeds eaten by finches are produced between May and September, and thereafter the stocks remaining are steadily depleted until the next spring, when seed-production begins anew. Hence, seeds are scarcest in early spring, just before the start of the new growing season, and during hard weather in winter. At this time the tree-feeders are most affected by glazed frosts, and the ground-feeders by snow lying for long periods. In summer all finches feed for preference on half-ripe seeds, exploiting different plants in turn as they come into fruit.

Bill-structure and feeding habits

A conical bill, a broad, powerful skull, and large jaw muscles are the main adaptations for crushing hard seeds which characterise all finches. But to husk seeds the bill is also modified internally (Nekrasov 1958, Ziswiler 1965). Two grooves, one down each side of the palate, accommodate the edges of the lower jaw when the beak is closed, but also function in husking (Fig. 28). With the aid of the tongue, a seed is first fitted in the groove of one or other side, a large seed near the base of the bill, where the groove is widest, or a small one near the tip, where the groove is narrow. The edge of the lower bill is then raised on to the seed from below to split the husk, and is next worked up between the husk and kernel. At the same time the seed is rotated by the tongue so the husk peels off against the edge of the bill, leaving the kernel within. The whole process takes but a few seconds, and a bird can retain several seeds in its bill and husk them one at a time.

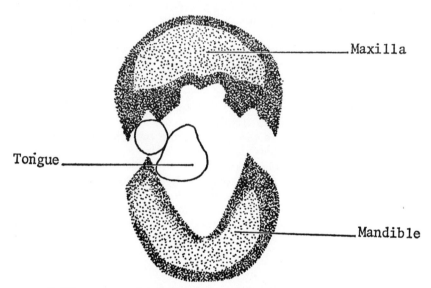

FIG. 28. The process of seed-husking in finches, as shown by a transverse section of the bill.

Seeds which have sutures or other weak points in the husk are always placed so that the edge of the lower bill presses directly on to them. They can then be cracked with less effort, which enables the bird to open seeds it might not otherwise manage. Nevertheless, each species of finch is restricted to seeds below a certain hardness and size. The limit to hardness is set by the strength of the jaws, and the limit to size by the width of the grooves. A seed which is too large to fit in the groove shoots out of the bill when force is applied and cannot be cracked, though some large soft seeds can be husked without the use of the grooves, because they do not need to be held so firmly. In general, the larger the beak of a finch, the more numerous the species of seeds in its diet, for while small-billed finches are restricted to small seeds, large-billed forms can eat large seeds as well. However, each species tends to concentrate on whatever size of seeds it can most efficiently deal with, so there is a correlation between the size of bill and the size of seeds preferred. Given certain features of common design, the finches vary greatly in the shape of their bills. This in turn is linked with differences in their feeding habits, as described below and summarised in Table 10.

Table 10. The adaptive radiation of the European finches.

Genus	Species	Beak	Chief foods	Comments
Fringilla	Chaffinch Brambling	Large and long	Seeds from the ground; insects from trees	Two species with almost identical feeding habits.
Coccothraustes	Hawfinch	Massive and conical	Large, hard tree-fruits	The most powerful species, able to split exceptionally hard fruits.
Carduelis and Acanthis	Linnet Twite Redpoll Greenfinch	Short and broad	Seeds picked from the ground, directly off plant-stems, or from pods and capsules	Four species differing in bill-size and size of preferred seeds. The Twite eats similar foods to the Linnet, but differs in habitat.
	Goldfinch Siskin	Long and narrow	Seeds from Compositae and the cones of alder and conifers	Two species differing in bill-length and depth to which they can probe for food.
Pyrrhula	Bullfinch	Short and rounded	Buds, tree-flowers, berries and seeds	Two species specialising on soft foods, the larger Grosbeak taking larger items than the Bullfinch.
Pinicola	Pine Grosbeak	Long and rounded	Buds, shoots, catkins, berries and seeds	
Loxia	Parrot Crossbill Common Crossbill Two-barred Crossbill	Mandibles curved and crossed at the tips	Conifer seeds	Three species differing in bill-size and in hardness of preferred cones.

Note: The Serinus finches have not been studied in detail, but they have more swollen bills than Acanthis and Carduelis and eat more buds. The same also applies to Carpodacus.

FRINGILLA

The Chaffinch and Brambling feed mainly from the ground in winter, in farmland or woodland, and mainly from trees in summer (p. 22–3, 28). They eat many more insects than the cardueline finches, and their relatively long beaks presumably help them to catch moving prey. Their beaks are also on the large side (Fig. 29), which enables them to take a wide range of seeds, up to the size of beechmast. Both species feed by rapid pecks, a method useful in catching moving insects and in securing seeds embedded in mud, but of little help in detaching seeds from plant-stems, where a long sustained pull is required. For this reason, they pick seeds almost entirely off the ground, and are quite incapable of opening any sort of seed-head. They pick insects off leaves, or catch them in the air during short flights from trees. Caterpillars are stunned by beating them on a branch before being eaten, while flying insects are taken back to a

FIG. 29. The palate and bill of the Chaffinch.

perch, dismembered and eaten there. The birds also catch falling conifer seeds in the air, and often feed around these trees in spring when the cones are opening. The feeding habits of the two species are more similar than those of any other pair of finches, but the Brambling is slightly more adept than the Chaffinch at detaching seeds from plant-stems and has a slightly deeper and stronger bill, which may explain its greater preference for beechmast.

COCCOTHRAUSTES

The large conical bill and the massive head and jaw muscles of the Hawfinch enable it to open exceptionally large, hard seeds, including the stones of olives (*Olea*), cherries (*Prunus*) and blackthorn (*P. spinosa*). The bulk of the food, however, consists of softer tree-seeds, such as those of elm (*Ulmus*) and hornbeam (*Carpinus betulus*), which are picked either directly from the trees or from the ground below. The species can also extract the seeds from a limited range of seed-heads, mainly by crushing them. The pods of peas and other legumes are 'popped' open in the bill, and the stones from soft fruits are obtained by squeezing the whole fruit and peeling off the flesh.

To deal with hard objects, the beak of the Hawfinch is more specialised in internal structure than those of other finches (Fig. 30). Behind the ridges on the palate is a pair of finely serrated knobs which meet in the midline and overlie a similar pair of knobs in the lower jaw. While small seeds are fitted in the grooves to be split, as in other finches, large ones are held between the four knobs (Sims 1955). The strain of cracking hard seeds is then shared equally by the muscles of both sides, and the resulting shocks are distributed more evenly over the skull. The four knobs consist entirely of horny material and do not develop until early in the bird's first winter, until which time softer seeds are eaten. The skulls of the young birds are also incompletely ossified and still have open sutures, so could not anyway withstand the stresses of cracking such hard seeds.

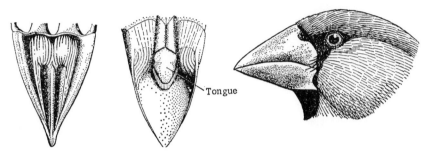

FIG. 30. The inside and outside bill structure of the Hawfinch.

In an apparatus designed to simulate the bird's bill, Sims (1955) measured the forces required to open the stones of cultivated cherries and olives. A series of trials was made with various loads and with the sutures of the stones lying in different directions. It was found that a greater force was needed to crack the stones quickly than slowly, and crushing loads were finally applied for about 20 seconds – which, incidentally, is longer than a Hawfinch takes to crack them. But under these conditions, cherry stones required loads of 60–95 pounds to break them, and olive stones loads of 106–159 pounds. The lowest average in both cases was obtained with the sutures of the stones lying vertical, which is how the Hawfinch places them, but still no small feat for a bird of only 55 grams (two ounces).

CARDUELIS AND ACANTHIS

These two genera, which include the goldfinch- and linnet-like birds, can be considered together because they have bills of essentially similar structure, and were formerly all classed together in the single genus *Carduelis*. They feed from a wide variety of plants, as well as from the ground, and can open many different types of seedheads, often using complicated bill-movements. Under most conditions, insects and buds form only a small part of their food. Their bills are unspecialised in internal structure (as in

Fig. 29), but come in two main shapes, short and broad or long and narrow (Fig. 31).

Species with short, broad bills feed mainly from plants whose seeds are either attached directly to the stem, such as grasses and docks (*Rumex*), or enclosed within pods or capsules, such as the various brassicas; they also frequently pick up fallen seeds from the ground. This type of bill is found in the Greenfinch, Linnet and Lesser Redpoll. These species differ, however, in size of bill and in size of seed preferred. The Greenfinch has the largest bill and eats mainly large seeds, such as certain tree-fruits and

FIG. 31. The bills of the Greenfinch and Goldfinch in overhead view.

cereal grains; the Redpoll has the smallest bill and eats small seeds of birch (*Betula*), grasses and other plants; while the Linnet is intermediate in size of bill and in the size of seeds it prefers, feeding mostly from farmland weeds. These differences are shown in Fig. 32, which has been drawn from the foods eaten around Oxford.

The Goldfinch and Siskin have long narrow bills which they use like a pair of tweezers to pick out seeds embedded deeply within certain types of seed-heads. The Goldfinch feeds mainly from thistles, dandelions (*Taraxacum*) and other plants of the family Compositae; while the Siskin feeds primarily from the cones of various conifers and alder (*Alnus*). The muscle for opening the bill is particularly well-developed and both species use a gaping movement to prise apart the bracts of cones and open other seed-heads. The basic difference between them is that the Goldfinch has a longer bill and can probe more deeply than the Siskin.

All the *Carduelis* and *Acanthis* finches, whatever the shape of their bills, open the unripe heads of Compositae by tearing down the sides to loosen the seeds, which are then picked out from above. But only the Goldfinch and Siskin, with their longer and more pointed bills, can pierce and probe into the tough seed-heads of thistles. The Goldfinch feeds from thistles from the time the seeds are formed in mid-summer, and throughout the autumn and winter it searches dead seed-heads on the ground for seeds. Other finches, in contrast, can feed from thistles for only a brief period in summer when the heads are blowing and the fluff is loose enough to be pulled out from above with the seeds attached.

The Goldfinch is also the only finch that can reach the seeds of teazles

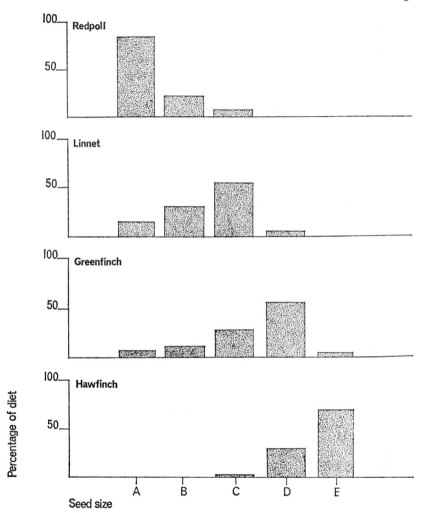

FIG. 32. The sizes of seeds eaten by four finches with different sized bills. Seeds in five size-categories, A–E.

(*Dipsacus*), which lie at the bottom of long spiked tubes (Fig. 35). The cocks are slightly larger than the hens, however, and their beaks average one millimetre (9%) longer, which enables them to reach the seeds more easily – a fact mentioned by Darwin (1871): 'I am assured . . . that the bird-catchers can distinguish the males by their slightly longer beaks. The flocks of males are often found feeding on the seeds of the teazle (*Dipsacus*), which they can reach with their elongated beaks, whilst the females more commonly feed on the seeds of the betony or Scrophularia.' Two hens I kept in captivity would sometimes feed from teazle, but before inserting their bills they first had to turn down the surrounding spikes; this was so time-consuming that, on average, they obtained only one seed to every four obtained by the longer-billed cocks. A difference in bill-length of only one millimetre may seem small to cause such a marked difference in feeding efficiency; but the differences in bill-depth between species are often no greater than this, and they are associated with even greater divergence in diet.

PYRRHULA AND PINICOLA

The beak of the Bullfinch is short, rounded and sharp at the edges (Fig. 33). The upper mandible forms a broad, shallow plate against which the lower operates, and the grooves differ from those of other finches in being of constant width along the length of the bill. Buds are particularly important to this species, as many a gardener knows to his cost, and may

FIG. 33. The palate and bill of the Bullfinch.

form up to a third of the annual diet. Seeds from globular fruiting bodies, like those of chickweed (*Stellaria*) also bulk large in the diet, as do seeds from soft fruits, such as rowan (*Sorbus*). The pulp of such fruits is discarded, and blackberries (*Rubus*) are eaten until late in the winter, long after the flesh has withered. Insects and spiders form a negligible part of the adults' diet, but are fed in quantity to the young.

The Bullfinch uses the same basic bill-movements for dealing with almost all its foods, whether these are seeds, buds, berries, pods or capsules (Nicolai 1956). The object is nipped off, held lengthwise and crushed in the bill, then turned by the tongue against the edge of the lower jaw so that the outer layer – the husk of a seed or the flesh of a fruit – is peeled off. It is also the only finch that eats small snails in quantity, crushing and de-shelling them by the same procedure.

For extracting the seeds of dandelions and other Compositae, the Bullfinch uses a different method from the finches just discussed. The latter have pointed beaks which they insert from above into a seed-head and pick out the seeds one at a time, but the Bullfinch attacks the seed-head at the side and bites out small pieces which are then turned in the bill to extract the seeds. The Bullfinch is thus limited to feeding from those Compositae which have small, soft, seed-heads, such as sowthistles (*Sonchus*) and groundsels (*Senecio*), and does not normally tackle the larger thistles (*Carduus, Cirsium, Onopordon*). With its rounded bill, the species also has difficulty in picking up seeds from the ground unless they are large. Abroad, it often takes maple (*Acer*) and large conifer seeds in this way, but in Britain it feeds on the ground extremely rarely. It also has difficulty in picking the seeds out of cones, so does not normally feed in this way either.

The Pine Grosbeak is about twice the size of the Bullfinch, with a similar, but larger and longer beak. Its feeding habits are also similar, as it eats many buds, shoots, catkins and berries. On average, it takes a greater proportion of large items than the Bullfinch, though there is a good deal of overlap and both species are fond of rowan fruits.

LOXIA

The curved, crossed tips of the mandibles are only one of several adaptations which enable crossbills to extract seeds from the hard, closed cones of conifers. The lower mandible of these birds twists either to the right or to the left of the upper one, and likewise the jaw muscles are asymmetrical, being larger on the side to which the lower jaw is deflected. The feet are particularly large and strong, and are used for holding the cones while they are worked with the bill. At these times, a crossbill gives the impression of using to the full the muscles of its whole body, as it heaves and strains to open the scales.

The feeding follows a consistent pattern. A bird first wrenches off a cone in its bill, carries it to some firm, horizontal branch, and clamps it between one of its feet and the perch. It then works the tip of its beak behind one of the scales, while the cone is held so that it points forwards and slightly to one side. A bird with the lower mandible deflected to the right holds the cone in its right foot, and vice-versa. The result is that, whether the bill crosses to right or to left, the tip of the lower mandible is always brought to bear on the cone itself and the upper one on the inside of one of the scales. The lower mandible is then moved sideways towards the body of the cone, so that the scale is raised by the tip of the upper one. The seed, once released, is scooped out by the protrusible tongue. (This last organ is longer than in other finches, with an extra piece of cartilage at the end.) The cone is thus opened primarily by the lower mandible being moved laterally in relation to the upper one, and the hinging mechanism of the jaw is specialised to permit this lateral play. From each cone a bird normally removes only a few seeds before dropping it and plucking another. Discarded cones can be recognised by their split or frayed scales. This feeding pattern is modified when the cones are opening, however, for then the bird simply clings to them and picks out the seeds in the same way as do other finches.

Such specialised feeding habits severely restrict the variety of other foods which crossbills can exploit efficiently. They find it difficult to pick up small seeds from the ground, and most of their alternative foods are ones that can be dealt with using the same bill actions as are used on cones. Thus they can prise off bark to get the insects beneath, open sun-flower seeds or beechmast, or split apples to get the pips. Apples have sometimes formed an important food of Common Crossbills during their invasions into southwest Europe, for example: '*there came a flocke of birds into Cornwall, about Harvest season, in bignesse not much exceeding a sparrow, which made a foule spoyle of the apples. Their bills were thwarted crosswise at the end, and with these they would cut an apple in two at one snap, eating onely the kernels*' (R. Carew 1602). Large apples are attacked on the tree and small ones detached and held in the feet like cones. Smaller fruits, such as those of rowan, are usually split open by being clasped in the base of the bill.

The three European species differ in size of body and bill (Fig. 34). The largest, heavy-billed, Parrot Crossbill feeds primarily from the hard cones of pine (*Pinus*), the Common Crossbill primarily from the softer cones of spruce (*Picea*), and the small, slender-billed, Two-barred Cross-bill from the small, soft cones of larch (*Larix*) (p. 74–81). This is true as a general tendency, but each sometimes feeds from cones of other types. Furthermore, some of the isolated forms of the Common Crossbill differ from the typical race in both beak and diet. Several races, including the Scottish *L.c. scotica*, have large beaks and feed from pine cones, whereas the Asiatic *L.c. himalayensis*, has a small beak and, like the Two-barred, feeds mainly from larch (p. 86). Also, the isolated race of the Two-barred, *L.l. megaplaga*, from Hispaniola, lives in pine forests and has a bill larger than that of the parental form in North America. In the crossbills, there-fore, the correlation between beak and diet is particularly close.

To summarise, the differences in beak structure between the various European finches are clearly associated with differences in their feeding methods. This is borne out well by the large conical bill of the Hawfinch, the narrow tweezer-like bills of the Goldfinch and Siskin, the rounded bill of the Bullfinch and the twisted mandibles of the various crossbills. Other species, perhaps, are less specialised, but none the less concentrate on particular types of food. The differences in feeding methods are most marked between genera; within each genus, the differences between species are mainly in size of bill and in the size of preferred food-items.

Leg-structure and feeding behaviour

The finches also vary in the proportions of food they obtain from the ground, directly from plants, or from the air. While the amount of ground-feeding depends partly on bill-structure, as mentioned, it depends mainly

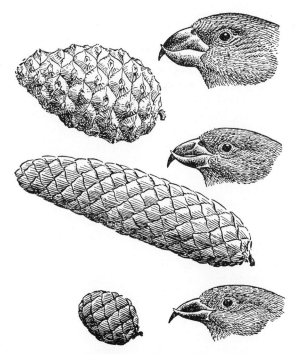

FIG. 34. The heads of the three crossbill species, and the main cones eaten. *Top:* Parrot Crossbill and pine cone; *Centre:* Common Crossbill and spruce cone; *Bottom:* Two-barred Crossbill and larch cone.

on the different positions in which the birds are able to feed. Those species which can most easily adopt clinging and hanging positions feed mainly from trees and herbaceous plants, while the least agile species feed mainly on the ground.

Six different feeding positions can be distinguished. Fig. 35 shows a bird (a) in a standing position; (b) in a normal perching position on a plant-stem bent horizontal under its weight; (c) leaning forwards; (d) perching on a bent plant-stem, so that the bird's centre of gravity lies over one of its feet; (e) clinging to a vertical stem; (f) hanging upside down. It can be seen that both feet are at more or less the same level in positions a, b, c and f, and on different levels in positions d and e. In addition, the Chaffinch and Brambling sometimes chase and catch flying insects, and the Bullfinch sometimes hovers to obtain seeds and insects from the ends of branches.

The standing position is adopted most frequently by the Chaffinch and Brambling, the latter being the slightly more willing of the two to settle on horizontal plant-stems. From these positions the birds reach upwards and forwards for food. Fitting with this, Chaffinches obtain most of their food from the ground, about a fifth from trees (while perching on horizontal twigs), and about 1% from the air. During the time they are in Britain, Bramblings also feed mainly on the ground and their behaviour at this time differs little from that of the Chaffinch. Another group (Hawfinch, Greenfinch and Linnet) stand less on the ground but more on horizontal twigs and stems than the last two species; they also perch on stems bent at an angle, but only rarely and momentarily do they cling to vertical stems. All three species obtain just over half of their food from vegetation, and the rest from the ground. The remaining species (Goldfinch, Siskin, Redpoll and crossbills) are exceptionally agile and can feed in all positions; they cling to vertical stems with ease and often hang upside down, but feed far less in a standing position than do other finches. These birds obtain almost their entire food directly from trees and herbaceous plants. An apparent exception is the Bullfinch which is less agile than the last four species and cannot hang inverted, yet still obtains almost all its foods from plants, but this is because with its rounded bill it cannot easily pick up small seeds off the ground.

The finches thus fall into three categories, those which feed mainly on the ground, those which feed mainly from vegetation, and those which feed commonly from both. The ease with which a species can cling and hang is in turn related to its leg-structure and body-weight. The most agile species are either light in weight (Goldfinch, Siskin, Redpoll) or have very short thick legs for their size (crossbills); those which feed best in a standing position have relatively long legs; while the remainder are intermediate in both leg-length and in behaviour. When feeding from plants with short, weak stems, like dandelions, moreover, all the carduelines use the same technique. They alight about half-way up the stem, then shuffle towards the head, depressing it to the ground, where it is held under the feet by the bird's weight. It can then be tackled by the bill.

The ground-feeding Chaffinch and Brambling are the only species that can walk or run. This enables them to cover the ground, and hence to find seeds, more quickly than the cardueline finches, which can only hop. The type of head-movement is also important here. In the Chaffinch, as the body shifts forward, the head is kept in an approximately constant position in relation to the surroundings, until the last moment when it is brought suddenly to a normal position. This head-movement is seen in other ground-feeding birds, such as chickens and pigeons, and is probably

FIG. 35. The feeding positions of finches.
A, standing; B, normal perching position on a plant-stem bent horizontal under the bird's weight; C, leaning forwards; D, perching on a bent plant-stem, with the weight on one foot; E, clinging to a vertical stem; F, hanging upside down.

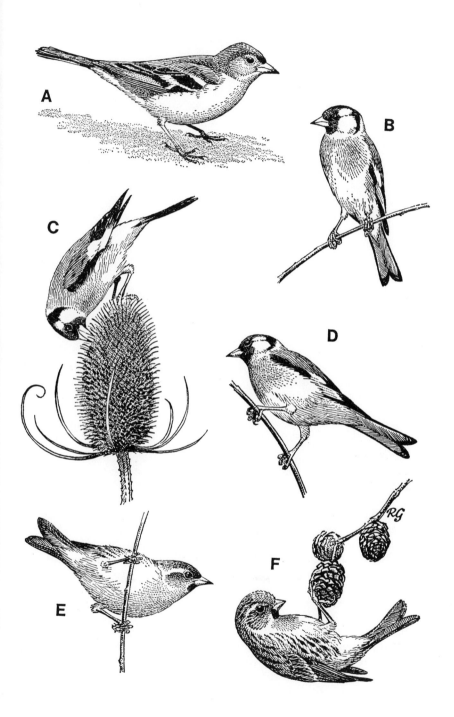

concerned with visual fixation, giving the maximum of 'still-viewing' and
the minimum of head-movement. In the carduelines the body and head
are moved as one, and the bird must stand for a moment between each
hop to scan the ground in front of it, which is a less efficient means of
searching than in the Chaffinch. However, hopping is probably a better
method than walking or moving through branches, and so presumably
helps to make the carduelines more suited to an arboreal life.

The use of the feet in feeding

The finches also vary in the use they make of their feet in feeding. The
Chaffinch, for instance, never uses its feet to hold food-objects (such as the
seed-heads of plants), but the Goldfinch does so regularly and can thereby
exploit foods which might otherwise be difficult for it to get. In general,
those species which are most adept at clinging to plant-stems are also
those which most often use their feet in feeding. Both types of behaviour
require a strong grip.

Furthermore, of those species which use their feet, some do so merely to
steady food-objects lying on the ground, while others can also pick up
detached food-objects in their bill, or pull in flexible plant-stems, and hold
them under their feet while the seeds are removed. The situation can be
summarised as follows:

Species which do not use their feet in feeding: Chaffinch, Brambling, Hawfinch,
Bullfinch, Pine Grosbeak.

Species which use their feet to steady food-objects on the ground: Greenfinch,
Linnet, Twite, Serin.

Species which also pull in food-objects in their bill, and place them under their
feet: Goldfinch, Siskin, Redpoll, Crossbills.

The co-ordination between foot and bill is well-developed in the
Goldfinch, Siskin and Redpoll, and can best be seen while the birds are
feeding in birches or alders (Fig. 36). The catkins of these trees hang
below the branches on thin, flexible stems, and to secure them, the bird
reaches to pull in a catkin with its beak, and at the same time extends its
front toes to clamp the catkin against the branch on which it stands. This
natural feeding behaviour has often been exploited by bird-fanciers, for
these finches can be taught to pull up food on the end of a long thread, the
pulled in loop being held under the foot, while the bird reaches with its
bill for the next pull. 'Goldfinches are so adept at this trick that they have
for centuries been kept in special cages so designed that the bird can
subsist only by pulling up and holding tight two strings, that on one side
being attached to a little cart containing food and resting on an incline,
and that on the other to a thimble containing water. This was so widespread in the sixteenth century that it gave rise to the name "draw-water"
or its equivalent in two or three European languages' (Thorpe 1956).

In recent years, the use of the feet by feeding birds has been studied in

PLATE 7. The Greenfinch (cock, *above*) in winter is a frequent visitor to feeding trays, where a favourite food is peanuts.

PLATE 8. Cock Greenfinch on a sunflower, one of the main crop-plants eaten by the species in southern Europe.

FIG. 36. The use of the feet by a feeding finch.

detail, again using food on the end of a thread. The results can be explained largely by the birds' natural feeding behaviour, those species which most frequently use their feet to hold food in the wild being most successful at pulling up and holding the string. The young of species like the Greenfinch and Canary, in which the co-ordination between foot and bill is normally poorly developed, are sometimes successful with practice, but the adults generally fail to learn (Vince 1958). Species like the Chaffinch, which do not naturally use their feet in feeding, seem completely unable to accomplish this task, given any amount of practice.

The avoidance of competition

One result of the variations in bill-structure, leg-length and body-weight among the European finches is that no two species have the same feeding habits. This situation is itself partly a result of natural selection. Thus if two species lived in the same area and had the same ecology, they would compete with one another, and in the course of evolution, they would either diverge in their feeding requirements or one would eliminate the other completely. This idea, called the 'principle of competitive exclusion', is often attributed to Gause (1934), who was the first to test it experimentally, but in recent years field-studies of birds have added much support (Lack 1944, 1947, 1954). In general, closely-related species either live in different habitats, in which case they might take similar foods, or if they live in the same habitat they take different foods, or they take the same foods from different places. A pair of species may differ in more than one of these ways, but the differences in diet are rarely absolute. The finches differ in diet more in winter than in summer (when food is less limiting), and more in natural habitats than in cultivated land (Newton 1967b).

The development of food-preferences

How do young finches come to adopt those feeding habits which are typical of their kind? With species taking such a varied diet, it is inconceivable that the young could 'instinctively' recognise all their foods individually. More likely, they inherit broad recognition patterns which are common to many potential foods, and then learn by trial and error which foods they can deal with most effectively, and come to concentrate on these (Hinde 1959). Evidence for this view was provided by Kear (1962). Soon after leaving the nest, young Chaffinches peck at any small spots which contrast with the background, and pick up and mandibulate a variety of objects, including seeds. They first learn to discriminate edible seeds from other objects, and then to prefer the largest seeds they can efficiently manage, so gaining the most good in a given time.

By this learning the young species with different types of bills come to concentrate on different types of foods, even though they might respond initially to the same range of objects. Thus young Greenfinches and Linnets reared in captivity begin by selecting the same small seeds from a mixture, but the Greenfinches, which have larger bills, learn to take large seeds sooner than the Linnets, and eventually settle on a diet containing a greater proportion of large seeds (Newton 1967b). In the wild, moreover, the young cannot help but have their attention directed to appropriate foods by their parents, and this might enhance the learning.

A similar process probably controls the development of other feeding behaviour. One might expect, for example, that those species which are structurally equipped to hang from vegetation would learn to do so, while others, less well equipped, would learn not to attempt it. This implies that all the differences in feeding habits between closely-related species might depend on their structural differences, the only 'psychological' factor involved being the learning in the young. Between more distantly related groups, however, some of the differences in feeding behaviour are probably inherited irrespective of structural features. For example, all cardueline finches can learn to pull out thistle fluff to get the seeds, a simple action for which no structural specialisation is required. Yet Chaffinches never do this, even in an aviary where they will watch other birds doing it and will pick off seeds from fluff pulled out for them. Here, it seems, the difference between the cardueline and fringilline finches is 'psychologically' rooted.

Food traditions

The foods eaten by a species are also influenced by social experience, the young learning from their parents, and the parents from one another. In this way novel feeding habits can soon spread through a population, as did the eating of *Daphne mezereum* fruits by Greenfinches. With such a common garden shrub, the habit is easily noticed, and by means of surveys its spread was mapped by Pettersson (1956, 1961). Apparently the habit started in the nineteen-thirties in a small northern town, but had spread over most of Britain by the fifties, and had reached the continent by the sixties. In the same way, the destruction of fruit-blossoms by

Redpolls in New Zealand started in the nineteen-fifties, and is now wide-spread there, and has recently started independently in Britain (p. 90). The best known instance of new feeding habits arising and spreading among other birds is the opening of milk-bottles by titmice (Hinde & Fisher 1951). But such habits can of course develop only within the limits set by the birds' structure and natural behaviour.

Since local traditions can arise in this way, this might explain why some finches take slightly different diets in Holstein (Germany) and Oxford, even though the same food-plants are common in both areas (Eber 1956, Newton 1967b). In Holstein cereals bulk large in the diet of the Linnet, but in Oxford are not taken, despite the quantity grown. Conversely, groundsel (*Senecio vulgaris*) seeds form a major food of the Goldfinch near Oxford for six months each year, but are not taken by this species in Holstein; they are, however, important there to the Linnet, which rarely takes them in Oxford. Further, in Holstein *Artemisia* seeds are taken commonly by the Greenfinch and Goldfinch, but in Oxford hardly ever. All these differences occur in summer, when the birds have a wide range of foods to choose from; in winter, when food is restricted, the diets of all species in the two areas are as similar as they can be.

To summarise this chapter, the various finches differ in the size of seeds they prefer and in the types of seed-head they can best exploit, and these differences are related to differences in the size and shape of their bills and in the way the bill is used. Species also differ in the proportion of food they obtain directly from vegetation as opposed to the ground, and in the extent to which they use their feet in feeding, both of which are connected with differences in body-weight and leg-length. The result is that no two species of European finches have the same feeding habits. Young finches respond initially to a wide range of food-objects, then apparently learn by trial and error what to eat and how to feed most effectively. In this way, through specialisations in structure, the young of each species could develop the feeding habits which characterise their species. They also learn from their parents, and the adults from one another, which enables new feeding habits to spread and local food-traditions to arise.

CHAPTER 6

BULLFINCHES AND FRUIT BUDS

THE natural feeding habits of some animals inevitably lead them to eat crops. In Britain the only finch of economic importance is the Bullfinch, which now removes the buds of fruit trees on such a scale as to constitute one of the greatest problems with which the fruit-growing industry has to contend. The damage is indisputable. Let any sceptic visit the orchards in the winter of a bad year and watch the birds in action. Let him later visit the orchards in spring and note the shortage of blossom. If he examines the trees closely, he will see that the blossom-buds have been nipped off neatly at the base, and that their remains litter the ground below. He will further note that the loss is greater on some fruit varieties than on others, and is greater on trees near woods and hedgerows than on those in the middle of the orchards. These are the characteristics of Bullfinch damage. This bird had a price on its head for the same offence as long ago as the sixteenth century, when one penny was offered in reward for '*everie Bulfynche or other Byrde that devoureth the blowthe of fruit*'. The damage has increased greatly in recent years, however, following the increase and spread of the species outside woodland (p. 90). Nowadays, in extreme cases, whole orchards of trees may be almost denuded of buds, and yield only a few pounds of fruit instead of several tons (Newton 1964b). In comparison, the damage to buds by other birds is negligible, though that by the House Sparrow (*Passer domesticus*) can be severe around human habitation.

The Bullfinch might have been expected to become a major pest in orchards, for in its natural habitat it takes a greater proportion and variety of buds, and for a longer period each year, than does any other small European bird. Indeed, it is well adapted to do so in bill-structure, feeding technique and digestive system, having a shorter and broader beak and a relatively longer gut than other finches (Eber 1956, Newton 1967d). All cultivated fruit trees, moreover, have buds of the size most acceptable to Bullfinches, and are derived from tree-species the buds of which are preferred under natural conditions. Various ornamental shrubs, such as *Forsythia*, are also attacked in spring, partly because their early flowering requires an early bud-swell, in advance of that in native trees.

A single Bullfinch can remove the buds of fruit trees at a rate of 30 or more per minute (Wright & Summers 1960, Newton 1964b). In winter, the feeding is remarkably systematic: a bird will alight at the tip of a branch and work towards the trunk, taking every bud in turn; and on reaching the older wood, which bears fewer buds, it will fly out to the tip of another branch and repeat the process. The birds enter orchards from the adjacent woods and hedgerows, attack the nearest trees first, and as the days go by, penetrate further, stripping every tree in turn. Since the birds often work in parties of a dozen or more, it takes them only a few days to devastate a large orchard. Not all their feeding causes damage, however, for at least half the buds can be removed from a pear tree without necessarily depressing the eventual yield of fruit (Wright & Summers).

In general, the buds of plum and pear trees are most vulnerable, with gooseberries and currants next, and apples and cherries least, though different varieties are preferred in different months. The usual sequence of preferences in Kent orchards through the year is shown in Table 11, but

Table 11. The sequence of bud-preferences shown by Bullfinches in Kent orchards. (From Newton 1967d.)

	Months of damage	Remarks
Apples	January-April	Damage rarely severe. The buds of some varieties, such as 'Lord Lambourn' and 'James Grieve', are eaten when dormant, but most varieties only at bud-burst or at the 'pink-cluster' stage. In general, dessert varieties preferred to 'cookers'.
Cherries	November-January	Only 'Morello' suffers severe damage in the dormant stage. Ovaries from sweet cherries are sometimes taken in spring, but damage is rarely severe.
Currants, red and white	December-March	Time of peak damage varies, but is often severe.
Currants, black	March-April	Usually attacked only after bud-burst, but often severely.
Gooseberries	November-February	Damage often severe. 'Leveller.' one of most favoured varieties.
Pears	January-March	Damage to some varieties often so severe as to result in no crop. In years when bud-feeding begins early, favoured varieties may be attacked in November, but usually the birds soon switch to plums and return to pears in January. The varieties 'Conference', 'Williams' and 'Dr Jules' are most vulnerable, 'Comice' and 'Hardy' least.
Plums	November-February	Damage to some varieties is often so severe as to result in complete loss of crop. Various gages, especially 'Golden Gage', preferred above all others.

in areas where other varieties are available the sequence may differ. And within any one type of fruit, certain varieties are more vulnerable than others. Among pears, for instance, the varieties 'Williams', 'Dr Jules' and 'Conference' are preferred; among plums, the various gages; and among apples, dessert varieties are generally preferred to 'cookers'. But the least favoured varieties are spared only when the birds have a choice, otherwise they too are eaten. There are no consistent differences in the appearance, size or texture between the buds of favoured and other varieties, and the preferences are probably governed by differences in time of bud-swell, nutritive content and palatability. At least in winter, the birds choose the buds which provide the most nutritious diet at the time, for feeding trials on captive birds have shown that the favoured varieties are also those on which the birds can best maintain their weight.

Only the small embryonic centres of flower buds are eaten – those parts otherwise destined to become fruit. Buds destroyed are not replaced by the tree in the same year, though most fruit varieties make good the loss in the following year through the development of ancillary buds. In some types of plums and gooseberries, however, the fruiting points do not regenerate, so the damage is cumulative. Occasionally, the leaf buds are also eaten, making it hard to train the tree to good shape, and thus permanently affecting its cropping potential (Wright & Summers 1960). The damage varies greatly from year to year, however, depending mainly on when the birds start eating buds: in some years they begin as early as November, in others not until March, but once begun, the attacks continue until the blossom is finished, around mid-May.

Early attempts to reduce the damage

In theory, the damage by any pest can be reduced either by protecting the crop itself (with some sort of enclosure, scaring device or repellent chemical), or by reducing the numbers of the pest. The latter may be achieved either by killing large numbers each year (by poisoning, shooting or trapping), or 'biologically' by altering the environment in some way so that the pest's population is held at a permanently reduced level.

Enclosing a fruit crop against Bullfinches is feasible in small gardens, but impracticable in large orchards; scaring devices (such as 'bangers') are effective only until the birds get used to them – which often takes only a few days; and all the chemical deterrents applied so far to buds have achieved little or no lasting success, in part because the Bullfinch peels off the outer layers bearing the chemical. Most chemicals are also washed off by rain, and when most needed (during cold weather) are difficult to handle as aqueous solutions. A systemic deterrent, that could be sprayed on to the ground and then taken up by the tree into its buds, might be more effective, but has not yet been tried.

For reducing the numbers of Bullfinches, poisoning is undesirable because it is unselective and therefore harmful to other animals, while shooting is expensive and incidentally damages the trees. The destruction of nests in the vicinity of fruit farms is too time-consuming to be practicable; and anyway natural predators are more efficient at this (p. 181–3). In the nineteen-fifties, however, Wright and Summers (1960) developed a trap that was not only effective, but also cheap, easy to operate, and harmless to other animals. It consists of a baited wire box which catches the birds alive, so that they can later be disposed of humanely. Used with a decoy, this trap has proved much the best way of reducing the damage.

General biology

It was nonetheless desirable to learn more about Bullfinches, to find what controls their numbers under natural conditions, and the factors that influence the quantity of buds they eat. I therefore studied for six years the birds living in some woods and orchards near Oxford (Newton 1964b,c, 1967d, 1968b). The winter seed-diet of these birds was obtained almost entirely from two types of herbaceous plants, two shrubs and two trees. The crops of all these plants were produced in late summer and not replenished by further seed-production during the winter. The seed-crops of dock (*Rumex*), nettle (*Urtica dioica*), and bramble (*Rubus*) were fairly consistent in quantity from year to year, but those of privet (*Ligustrum vulgare*), birch (*Betula*) and ash (*Fraxinus excelsior*) varied greatly. This was especially true of ash, which in some years produced a tremendous profusion of seeds and in others none at all. Previously no animals were known to eat ash seeds in quantity and to my palate they were distasteful. Bullfinches, moreover, were extremely selective, feeding consistently from a few trees and leaving most untouched.

As seeds became scarce during winter, and their variety restricted, buds became increasingly important in the birds' diet, especially those of hawthorn (*Crataegus monogyna*), but also of crab-apple (*Malus sylvestris*), wych elm (*Ulmus glabra*) and other trees. But feeding trials on captive birds showed that, in winter, Bullfinches could not maintain their weight on buds alone, neither those of native nor of orchard trees, and needed some seeds in order to survive. Only after the end of February, when buds were larger and days were longer, could the birds subsist entirely on buds. It thus seemed likely that wild Bullfinches ate large numbers of buds in winter only when seeds were scarce, and to test this view I measured the seasonal decline in seed-stocks in the woods each winter, and at the same time checked the neighbouring fruit-farms for damage. The seeds disappeared from the various food-plants during winter mainly through the activities of Bullfinches, but also many fell to the ground and were lost, and some of the birch seeds were eaten by other birds.

Fig. 37 shows the decline in seed-stocks during the winter of 1962/63, when the ash crop was good. Although the entire crops of three of the food-plants had gone by January, half the crops of dock and bramble remained by April. And so plentiful were the ash seeds that, although they had formed the main food of Bullfinches throughout the winter, less than 1% of the crop had been removed. Hence, in this year large quantities of seeds were left at the end of the winter.

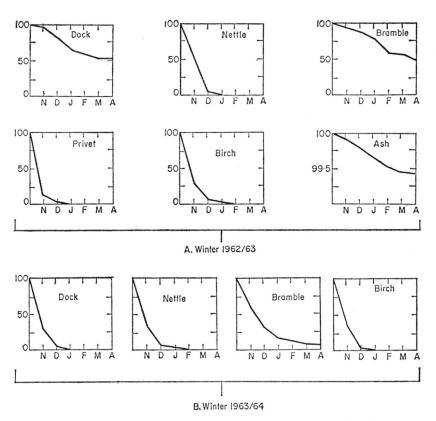

FIG. 37. The decline in seed-stocks in an Oxford wood during two successive winters.

Fig. 37 also shows the contrasting situation in 1963/64, when ash seeds were lacking. All the privet seeds had been eaten before mid-October, when measurements were started, as had all the seeds of three other plants by January. All that remained at the end of the winter was about 7% of the bramble seeds. Hence, in this winter Bullfinches ate practically all the seeds available to them in woodland.

In the first of the two winters just described, when seeds were plentiful, the buds of various native trees formed less than one-fifth of the diet of Bullfinches from October to April, and were not taken in quantity before March. Damage on fruit farms was negligible. In the second winter, when seeds were scarce, buds formed nearly a half of the total winter diet and were taken in quantity as early as mid-December. Damage on fruit farms was severe. Results consistent with these were obtained in the four other winters, two with ash crops and two without.

Ash-crops and bud-damage

From the fruit-growers' viewpoint, the seeds of ash are thus the most important winter food of Bullfinches, because they are often the only alternative to buds at a time when other seeds have been eaten. Past records show that good ash crops usually occur every second year in England, with little or no seed produced in the intervening years. Replies to questionnaires sent to fruit-growers in various areas showed that, as expected, most had suffered severe bud-damage in their orchards only in the alternate years in which the ash crop failed. Also, since the fluctuations in the crop were synchronised over the whole of southern Britain, so was the extent of bud-damage, and all areas had it bad together.

It might be thought that one solution to the problem would be to break in some way the biennial cropping of ash so that seeds were available every year, or else to supply an alternative source of seeds in the lean years. In this way the birds would never have to eat buds in quantity. However, even if this were feasible, it would not be a satisfactory solution, for Bullfinches are almost certainly held in check by food-shortage in the winters when seeds are scarce. Around Oxford their mortality was always heaviest in the years without an ash crop, for then most other seeds had gone by January, before buds were large enough to provide adequate nourishment. Hence, if food were provided artificially, the birds might survive the lean years in larger numbers than at present and increase to an even higher level set by this new food-supply. Having eaten it, they would turn again to buds. Also, putting seeds in orchards might make the birds concentrate there in even greater numbers than at present.

The most effective means of control

Nonetheless, the relationship between the ash crop and the damage to buds means that fruit-growers can predict the years in which severe attacks are likely, and plan their control accordingly. At first, the growers used their traps mainly in spring, when the attacks were occurring and, although damage was reduced in this way, it was still severe. But from a better understanding of the bird's ecology, I was able to suggest a more effective trapping programme. The logic ran as follows: since seed-stocks are not replenished during the winter, the more birds present in autumn, the sooner they will eat these seeds and turn to buds, and the greater will be the damage. But by removing some birds in the autumn, the natural seed-stocks might be conserved, the date at which the birds turn to buds delayed, and the total damage reduced. So the plan was to trap in the autumn, in the nearby woods and hedges, instead of in spring in the orchards themselves. This was started in 1963 on about a dozen farms in Kent, which then obtained good crops in 1964, even though the damage was generally bad in this year. The system is now in general use, though some growers play safe by trapping for the whole year, not just in autumn. It works because most Bullfinches move over only short distances (less than five kilometres), so immigration is limited, and because several of the important natural foods are not eaten regularly by other animals, so if Bullfinches are removed these foods last longer.

The principal effect of trapping on the birds themselves is to bring the main period of mortality forward from mid-winter (natural starvation) to early autumn (artificial control). But compared with the Bullfinches that die naturally, those killed by fruit-growers contain many more first-year birds. For instance, from October to December 1964, the ratio of first-year to older birds which I netted in woodland was 2:1 (which fits with the reproductive rate), whereas among nearly 300 killed in orchards in the same months, first-year birds outnumbered adults by 38 to 1. This is partly because young birds are easier to trap, and partly because they move around more than the older birds, so that more come within range. On the average fruit-farm, a few hundred Bullfinches might be destroyed annually, but on a large one in well-wooded country, over a thousand. This may seem a lot, but even with the birds moving over only five kilometres, the potential of a single trap extends over 80 square kilometres. Further, although trapping has reduced the damage, it has not, apparently, caused any long-term reduction in Bullfinch numbers, for the totals caught by individual fruit-growers have not declined over the years, as might otherwise have been expected. Trapping requires one man, part-time, for a few months each year, and sometimes makes the difference between a good fruit crop and none at all, so is clearly worth the cost to the grower.

In the past, attempts to deal with pest-species have often begun with the use (or misuse) of chemical deterrents and poisons. Most of these methods achieved little or no lasting success, but have resulted in a wastage of public funds, pollution of soil or water, and an unnecessary destruction of other wildlife. Recent studies of several pest-species have shown that any attempt at control must be preceded by a thorough study of the pest's biology – work that many would consider a needless delay or of academic interest only.

CHAPTER 7

FLOCKING AND ROOSTING

MANY species of birds feed or roost in the company of others for at least part of the year. A more efficient usage of the food-supply, an increased awareness of predators, and other reasons have been put forward to explain gregariousness, but the main function undoubtedly differs from family to family. The cardueline finches feed in flocks at all times of year and the fringilline finches at all times except when breeding. The flocks may contain anything from a few individuals to several thousands or, in the Brambling, even millions. The largest concentration on record is a roost containing 70 million Bramblings which some years ago congregated each night in conifer plantations in a small Swiss valley (p. 30). But flocks of more than a few thousand finches are exceptional; in most species tens or hundreds are the rule, and in Bullfinches groups of less than a dozen.

Outside the breeding season the lives of finches follow a set routine. At daybreak parties of birds leave the roosts and assemble on the feeding grounds. The flocks that form are largest and most integrated in the early mornings, when the birds are hungry, but tend to break up in the middle part of the day, when groups of birds leave to rest, preen, drink and bathe, only to reassemble again in the late afternoon. The slack period varies in timing through the year: in mid-summer in Britain it lasts from around 9 a.m. till 4 p.m., in September from around 11 a.m. till 3 p.m., and in mid-winter is reduced to an hour around midday. Throughout the day individuals also move between the different flocks, but towards evening, the flocks again break up as the birds leave in separate parties and fly on direct course for their roosts, in thick scrub. If the roost is large, the flocks tend to merge as they reach it, the smaller joining the larger. The same roosts are used night after night, but change irregularly in size and composition, for some birds use different places on different nights. Thus at one roost near Oxford less than 300 Greenfinches were usually present, but on certain nights up to 1,200; and some birds ringed here were later caught at other roosts in the area (Dickinson & Dobinson 1969).

The constant movements of finches between different roosts and feeding places are well known to bird-ringers, and not just from the recoveries, but because many more birds are often caught at a place over several days than are present at any one time. In one garden, for instance, over a thousand Greenfinches were ringed in two months, but at no time were more than a dozen present. As yet, ringing recoveries have given little indication of the size of area served by a roost, for unless a bird is caught twice in 24 hours, a particular roost cannot be linked with a particular feeding place. However, one Greenfinch was caught at a roost three kilometres from where it had been ringed a few hours earlier, and probably many move further than this. Some Hawfinches were seen to fly more than ten kilometres between their feeding and roosting place (Mountfort 1957), yet these birds will also roost within a hundred metres of where they have spent the day.

Mixed flocks of seed-eaters result mainly from different species sharing the same feeding grounds. Chaffinches, Bramblings, Linnets, Greenfinches, Tree-sparrows (*Passer montanus*) and various buntings, for example, often assemble together on farmland. On the ground the birds usually move as a unit, but once in the air the different species form compact groups of their own, the Linnets circling and settling some distance away and the rest making for cover. The Chaffinch and Brambling, in contrast, behave in a flock as though they were members of a single species and are at all times thoroughly integrated.

It is the way in which their food is distributed, in local concentrations, which enables finches to feed in flocks. At any one place there is usually more food than can be immediately consumed (or defended) by the bird that finds it, so it is of no serious disadvantage to such birds to feed in company. But gregariousness also helps each individual to find food. Especially when hungry, flying finches react instantly if they see a feeding flock. Sometimes they merely dip in flight before moving on, but usually they join the feeding birds, alighting near the edge of the flock. In this way a small group that has found a good feeding place may rapidly swell in size as it is joined by others. For example, I once saw five Greenfinches feeding on a patch of freshly seeding charlock; an hour later 20 birds were present, the following day over a hundred, and on the fourth day several hundreds. The flock persisted for only a few days, and then dispersed within two days as the seeds were consumed.

To appreciate the advantage of this method of feeding, remember that finches are specialist feeders and for much of the year their food is extremely patchy. To find a small plot of suitable feeding within a large tract of country would require each individual to waste a lot of time searching. But if all individuals are looking for food, some will be lucky by chance alone. If such birds stay to feed, it only requires other individuals to react appropriately for numbers to accumulate rapidly on the best feeding grounds. Indeed, 'local enhancement', that is, flying to join others seen feeding, is the easiest way to locate food and may also be an important way in which young birds learn what to eat. On the other hand, any birds consistently failing to respond to a feeding flock would risk starvation and might be eliminated by natural selection. Hence, while it is the local abundances of food which permit flocking in finches, gregariousness itself is a help to the birds in finding them.

The distribution of finches cannot be explained by gregariousness alone, however, otherwise they would all concentrate in a single large flock, but at any one time the population is instead dispersed in several flocks of differing size, and moreover the pattern changes through the year. The food supply has an obvious influence. In early summer, pairs and small groups are the rule, and it is chiefly in winter, when the number of possible feeding places is much reduced, that larger numbers occur together. At this time, some species habitually feed in larger flocks than others, but this is probably because their food is locally more plentiful, and within each species flock-size varies greatly. Thus Greenfinches feeding in fields, with a wide expanse of feeding, often number several thousands, yet on a garden feeding tray only a few individuals. The number that can feed at such a place depends on the standing room, for each bird defends its position, and only as one leaves or is driven off, can another take its place. This may seem obvious, but it is an important way in which the population as a whole is dispersed and the size of each flock is reduced to correspond with the feeding available. The position on farmland, where at any one time a flock might occupy only a small part of a feeding area, is less easy to explain.

Another advantage of flocking, already mentioned, is that it gives increased protection from predators and enables the birds to feed more efficiently (Lack 1968). For most of the time, feeding birds are on the move with their heads down, so the chances that an approaching predator will be noticed is much greater by a flock than by a solitary individual. Moreover the birds act as though aware of this, for one on its own is constantly looking around and spends more time on the alert and less in feeding than a bird in a group. Like many other flocking birds, finches have special alarm calls and conspicuous marks on their wings, tail or rump to warn their kind if danger threatens. The calls are audible only over the short distances for which they are needed and the colour patterns become exposed suddenly as the birds take wing. If a flock is feeding in a field, and there is sudden danger, the birds will take off in a body, with a rush of wings, without calling, and make for the nearest cover. The birds move in this way on seeing a predator or on hearing the alarm call of their own or another species.

The importance of keeping in flocks is also shown by the evolution of special 'contact calls', uttered whenever a bird moves away, and if an individual loses touch with its companions it shows special behaviour until it rejoins them. For instance, a Bullfinch isolated in this manner calls loudly, flies up to the treetops, looks round, perches in open places and makes itself conspicuous by flicking its wings and tail, until it sees or hears its fellows.

Flock Structure and Behaviour

As well as the factors promoting gregariousness, such as the mutual

attraction between individuals, there are within each flock others promoting dispersion (Hinde 1961). In particular, each feeding bird main-
tains a space around itself – the 'individual distance' – by threatening,
attacking or fleeing from other birds that approach too closely. This behaviour is found in almost all flocking birds, not just finches, and it
probably serves to reduce the chances of food-robbing and to ensure that
each bird has enough room for a sudden take-off. But these are not the
only functions for there are also sexual differences. In an aviary cock
Redpolls keep at least 10 cm. apart in winter, but hens only 4 cm. (Dilger
1960). Cock Chaffinches keep at least 20 cm. apart, and hens 5–10 cm.
(Marler 1956a). In general larger species defend a larger area, and individuals of all species keep further apart than usual during the courtship
period, when the cock may also drive off other birds from a wide area
around himself and his mate.

At any one time the structure of the flock thus depends on the outcome
between the conflicting tendencies of gregariousness and solitary life, and
in finches the degree of flock-cohesion changes seasonally. In summer, the
flocks are little more than loose aggregations of individuals at an abundant
source of food, each bird going about its own separate business of feeding
young and so on, and paying little attention to its neighbours, except to
keep a short distance away from them. When flushed the birds usually
scatter in different directions. In winter, in contrast, the flock is more
integrated and the behaviour of different individuals is more synchronised,
each feeding, drinking, bathing and resting in the company of others.
Only in winter does the whole flock move as a unit. Such synchronised
movements are initiated by the calling of one of the flock members. Others
join in and feeding stops. Eventually a small group takes off and the rest
of the flock follows, gradually peeling off the ground. Once in the air
the flock may circle a few times and land again close by or move right
away. Although the movement is initiated by a few individuals, the rest
will not leave unless they are ready, for the few might take off after making
all the preparations, and then perceiving that the rest are not following,
circle and land again (Marler 1956a). These are some of the ways in
which the activities of the different flock members are synchronised and
flock cohesion is maintained.

The feeding behaviour of birds in a flock also changes through the year.
In summer when seeds are plentiful, a flock feeding on the ground tends to
spread widely and the different members hop around more or less at
random. As food becomes scarce, not only do the flocks become fewer and
larger, but the members adopt a different feeding method. They all face
the same way, usually into the wind, and begin to hop forward, and other
parties joining them fall in with the general movement. Any bird stopping
to pick up a seed is passed by others, and eventually a bird which started
near the front finds itself near the back of the advancing flock, where few
seeds remain; it then flies over the birds in front to drop in the van where

its chances of finding food are greater. Each bird holds this privileged position for only a short time until others fly over it and hop by each time it makes a stop for a seed. In this manner the whole flock rolls steadily over the ground. The term 'drifting' has been used to describe this type of motion (Crook 1960), an expression implying a casual movement which this is not: rather it is efficient food-seeking behaviour in which the whole ground is searched thoroughly and all individuals spend at least some time in the front ranks (Ward 1965).

Somewhat similar behaviour is seen among Siskins and Redpolls feeding in trees. For some minutes a flock will wheel above the forest, then drop suddenly to a particular tree. After a time a party will take wing, pass over the rest still feeding, and alight on the next tree so that the whole flock leapfrogs through the forest. On each tree the birds normally start at the top and work rapidly down. In alders (*Alnus*), they are highly selective, search only the few fruits that are open at the time, and leave the rest for another day. Their feeding contrasts with that of the Bullfinch and Pine Grosbeak, which normally sit for long periods over a bunch of berries, methodically munching them all, and stripping the trees in turn. The first method is useful to the cone-feeders, which have to select individual fruits from a tree and the second to the larger, more sluggish species which do not.

Fighting

In most situations, on the ground or in trees, little fighting occurs in connection with individual distance, for as more birds join the flock they alight at the edges to increase the area occupied. The same is not true, however, where feeding is limited, as for example on a restricted number of food-plants or at a feeding tray. Here, birds continually fight over standing places, and in general larger individuals dominate small ones and cocks dominate hens, though exceptions exist (Hinde 1955–56).

Three types of postures are used in fighting among finches (Fig. 38). The commonest is the 'head-forward threat', in which a bird faces its

FIG. 38. Chaffinch postures: A threat ("head forwards"); B, submission

opponent, crouches, raises or flutters its wings and threatens him with open beak. The more intense the aggression the more exaggerated the posture, but *Carduelis* and *Serinus* finches more commonly flutter their wings than do others. In most species, this display is accompanied by a special aggressive note, but in the Chaffinch, Brambling and Hawfinch by bill-snapping instead. Sometimes the attack is pressed home, and the aggressor lunges forward, stabbing at its opponent and fluttering to maintain balance, and this continues until one gives way or starts a chase. A more decisive encounter is the 'supplanting attack', in which one bird, perched some distance from another with food, may suddenly sleek its feathers and fly at its victim, which flees, the aggressor perching in its place and remaining to eat the food. Neither aggressor nor victim show any hesitation in their behaviour, one with confident attack and the other with prompt escape (Marler 1956a).

Fighting is time-consuming, however, and potentially dangerous, so is kept to a minimum. More common than either form of aggression is 'avoidance behaviour', in which each bird merely ensures that it does not approach others too closely. Imagine birds are feeding on scattered grain. One hops close to another, perhaps sleeking its head feathers, and the second immediately moves away keeping a certain distance between them. This second bird often assumes the 'submissive posture', with feathers fluffed and the neck pulled in (a reversal of the threat display) and turns its back on the aggressor to avoid looking at him, behaviour which averts attack.

Learning also reduces the amount of fighting through the development, in small groups, of a social hierarchy. Each individual learns by experience, bitter or otherwise, which of its companions are stronger and must be avoided, and which are weaker and can be intimidated. In this way a peck-order develops rapidly, in which each individual knows its place, and conflicts are settled without a fight. Peck-orders depend on the birds being able to recognise one another, and have been studied in detail among caged Canaries (Shoemaker 1939), Crossbills (Tordoff 1954), Chaffinches (Marler 1956a) and Redpolls (Dilger 1960). In general, when a hen takes a mate she assumes a status in the social hierarchy equal to his.

In finches, as in other birds that have been studied, aggressive encounters over food are most frequent when food is scarce or feeding sites restricted. The advantage to the dominant birds, which attack more often than they retreat, is obvious. But submission also has survival value, even to the lower members of the hierarchy which are often displaced, since they do not waste time and energy disputing with stronger individuals when they would lose anyway (Lack 1954). When food is short it will pay them to look elsewhere, rather than to stay and wait in vain for a feeding place. This again can be easily seen among Greenfinches on a feeding tray, where a few birds get most of the food, while others wait for a time in

PLATE 9. The Goldfinch, with its long sharp bill, specialises on seeds of plants in the family Compositae, especially thistles (cock, *above left*). The hen (*above right*) has gaps in her wings produced by moulting primary and secondary feathers. *Below* is a pair at their nest, well-secured among swaying branches.

PLATE 10. The Siskin (cock *above*, hen *lower left*) breeds in conifer forests and has recently spread in Britain as a result of increased afforestation. In winter it becomes more generally distributed, and is usually seen in alder trees (*lower right*).

trees near by, and if they are not soon successful move away. This, as mentioned, is one of the ways in which flock-size is adjusted to the food available.

Submission as well as dominance is thus of advantage to all individuals whatever their position in the peck-order, because combat is thereby avoided and time and energy saved. The same individual might show different degrees of aggression at different times, depending on its general condition, the state of its gonads, its position in space with respect to other individuals, whether it is on or off home ground and so on. Also, weak individuals can approach aggressive ones more closely than otherwise if they adopt the appeasing submissive posture.

Nevertheless the outcome of fighting is that, when food is short, not all birds are affected similarly, for some can get enough and maintain their weight, while others cannot. At most times in winter only a small proportion of birds in a population are underweight and starving, for as food becomes scarcer the population is trimmed down accordingly, and as some birds weaken and die, others take their place. By this means, even though mortality is heavy over a long period, only a few birds are starving at once. This is certainly so in the Bullfinch, the only finch studied in this respect, though it has also been recorded in the Wood-pigeon (Murton 1965). In general, only when food is reduced suddenly, as for example by snow, is a large proportion of birds short of food and underweight at the same time.

Roosting

During the breeding season, finches roost singly, in pairs or small groups, but from late summer some species gather into fewer, larger, roosts containing hundreds or thousands of birds. They favour clumps of evergreens, such as rhododendrons, gorse or young conifers, and other scrub patches, especially in hollows or in woodlands that are sheltered from wind. Species differ in their preferred roosting sites (Table 12), however, and when several use the same area they tend to keep apart. In America certain rosy finches (*Leucosticte*) roost in caves or mine-shafts (French 1959), and in the Arctic, Redpolls make holes in the snow (Sulkava 1969).

The larger finch roosts are often used year after year. This cannot always be explained by shortage of sites, because some apparently suitable places are not used or are used only irregularly. In my experience, roosts of the commoner species, such as the Chaffinch, Brambling, Greenfinch and Linnet, are easy to find, but those of the others are not. Records of Goldfinch roosts for example are few, partly because in Britain they tend to be small and temporary. An exception, in the trees bordering some streets in Kensington, London, contained up to 105 birds in one winter (Ruttledge 1965). Sometimes Goldfinches use mixed roosts, and at one site in Bedfordshire up to 70 regularly joined Greenfinches, Linnets and Chaffinches in the elder and hawthorn scrub in an old quarry (F. Hamilton, *in litt.*). On the continent Goldfinches form much larger roosts.

On arrival at the roost, up to an hour before dusk, these various finches do not normally settle immediately. They often seem nervous and, when in large groups, they perform 'communal displays' beforehand. Chaffinches often circle a roost for some time, with a hesitant bounding flight, and then alight in the tree-tops, where they call for a while before dropping to the bushes below. Greenfinches assemble first in the tree-tops, calling and singing, and now and then they take off in a body and perform rapid wheeling flights over the roost. Linnets behave similarly but may circle round for an hour or more before settling. The chief features of this pre-roost behaviour are its conspicuousness, its noisiness and, in some species, co-ordinated flights in which the participants twist and turn in unison. When the birds finally enter the roosting bushes, they do so suddenly, silently, and in a body. Similar behaviour occurs in some other birds which roost in flocks.

Once in the roosting bushes, finches may sometimes be heard to squabble over perching places, evidently because they maintain their individual distance, as on the feeding grounds. Also, despite the fact that some birds use several roosts, certain perches in every roost are used night after night, as can be seen from the droppings below; and if individuals are disturbed, they will return repeatedly to their chosen perches. Like most birds, finches sleep with the head turned back and tucked beneath the shoulder feathers, the body feathers fluffed and the legs flexed; they often perch on only one leg, the other raised into the feathers.

It is not immediately obvious why birds roost communally rather than singly, but the avoidance of predation is a frequent suggestion (Lack 1968). The roosting sites themselves, in thick or thorny cover, must offer some security, but if this alone were needed the birds could get it by roosting singly. Also, whether the birds sleep alone or in groups, they have to contend on their way to the roost with diurnal predators and then in the bushes at night with nocturnal ones. But a large roosting flock, like a feeding flock, must surely be more aware of an approaching enemy, whether by day or by night. This was made clear to me when I tried to catch Bramblings by hand in the dark. I could sometimes catch isolated individuals or birds on the edge of a group, but never those from the midst of a group, because nearly always one was awake to sound the alarm. If the same holds for natural predation, here is a clear advantage in a communal roost.

A large group, performing a conspicuous display over the roost, is also more likely than a single bird to attract a predator, especially when the same site is used every night. Probably, however, the chances that any one bird gets caught are still less than if it roosted singly; most species of predators are themselves territorial, so this would limit the number that could attend each roost. The greatest threat is not from diurnal birds of prey, which can be seen and avoided, but from the owls and small mammals which can approach in the dark undetected. It is against these, I believe, that the pre-roost displays function, by synchronising the activities of the birds, so that they all enter the roost at the same time and in the same place. Without this co-ordination, the birds might enter the bushes at different times and perch far apart, thus increasing their vulnerability then and throughout the night.

In some species communal roosting might also help individuals to find food. Referring to an African weaver finch (*Quelea*), Ward (1965) has written: 'It seems reasonable to suppose that when the members of a roost fly out at dawn, their behaviour will depend partly on their success the previous day. Those individuals which have left a good feeding place the evening before probably return to the same area, while those which have been less fortunate do not. It would obviously benefit the latter if, instead of going on a random search of new feeding grounds, they could simply join a group whose behaviour indicated that they were heading for an area where food was to be had. While it is impossible to see exactly what is happening when a roost empties, soon after dawn, the general pattern is that the birds leave in waves, each of which comprises two elements. A large number of birds fly straight out of sight. Many others, however, go only a few hundred metres and settle on prominent trees or bushes; then as subsequent waves pass overhead, they fly up in groups to join them. This is perhaps the mechanism whereby knowledge of good feeding places is shared within the roosting population.'

As far as the behaviour is concerned, the same could be said of some European finches, but whether it helps them to find food is difficult to say. Nevertheless, the foraging and roosting habits of the different species are correlated (Table 12). Large communal roosts, containing hundreds or thousands of individuals, are found only in species which wander widely for food, chiefly in open country. These include the Greenfinch, Linnet, Chaffinch and Brambling. These birds may feed at several places and travel many kilometres each day, but they often visit the same places on successive days. Most of them feed on the ground. Their main roosts are used year after year, irrespective of the position of the roosts in relation to food-supplies, though other sites are used occasionally. In general, the roosts become fewer and larger as the winter progresses, when the need for social food-finding might be expected to increase.

In contrast, species which either forage over a small area, like the Bull-finch and Hawfinch, or whose food is conspicuous within their habitat, like the Crossbills, usually roost in groups of less than a dozen and at temporary sites, wherever they are feeding at the time. Unless their numbers are large, they do not display beforehand. Moreover, immigrant Chaffinches wander widely for food and roost communally, whereas resident ones feed chiefly around their territories and usually roost alone. Hence, while it is impossible to test Ward's view, these facts are not in-

Table 12. The roosting and foraging habits of finches.

		Size of roosts	Roosting sites
	Greenfinch	Usually 50-300, regularly up to 2000.	Clumps of evergreens or bramble, usually in woodland. Rhododendrons favoured.
	Goldfinch	Usually 10-20, on continent up to several hundreds.	In summer in tall deciduous trees in avenues, large gardens, parks and wood-edges. In winter in holly and other evergreens, or oaks and beeches that have retained dead leaves, and occasionally in the exposed bare branches of small trees.
Group A Diet varied; wander widely for food, mostly in open country, feeding at several places and travelling many kilometres each day, but often visiting the same places on successive days. Roosts mainly fixed and traditional, larger than feeding flocks.	Linnet	Usually 50-300, regularly up to 1500.	Gorse patches favoured, also in thorn scrub, brambles, young oaks and beeches that have retained dead leaves, or reed beds.
	Twite	Usually 50-100, sometimes up to 500. Often mixed with Linnets.	Gorse patches, heather, reed-beds and other low herbaceous cover. On Scottish islands, sides of corn stacks, and on continent town buildings.
	Chaffinch (immigrant)	Usually 50-100, regularly up to 2000. Often mixed with Bramblings.	Clumps of evergreens or bramble, and conifer plantations.
	Brambling	Usually up to 500, but regularly more. Roosts of 11, 50 and 72 millions recorded on continent. Smaller roosts often mixed with Chaffinches.	Young conifer plantations favoured, also other evergreens, bramble and other scrub.

continued

Table 12. (continued)

	Size of roosts	Roosting sites
Group B Diet varied; wander very locally, mostly in or near woodland. Roosts mainly temporary, and about the same size as the feeding flocks.		
Bullfinch	Usually 1-6, sometimes up to 20.	Tall thorn trees and evergreens.
Hawfinch	Usually 5-6, sometimes up to 30.	Tall evergreens, clumps of thorn trees or ivy; not always in woodland.
Chaffinch (resident)	Singly or in pairs.	Thorn trees, evergreens, ivy or other thick cover.
Group C Diet restricted; stay for some time in a district, mostly in woodland, exploiting food locally, and then moving on. Roosts mainly temporary and about the same size as the feeding flocks.		
Siskin	Usually 10-20, up to 50.	Clumps of tall conifers and thorn scrub. Rarely reed-beds or low alders.
Redpoll	Usually 10-50, sometimes up to 200.	Thorn, birch or sallow scrub, and young conifer plantations.
Crossbill	Usually 5-10, sometimes up to 50.	Thick cover in tall conifers.

Note: Table compiled mostly from my own records; also from Gueniat (1948), Mühlethaler (1952), Schifferli (1953), and Sutter (1948) for Brambling; and Tomialojc (1967) for Twite.

consistent with it: those finches which might be expected to have the greatest difficulty in finding food form large communal roosts in traditional sites; the rest, whose roosts are small and temporary, either feed consistently over a small area they know well, or eat conspicuous fruits from trees.

By roosting communally, rather than singly, birds might also lose less heat overnight because the local temperature of the roost is raised above that of the surroundings. While this might be significant on some nights, it is at most a subsidiary function of communal roosting in finches, and can hardly be important in the tropical species which share the habit. Whether sleeping singly or in groups, they choose a sheltered site. (On the other hand, in birds like the Treecreeper (*Certhia familiaris*), in which several individuals may huddle together on cold nights, the behaviour clearly serves for warmth.)

A fourth view is that birds can control their own populations in relation to food-supplies and that communal roosting is a way in which they are all brought together at one place and one time to assess their numbers (Wynne-Edwards 1962). The birds are supposed to do this during the communal displays beforehand (which I interpret differently). On general grounds, this idea is difficult to accept, and suffice it to say that at finch roosts the numbers fluctuate so much from night to night that they could provide no good indication to a bird of the total in the area.

Summarising the chapter, an increased immunity from predators is probably one main reason why finches both feed and roost in flocks. Ease of food-finding is another major advantage of feeding in flocks and perhaps to some species of communal roosting. Fitting with the latter view, the roosts are largest in species which forage widely in open country and in these same species the roosts become larger in winter, when food is more localised. Increased warmth on calm, cold nights is at most a minor advantage of a communal roost, though a sheltered site is usually chosen.

CHAPTER 8

THE BREEDING BEHAVIOUR OF
THE CHAFFINCH

CHAFFINCHES, to recapitulate, breed commonly over most of Europe, in woods, hedges and gardens, and space themselves by territorial behaviour. They build compact nests in trees or shrubs, lay 3–5 eggs in a set and raise 1–2 broods each year. This chapter is concerned with their behaviour in the breeding season, and is based mainly on the work of Dr Peter Marler (1956a) near Cambridge. To begin with, it is convenient to follow the breeding cycle from the establishment of territories in spring to their abandonment in late summer, when the young have been raised.

The territory is an area which the cock will defend vigorously against other cocks of his species; into which he will attract a mate; within which nesting and all sexual behaviour will take place; and which will later provide the food for the young. Without a territory a Chaffinch cannot breed. In its advertisement and defence, the song plays a key role, repelling other cocks and attracting hens. Most cocks defend up to several thousand square metres, the exact area depending mainly on the habitat (p. 20–1).

Old birds usually return to exactly the same territories year after year. They often feed and roost there in winter and are first to establish themselves in spring, when they move in with ringing 'chink' calls, and singing loudly to advertise their presence. At first an old cock normally respects the original boundaries of the territory, and if all his neighbours of the previous year return, these boundaries will be accepted with little conflict. But if an adjoining territory has been vacated the cock will soon begin to invade and incorporate more ground into his own, though he may relinquish it again later. At first the cock is present only in the mornings, but as the season progresses, he spends more and more of the day there.

A young bird establishing a territory behaves differently from an old one. He begins about a week later, at the end of February, when many areas are already full of older birds who drive him away if he shows any signs of lingering. On finding an unoccupied area, he enters and begins to move uneasily through the trees and bushes. After a few minutes, if he is not disturbed, he begins to give the 'chink' call and to utter a quiet rambling inconsequential series of notes, known as the 'subsong'. He continues this irregularly, interspersed between periods of feeding on the ground and moving restlessly among the trunks and branches.

Two types of behaviour indicate that the young cock tests the suitability of an area as a breeding place. When he is calling, he uses more and more certain conspicuous perches, which later become the song-posts, used regularly through the season. The presence of such exposed perches, from which he can scan part of his ground, is the first essential for an area to be suitable. Second, the young cock passes much of his first week moving restlessly around the trunks and branches. He shows particular interest in crutches formed by the junction of two or more branches or between branches and the main trunk. These he will examine first with one eye and then the other, and with occasional tail flips, he will hop into a crutch and circle in it, brushing his tail past the enclosing branches. Then he will move away along another branch and repeat the procedure. It is in crutches such as these that the hen will later build her nest; and since the cock subsequently plays no part in selecting the nest-site, it seems that here his behaviour serves only to check that a territory is adequate for breeding. In this way a young cock is at once distinguishable from an old one, who, returning to a familiar territory, does not inspect possible nest sites, and is much less restless.

Vigorous fighting develops only when the bird has become familiar with the area. The minimum time needed for this is probably quite short, perhaps 30 minutes or less, but it is always possible that the bird has accumulated experience from short visits on previous days. Most young cocks find themselves pitted against older ones on one or other of their flanks. The presence of rivals may be betrayed by song or 'chink' calls, but usually they are seen first. Fighting soon becomes intense at particular points, centred on commanding song-posts, and if the territory is large these may be a hundred metres or more apart. Once established, the young cock tends to expand his boundaries until checked by another bird. This sometimes results in very large territories, particularly in the less good habitats, but often natural boundaries such as a drive or a fence are adopted. Within continuous woodland some boundaries are clearly demarcated, so that one tree belongs to one cock and the next to another, especially where a boundary has been hotly contested. Elsewhere, however, the boundary is usually a zone rather than a line, and for hens all boundaries seem to have this form. In other words, the territories overlap.

Territorial aggression differs from other types and involves distinct postures. Thus once a territory is more or less established, two types of fight may be distinguished, according to how close they are to the territorial boundary, and whether or not the intruder is known to the territory-owner. If a stranger lands well within the territory, the occupant is likely to fly at him directly. His approach is rapid, involving a series of dashing flights, in which the white wing flashes are exposed to full advantage. When within range, he makes a supplanting attack on the intruder, who flees, his vacated perch being occupied a fraction of a second later by the aggressor. Usually, the victim flees straight away, but if not, this procedure is repeated until he leaves the territory. The second type of fight involves encounters at territory boundaries between rivals who know one another. Assume that an old cock has returned to his territory a few days before his immediate neighbour, also old, and begins to sing, first on the boundary and then, hesitantly, actually within his opponent's old territory. His rival then arrives, and lays claim to the stolen portion, and for several days a battle will rage across the old boundary, with fights that are quite characteristic. As one bird approaches, the other comes down to meet him and the two move back and forth over the boundary, displaying vigorously but rarely attacking one another. This may continue for half an hour or more during which time the two may cross the boundary 20 or 30 times. These movements to and fro are accompanied by changes in the displays, pronounced postures being adopted by the aggressor at the height of his advance, and weaker ones at the moment of retreat (Fig. 39). At first, therefore, the territory boundaries are fluid but after three weeks they stabilise, and from then on the distribution of the breeding population for that year is more or less fixed.

FIG. 39. The aggressive posture of a cock Chaffinch displaying to a neighbour at a territory boundary. At the height of his advance, the head and neck are sleek and extended, the beak points upwards at 30°, the breast is swollen, and the wing-flashes exposed. In this posture, the cock pivots jerkily from side to side so that the image of his opponent is cast from one eye to the other, the tail and wings being flipped with each turn of the body.

Pair-formation

A few days after he has come on to full song, the cock Chaffinch is usually joined by a hen, who, upon arriving in the territory, moves from tree to tree, apparently attracted by the loud regular song. She gives the 'tupe' flight call frequently. At this time the cocks seldom use this call, and probably it serves to identify hens, because cocks may show signs of courtship before even seeing a hen if they hear this call. From the first meeting the response of the cock to the hen is distinct from that to another cock. On seeing her, he sleeks his feathers so that the white wing flashes become exposed, flies beneath her and adopts a special 'crouching lop-sided posture', in which he turns away from her so that she gets a side-view of him. Then with his body sleeked and horizontal, he tilts his body and raises the wing nearest her, thus exposing an expanse of red flank and

belly (Fig. 40). After a few seconds he relaxes and moves to another perch
to repeat the display, keeping the same distance from the hen, all the time
uttering a special 'kseep' call. While the cock courts her, the hen fluffs
her feathers and, apart from an occasional glance, seems almost to ignore
him. Soon, however, she begins to hop among the branches and make
occasional short flights. The cock then gives the 'moth flight', involving
rapid wing beats of small amplitude, which he directs towards the heart
of the territory, and if the hen follows, he repeats, gradually leading her
round his ground.

What follows depends on the hen's subsequent behaviour. If she is
inclined to wander away the cock may leave her, resume song and wait
for the next hen. But if she remains he sometimes makes supplanting
attacks on her, followed by sexual chases in which the two dash headlong
among the branches. Then just as quickly both may feed on the ground
together without any sign of aggression. As soon as she is more or less
accepted, the hen begins to explore, examining nest-sites in the same way
as the young cock. Also, she soon begins to attack any other hens she
encounters, though her attacks bear less relationship to the territory
boundaries than those of the cock.

An unmated hen does not necessarily pair with the first cock who courts
her. What determines her final choice is not clear, but the intensity of
courtship is probably one factor. At first young cocks are much less ardent
than old ones and tend to pair two or three weeks later. They also lose
interest more quickly, and at first will seldom pursue a hen beyond the
territory. Older cocks sometimes pursue a hen across several boundaries.
They never display aggressively against the occupants, who of course
attack violently, but will remain on foreign ground for a long time,
evading attack and attempting to entice the hen back by singing, courting,
and by the use of the 'moth flight'. It is probably in this way that the
hen first learns the territory boundaries.

Once the pair is established, there is little likelihood of a change, and if
both survive until the following year they will probably pair again, as
shown by ringing. They may often be seen together near the territory in
winter, but in a flock there is no obvious bond between them, and the
territory is probably important in renewing it in spring. However, about
one third of adult Chaffinches die between one breeding season and the
next, thus reducing considerably the number of pairs that can remain
intact. Even in Fenno-Scandia, where Chaffinches migrate, the surviving
adult cocks almost always return to the same locality (p. 26).

After the pairs are established each year, feeding, preening and resting
are largely confined to the territory. Drinking and bathing are conducted
here if possible, but most pairs have to seek water elsewhere. If the only
water in the vicinity lies within a territory, the owners tolerate the visits
of other birds, but only while they show no sign of attacking or escaping.
It is not clear whether this situation pertains from the start, or whether

repeated intrusions mitigate the owner's attacks. In addition, some cocks regularly go through other territories, moving silently and cryptically, keeping in dense cover. This is particularly true of cocks whose mates begin to incubate early, while neighbouring hens are still soliciting for copulation.

Pre-nesting behaviour

Usually the pair remain together for about six weeks before starting to nest, during which time courtship by the cock intensifies and the hen becomes dominant. This results not merely from an increase in the hen's aggressiveness, though this plays a part, but mainly because the cock avoids close proximity with her. At first there is a neutral period, when neither partner shows any overt aggression towards the other, and only later does the hen lose her fear of the cock and attack him for the first time. The timing of these events varies in different pairs, extended acquaintance is not necessary, and in pairs formed late, the hen may be dominant from the start. Once the change has occurred, however, the hen can then feed without fear of her mate and can get priority at food, which must help her to form her eggs.

As in many other birds, courtship in the Chaffinch is characterised by tentative ambivalent behaviour involving conflicts between fear, aggression and sexual attraction (p. 159). The reversal of dominance before breeding has also been noted in other birds and is accompanied by changes in the cock's courtship (Hinde 1955–56). Initially when the cock Chaffinch is dominant, his displays are forms of the 'crouching lop-sided posture', described earlier, which contains elements of attack; these are largely replaced in the 'upright lop-sided posture', which develops at this stage, by signs of fear. These two postures are similar, except that in the latter the cock stretches himself upright and pulls his head back, instead of crouching (Fig. 40). This posture reaches its highest development in the 'pre-copulatory dance', in which the cock patters to and fro before the hen with short quick steps, tilting first one wing and then the other as he passes in front of her. At this stage the hen plays a mainly passive role in courtship, except in sexual chases. These are often instigated by the hen, sometimes in response to the cock's display, and sometimes not. Typically, while feeding near her mate, she may suddenly sleek her feathers and crouch tensely for a moment watching him, seeming to wait until he is looking at her, before flashing off through the bushes with him in pursuit. When they settle, the cock often courts vigorously.

Nesting

As the weeks pass, the cock's displays and sexual chases become frequent, and quite suddenly, during mild weather in April, the hen begins a frenzy

FIG. 40. The courtship postures of the cock Chaffinch.
A, the 'crouching lop-sided posture', which is seen mostly between the
time of pair-formation and nesting. With the head sleeked, the wing-flashes
exposed and the tail spread, the bird tilts his body to one side, exposing
an expanse of red flank to the hen; B, the 'upright lop-sided posture',
which is seen mostly during nest-building. The bird stretches his legs and
body upwards, with the neck drawn up and back, beak pointing downwards, and the crest slightly raised.

of nest-site examination. Moving around at various levels in the trees, she
alights on a branch and hops to where it joins another. If they meet in a
deep crutch, she hops into it, flexes her legs and fluffs her feathers, turning
first this way and then that. After a moment, she emerges 'chinking'
excitedly as she alights and looks for another. Suddenly, she begins to
carry nest material to a particular site, and starts to build.

   The hen is entirely responsible for building the nest. The different birds studied by Dr Marler took between 3 and 18 days to build, on average 7 days. The longest periods were in young inexperienced birds, which brought materials in the wrong proportions for rapid building. The shortest periods were observed when nests of birds which were about to lay were destroyed, in which case materials were often transferred from the first to the second site. During building each hen made about 1,300 visits to the nest, at up to 20 per hour.

The nest itself consists of four concentric layers. On the outside is a shell of lichen and spider silk, then a layer of moss and grass, a third mostly of grass, and a lining of thin roots and feathers. The various materials are dealt with in different ways, appropriate to the part they play in the nest-structure. For example, two movements are used to attach cobwebs. The first is used only when the nest is supported by thin twigs, around which loops of thread can be bound. One end of a thread is attached to a branch, then the bird leans to the other side of the branch, and retrieves the loose end so that the twig is completely encircled; there may be several loops on each twig. In a second action, by which moss fragments are secured, one end of the web is attached to the nest, then the free end is drawn away and attached elsewhere, and so on. Fragments of moss and grass are inserted into the cup wall by stabbing movements of the bill; and to shape the nest cup the bird sits in it, fluffs its plumage and turns round and round. There is also a scrabbling movement in which the bird supports its body on the rim of the nest, using head and tail, and kicks back with its feet.

During building the attention of the cock is more firmly fixed on the hen than before. He follows her almost everywhere, but she often attacks him, especially when he approaches the nest-tree, which he soon learns to avoid. By this time sexual chases have become common and the cock makes increasingly frequent attempts to rape the hen, without success. It is during building that the 'crouching soliciting posture' of the hen is first seen, to be soon followed by copulation. If nesting is successful, copulation is confined to a period of about ten days ending with the start of incubation, but is resumed if the first nest suffers disaster. It is during the copulatory phase that the only purely reproductive call of the hen – 'seep' – is given. Copulation is sometimes preceded by the cock displaying to the passive hen, but more often by the hen soliciting the passive cock.

Most clutches are started in late April or early May (p. 188). Laying occurs in the early morning, at daily intervals, until the clutch is complete. Regular incubation begins with the penultimate egg, and is entirely by the hen. She feeds herself throughout and rarely has more than an hour on the nest without a break of five or ten minutes, the cock escorting her when she goes to feed. He does not normally feed her himself, though a few records exist of a cock passing food to his hen on the nest (e.g. Barrett 1947); this was usually in the nestling phase, however, so the food might have been intended for the young but taken by the hen as she happened to be on the nest at the time.

The eggs hatch after 11–14 days, the last to be laid up to a day later than the rest, and the shells are then eaten or carried away by the hen. At first the young are blind, helpless, and naked except for a sparse covering of thin wispy down. They are capable only of raising their heads and opening their mouths for food, which they do automatically as soon as the hen lifts herself from the nest. But within a few hours of hatching, the young have also arranged themselves with their hind ends outwards and their heads inwards. When a parent comes to feed them, they all stretch up together and open their beaks. This system works well for broods of 3–5 young. In broods of six, the young have to struggle for positions, and food is shared unevenly, resulting in great size-differences between them, with one or two 'runts' in the brood. In broods of one or two, the young often have difficulty for the first few days in keeping balance, while raising their beaks for food. (It is well known among canary-breeders that a single youngster often starves to death because its mother has difficulty in feeding it.)

By the fourth or fifth day, the young become capable of other movements. Their eyes begin to open and their feathers begin to emerge, the flight and tail feathers first, and the body feathers a day or two later. The feathers push out the down which clings to their tips until they are almost fully formed. As the young grow, they are brooded less, and after the sixth day hardly at all, except perhaps at night. Most of their food at this stage is provided by their mother, only 15% of the feeds witnessed by Marler being from cocks. The stage at which the cock began to visit the nest varied between pairs: in one he was seen carrying food on the first day, and in another not until the eighth. Including visits by both parents, the chicks were fed on average 3–4 times an hour at the start, increasing to about 6–9 times at the end of the nestling phase. After each feed the parent usually waits for a dropping. The faeces of the young are eaten for the first two or three days, and carried away after this, until the last few days when they are allowed to accumulate on the nest rim. Once the young have left the nest, both parents play an equal role in feeding them.

Small caterpillars from various trees form the bulk of the nestlings' food. These are sometimes broken up and fed to several chicks at each visit. Usually only a single caterpillar is brought, but sometimes three or four. The newly-hatched chicks at first beg silently by raising their heads and gaping, exposing the cream flange and pink interior of the mouth. Later they raise the body on their legs and utter a 'cheep' call; and later still they begin to flutter their wings when begging for food. During the last four days in the nest, the chicks, which have previously kept still while the parents were absent, begin to stretch, preen and flap their wings. They spend long periods drawing their flight feathers through their beaks, freeing them from the bursting sheaths.

Most young leave the nest on the 13th or 14th day, but some as early as the 11th and others as late as the 18th (Newton 1964a). The short nestling periods are probably due to the young being disturbed from the nest prematurely, and the long ones to shortage of food slowing their development. The parents continue to feed their young for about three weeks after they have left the nest, bringing the total period of parental dependence to five weeks.

On departure, the young hop out on to branches around the nest and then scatter in different directions. They are capable only of brief clumsy flights and their tails are still very short, but within six hours they may get up to 20 metres from the nest, moving further on successive days. Both parents help to place the fledglings. They use elaborate leading behaviour, often tempting the young with a caterpillar into dense cover, and this is repeated if they move into the open again. The parents at this stage show no sign of trying to collect the young together; and presumably the dispersal of the young reduces the chance of the whole brood being found by a predator.

During the first 'cryptic' phase, just after leaving the nest, the young are exceedingly difficult to find, because they remain in dense foliage, motionless except when being fed. It seems that each chick is usually adopted by one parent, probably because the parents have difficulty remembering where all their young are. Perhaps to help this, the begging of the young soon becomes more elaborate. On the approach of a parent, a juvenile raises the feathers of its breast and head, lowers its body and pivots from side to side, opening its beak and uttering a characteristic 'chirrup' call, which now develops. Each young is visited about four times an hour. Well-fed chicks call only when a parent approaches, but hungry ones whether an adult is present or not, thus making them more vulnerable to predators.

At the start of the next, 'free-moving' phase, instead of remaining on their perch, the young follow the parent after being fed. As each parent picks up successive birds, families are re-formed, either with both parents leading all the young, or, more often, with the cock and hen leading separate groups. Probably it is the attraction of young to the parent rather than a general social tendency that makes the group cohere. At first, the parents try and keep the young within the territory but by the 21st day, when the juveniles can fly well, this becomes difficult and the groups begin to wander round the neighbourhood concentrating on local sources of defoliating caterpillars. In this way the territorial system gradually breaks down, but for some further days the broods remain discrete. It is at this stage, which lasts 4–5 days, that the young make the greatest demands on their parents; their begging becomes more persistent, they are fed more frequently and may often be seen pursuing their parents for food, because as yet they cannot feed themselves.

Soon, however, the young begin to peck at leaves and twigs and attempt to catch flying insects. At first they are rarely successful and this exploratory behaviour occurs mostly when the young are satiated; when hungry, they continue to beg from their parents. Within a day or two they learn to catch food for themselves, and in this final 'semi-dependent phase', which lasts 10–14 days, they beg only if actually approached by an adult with food. But the family groups are maintained for a time, and the young begin to take seeds, which they seek mainly on roads and tracks, and other bare ground. At first they merely pick up and mandibulate any hard objects, but soon they distinguish edible seeds from inedible grit, and finally learn to shell the seeds. The parents stop feeding the young between the 32nd and 37th day of their lives (Barrett 1947, Marler 1956a).

Some days after becoming independent, when they are 40–50 days of age, juvenile Chaffinches aggregate into small groups and begin to moult. At this stage they may move several kilometres from their birth place but towards the end of the year the range is narrowed to a particular area, from which most individuals will not wander for more than a kilometre or so for the rest of their lives.   ·

Soon after shedding their young in late June or July, parent Chaffinches become skulking. They cease all reproductive behaviour, but still spend most of their time around their territories. For a short time they may continue to attack other adults they meet there, but even this soon stops as moult begins. The breeding cycle is then complete.

Three aspects of their breeding can now be discussed more fully.

Nesting success

One of the hens studied by Dr Marler built six nests in a season, and another hen four without rearing young. Of seven other birds that were closely watched, two were successful with the first nests, two with their second, two gave up after the second, and one was successful with the third. Thus four birds out of nine reared no young in one season, and only five out of 23 nests were productive.

The records of the British Trust for Ornithology for Chaffinch nests suggests considerable annual variations in their success over the country as a whole (Newton 1964a). In the eleven years from 1950, the proportion of nests that produced young varied from only one-fifth in 1960 to three-fifths in 1956 (Appendix 3). But the number of pairs producing young was probably higher than these figures suggest because they are based on all the nests found each year, irrespective of whether these nests were first or later attempts, and as mentioned, a pair might lose several clutches before eventually producing a successful one or giving up. The main causes of nest-failure were the various animals which ate the eggs and young, and these predators accounted for most of the annual differences (Appendix 4). Also many nests were deserted, some without apparent cause, others during a cold snap, and others after heavy rain had soaked or tilted the nest. In some years prolonged rain also accounted for the loss of many nestlings; and a storm which swept the south of England in May 1955 destroyed in

PLATE 11. The Linnet forages mainly on open land eating the seeds of various weeds.

PLATE 12. A cock Linnet at his nest of well-grown young in a gorse bush. This is a favourite nesting site, especially in early spring before deciduous shrubs come into leaf.

some areas half the broods under observation at the time. The success rate also varied with the time of year; only two-fifths of the clutches started before mid-May produced fledged young, compared with about half of those started after mid-May. Again this was due mainly to a seasonal decline in predation, itself probably the result of a gradual thickening of the vegetation making the nests more difficult to find (see also p. 182). In addition to the factors which caused the loss of whole clutches and broods, many nests contained at least one egg which failed to hatch. Nevertheless, the most important factor influencing the number of young produced each year was the extent of predation on eggs and nestlings.

The functions of the territory

The provision of food for the parents and young, the avoidance of predation, and the prevention of epidemics, have all been suggested as reasons for territorialism in birds. Probably, however, the territory serves a different function in different species, and perhaps more than one function in any one species. As regards the Chaffinch, Dr Marler did not commit himself as to the main purpose of the territory, though his study showed that each pair spent most of its time there in summer. The territory at least provided a place where the pair could display and mate without disturbance from other Chaffinches. In captivity, the reproductive activity of a cock is largely inhibited by the presence of a rival cock, and any bird attempting copulation is violently attacked by others. This is common among other birds, and has led to the suggestion that privacy for sexual behaviour is the primary function of the territory. A much smaller area would suffice for this, however, and anyway it is impossible to say which came first in evolution, territoriality or the intolerance towards copulating pairs.

In my view, the main purpose of the territory of the Chaffinch is to help to ensure easy feeding for the adults around the nest. As evidence, most pairs obtain almost all their food from within their territories in summer, and secondly, they defend smaller areas in deciduous than in coniferous woods, the latter being notoriously poorer in suitable insects (p. 20–1). It is true nonetheless that some pairs obtain part of their food on neutral ground outside the territory, and that when the young leave the nest, the boundaries largely break down. The same occurs in other insectivorous birds, and for these reasons, some authors have discarded the provision of food as the chief function of the territory. But one could not expect a pair of birds to be as active in defence while they were busy collecting food for their young, as they were earlier in the season when they had little else to do. By establishing a large territory at the start of the season, the cock has at least ensured that no other Chaffinches have settled so close that they feed regularly from the same source of food later in summer when there is less time for fighting. In the absence of territorial behaviour, all the birds in an area might have crowded into the best habitats and put so much pressure on local food-supplies as to jeopardise all their chances of raising young. As it is, territorialism disperses the population through the available habitat, and limits the extent to which different pairs feed in the same places. The other advantages of the behaviour, such as the lack of disturbance while mating, I regard as subsidiary in the Chaffinch.

Two sources of confusion are prevalent in discussions of territorial behaviour in birds. The first concerns its role in population regulation. Territorialism almost certainly limits the number of pairs which can settle in an area, and causes others to disperse elsewhere, or perhaps not breed at all. But such behaviour cannot have evolved as a means of regulating population-size: any regulation which might be achieved locally is only an incidental result of behaviour evolved to ensure the needs of individual pairs. Another source of confusion results from failure to distinguish between the ultimate and proximate reasons for territorialism. A bird might be said to hold a territory in order to ensure a food-supply or because it behaved aggressively. Both would be true, but the first is the ultimate reason for holding a territory of a certain size, while the second is the immediate means by which the territory is acquired.

The Song

The song of the Chaffinch is one of the most familiar sounds of the English countryside in spring. It is fairly stereotyped, lasting 2–3 seconds and consisting of a succession of notes, followed by a flourish. Its functions, as mentioned, are to attract hens and repel cocks, and to these ends it is loud, clear, and easy to locate. It is uttered for long periods at fairly regular intervals. An unmated cock will sing every 7–15 seconds for most of the day – or six times a minute, 360 times an hour and more than 3,300 times in a 12-hour day, feeding between times. (If this performance seems incredible, it is meagre compared to that of some other territorial birds, for example the Red-eyed Vireo *Vireo olivaceus* in America, which sings 22,000 times each day – de Kiriline 1954.) Once he has found a mate, the cock Chaffinch sings less often, partly because he has less time then, and partly because one of the functions of the song has been fulfilled. Moreover the hens can apparently detect the difference in frequency of singing between mated and unmated cocks and seek out the latter (Marler, in Thorpe 1961).

The attraction of the cock's song to the hen can be demonstrated in an aviary, where an unmated bird will move towards an appropriate tape-recording. The same may be seen in the wild, both at pair-formation and later, for during the copulatory phase the hen often moves towards the song of her mate. The song might also stimulate her sexually because she sometimes solicits just on hearing it. The repellent effect of the song on other cocks is less easy to demonstrate, but when prospecting for territories, young cocks may be seen to avoid the vicinity of a singing bird, without necessarily seeing him.

Although the song of the Chaffinch is easily recognisable, the number of notes, timbre and intonation vary between individuals. This enables neighbouring cocks to recognise one another (and hence detect new-comers) and the hens to find their mates. Each cock, moreover, may have several slightly different songs in his repertoire. Most have up to three, though some have up to six. Usually a bird gives each song-type 10–20 times, before switching to another at random, without a fixed programme; but when counter-singing against a neighbour, a bird tends to reply with whichever of his own songs is closest to that of his rival (Hinde 1958). The reason for this is not known, but perhaps such a close retort has more effect: at least the bird is 'giving as good as he gets'.

The songs of birds separated by some geographical barrier, such as a river or a treeless plain, are even more different, as is especially obvious in the songs of some Scottish Chaffinches living in isolated glens. Those in Glen Orchy, for example, are quite different from those on the other side of the barren Rannoch Moor, and different again from those across a mountain ridge, in the very isolated Glen Lyon. Similar contrasts some-times exist across much less impressive barriers, such as a road or a large field, as shown by a study in Devon (Brooks King 1949).

Thus, not only are the voices of cock Chaffinches individually distinct, as in human speech, but also geographically variable as in dialects (Fig. 41). In the Chaffinch one dialect area differs from another chiefly in the frequency with which different song-types are given, though certain songs are confined to only one or a few areas. Also, the dialect areas are small, distributed in a mosaic, each separated from the rest by unsuitable terrain. Here the parallel with human speech ends, for in the Chaffinch the same dialects recur by chance in different parts of the bird's range. Thus all the song-types recorded during a survey in Russia (Promptoff 1930), were also recorded in Britain (Marler 1952b). The converse was not true, however, for many of the more complicated songs found in Britain and other parts of western Europe were lacking in the east, where the songs tended to be simpler.

Dialects are not confined to song, but also occur in another note, known as the 'rain call', because it often seems to herald a change in weather. Paradoxically this note is hardly heard in Britain, but is common on the continent and varies greatly in form, from a single 'twit' to polysyllabic sounds like 'fit-fit', 'flit-flut', 'hwit-ziwit' and so on. Several of these forms, studied in detail in the suburbs of Stuttgart, were found to be distributed in dialects in exactly the same way as song, separated by boundaries, like a street or a railway (Sich 1939).

Studies of the development of song in young Chaffinches have helped to explain how the dialects originate, for the song is partly innate and partly

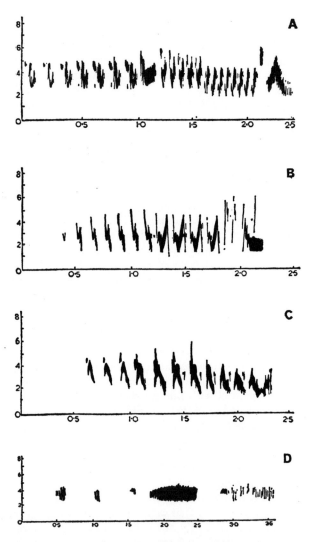

FIG. 41. Sonograms of the songs of three Chaffinches and a Brambling.
A and B refer to Chaffinches from different dialect areas; C a bird hand-
reared in auditory isolation; and D the Brambling. Vertical scale:
frequency in kilocycles per second; horizontal scale: time in seconds. (From
Thorpe 1958.)

learnt (Poulsen 1951, Marler 1952, 1956a, c, Thorpe 1958, 1961). In one experiment, young cocks which were taken as nestlings and reared in groups in auditory isolation, developed a song that was simpler and more restricted than normal, the end phrase consisting of a single squeak, instead of the usual run of up to six notes (Fig. 41). But the song of each group was uniform, even though the birds were unrelated, implying that they had been learning from each other. In another experiment with Chaffinches reared by their own parents, and not isolated until their first winter, the songs which developed were nearly normal, although again the end phrases were sometimes atypical.

It seems, therefore, that each young cock begins to learn the song in his first summer, before he can produce any such sound himself. At this stage he absorbs the general pattern of the song, and its division into separate phrases with a flourish at the end. But the range of sounds that he will pay attention to, and try to copy, is rather limited, thus ensuring that he picks up the songs of other Chaffinches rather than those of other species. And not until the following spring, when he can practise on his own territory, and copy the sounds of his neighbours, are the finer details added. He may in fact learn several slightly different songs from his neighbours on different sides, thus acquiring a varied repertoire, and to any of these songs he may add his own personal touch. Learning stops after the second summer, and whatever songs the bird then has will stick for life.

It is this second phase of learning in the spring on which the dialects depend. To give an example from Marler's field study, one young cock took a territory adjoining those of three old ones, A, B and C. First he sang vigorously against A, and developed a copy of his most frequent song. Then he moved to the boundary with B, and began to acquire a second song from him. But after a few days, when B obtained a mate and became silent, his song was dropped and never heard again. The young cock then returned to sing against A and copied another song from him, and finally a third from his other neighbour C. He thus acquired his complete repertoire of three songs in only three weeks.

It appears then that dialects arise by young birds learning from old ones, and keeping to the same area in later years. This process will itself encourage the persistence in one area of a limited number of song-types in a fairly stable state, but counter-singing also encourages stability by tending to eliminate the less common songs. Disruptive factors are also at work however. For example when trees are cut or blown down, the occupants may be forced to move elsewhere, thus introducing their songs into new areas. Also, if one bird dies and others take over the territory, their songs become audible to birds further on. As a result, the dialect areas are often roughly defined, except when the habitat places a firm check on movement, as in the mountain glens described above.

In addition to song, Chaffinches have a vocabulary of fourteen basic calls, some of which can be subdivided into variants, giving a total of twenty-one different signals. This figure is minimal, however, for more subtle variations may exist that have been overlooked. While the song is partly learnt, the calls appear to be entirely inborn, except the 'rain call' mentioned above. The responses of other Chaffinches, which are also inborn, shows that these various sounds act as a language. They may convey the identity of the calling bird, its sex and age, its position in space and time, and its feelings – whether hungry, afraid, and so on. Usually different calls communicate different information and only the most complex signal, song, provides all four types of information simultaneously.

As may be seen from Fig. 41, the song of the Chaffinch bears little resemblance to that of its relative, the Brambling. Such a marked difference is not uncommon among closely allied species, and the usual explanation is that, since the song serves partly to attract and stimulate a mate, it also helps individuals to distinguish their own from other species. Hence, among related species, selection might act strongly in favour of a divergence in their songs to help to avoid cross-matings.

To end this chapter, it is worth re-emphasising that, despite their songs, the Chaffinch and Brambling are closely similar in most aspects of their breeding. Equivalents of the two 'lop-sided' displays of the Chaffinch exist, and are given in similar circumstances in the Brambling (but in this bird the body is not tilted to one side, the wings are drooped more and the tail is slightly raised, exposing the white rump). Furthermore, both species hold large territories while breeding and feed their young on insects, which they carry to the nest in their bills. In both, sexual behaviour is restricted to the territory and neither species shows courtship feeding. These last five features of the sub-family Fringillinae form the main behavioural differences from the Carduelinae discussed in the next chapter.

CHAPTER 9

THE BREEDING BEHAVIOUR OF
THE CARDUELINE FINCHES

THE main differences in breeding behaviour between the fringilline and cardueline finches are in their nesting distribution and in their feeding habits. The fringillines, to recapitulate, rear their young on insects and defend large feeding territories, spreading themselves fairly evenly through the habitat. The carduelines, in contrast, feed their young primarily on seeds (p. 178-9); they nest in loose colonies, within which each pair defends a small territory around its nest; and they forage away from the colonies in flocks (Fig. 42).

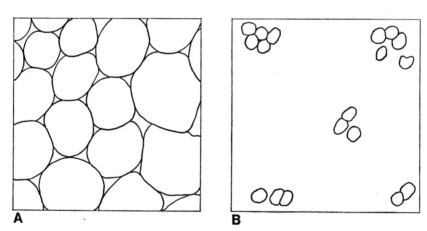

A　　　　　　　　　　　　　　　　**B**

FIG. 42. The nesting dispersion of the fringilline (A) and cardueline (B) finches, showing the territories of individual pairs.

The differences between the two groups probably arose through adaptation to the way their food is distributed. Insects suitable for Chaffinches are found on almost every tree in woodland and remain available through the summer. A bird defending a feeding territory is sure to find insects there whenever it needs them, and can procure them without competing with others of its species. Seeds suitable for carduelines are found in local concentrations, which are not only widely spaced, but also continually changing in distribution as different food-plants come into seed. At any one place, food might be available for only a short time, corresponding to the period in which the plants which happen to grow there

come into fruit. Any carduelines defending feeding territories might therefore soon find themselves without food. Instead, they defend only a small
area around their nest, and forage wherever food happens to be available
at the time. And because their food, where present, is usually abundant,
many individuals can feed together without interfering with one another,
so flocking persists through the year. After the breeding season, when the
Chaffinch and Brambling turn to seeds, they also flock. Thus it is probably
not the *type* of food which is important in influencing dispersion, only the
way in which it is distributed, productive patches of seeds being fewer
and further between than of insects.

The idea that the type of nesting distribution in finches is linked with
diet is almost impossible to test experimentally, but as circumstantial
evidence, the same two systems recur in another group, the weaver birds
(Ploceinae), which also contains both insectivorous and granivorous
species. The insect-eaters hold large territories in which they feed solitarily,
whereas the seed-eaters nest in colonies and feed in flocks (Crook 1962).
(Unlike the carduelines, however, the latter are also polygynous, each
cook having more than one hen.)

To find seeds, the carduelines often travel considerable distances, sometimes more than three kilometres from the nest. They have a storage organ
in which a large quantity of food can be carried to the nest and then
regurgitated to the young. In some species this takes the form of special
pouches under the lower jaw, as noted in the Bullfinch, Pine Grosbeak,
Trumpeter Finch (*Rhodopechys*), and certain rosy finches (*Leucosticte*)
(p. 66–7). Other species, it seems, use their distendable gullets for this
purpose. But either way, the ability of the birds to carry relatively large
quantities of food means that, though feeding at a distance, they do not
waste too much time in travelling back and forth. One result is that the
young are fed infrequently, usually at intervals of 20–60 minutes, but
each time they get a large meal, which they in turn store temporarily in
their expandable gullets (p. 178). This contrasts with the insectivorous
Chaffinch, which forages mainly near its nest, brings one or a few items
at a time in its bill, and feeds its young every 7–10 minutes.

Other differences in the breeding behaviour of the fringilline and
cardueline finches can be linked with this basic difference in their nesting
distribution. First, consider the territorial behaviour. In the Chaffinch,
individual cocks are always competing for ground, defending a large
area which is usually expanded until checked by other birds. Their territorial behaviour is prolonged and elaborate, involving a special song and
special postures, used only in territorial fighting. In the carduelines, individual pairs defend a very small area; usually there is no shortage of
nesting places and much of the habitat remains unoccupied. Their territorial behaviour is short and inelaborate, their songs are less specialised,
and they have no special fighting postures confined to the breeding area.
Second, there are associated differences in the behaviour between the

pair. In the Chaffinch the very restriction of the birds to their territories helps to keep the pair together, by compelling them to remain in a circumscribed area where the chances of meeting other individuals is limited. In the carduelines, while the hen is on the nest, the cock is mostly away foraging, and later when the pair are feeding young, they may be present in the territory for only a few minutes each day. For most of their time, they wander widely for food, moving from flock to flock and constantly mingling with other individuals. Under these circumstances, it would be easy for the pair to lose touch with one another. Special behaviour, including mutual displays, helps to maintain and strengthen the pair-bond; and while feeding young, the pair remain side by side, foraging and visiting the nest together. If they do become separated, it is particularly important that the hen recognises her own mate. It is perhaps for this reason that the voice and song-patterns of the carduelines are more variable between individuals than in the Chaffinch. The cock cardueline spends less time in territorial defence than does the cock Chaffinch, but more on parental duties, making the roles of the sexes less distinct.

The cock Chaffinch must acquire a territory before he can get a mate. The cock cardueline finch finds a mate first, and he does this, not by singing to attract one, but by courting a hen, while they are both in a flock. Only after they have paired, do they decide where to nest, and only then do they begin to defend the surroundings against others of their species. In fact, the carduelines are almost unique among song-birds in establishing their territories after the nest-site has been chosen, and in maintaining them only while the nest is in use. Furthermore, a pair may raise successive broods a long way apart, setting up different territories around each nest. This is another adaptation to a sporadic food-supply, for the birds tend to settle wherever their food is temporarily plentiful.

In the following paragraphs, I shall discuss some of these aspects of cardueline behaviour in more detail. The account is generalised but, for the most part, only minor variations exist from species to species.* The Hawfinch and Bullfinch, which in some respects deviate strongly from the typical cardueline pattern, are discussed separately at the end of the chapter.

Pair-formation

Cardueline finches begin to pair off while they are still in flocks – in Britain around mid-February. Pair-formation is a less definite affair than in the Chaffinch, as the relationship between two birds develops over several days or weeks, and is not marked by any particular event. The

* In preparing this account I have consulted the following: Andrew (1961), Andrew & Hinde (1956), Boase (1948), Conder (1948), Coutlee (1968), Dilger (1960), Grinnell (1943), Hildén (1969), Hinde (1954, 1955–56), Lang (1948), Linsdale (1957), Newton (1967b), Nickell (1951), Nicolai (1957), Skead (1960), Stokes (1950), Swenk (1929), Tast (1968, 1970), Thompson (1960), Thorpe (1961), Weaver & West (1943).

first signs of approaching breeding are when the cocks become more aggressive among themselves, threatening, supplanting and chasing one another more than usual. This occurs mainly when the birds are not feeding, at slack times around mid-day and evening, when they sit in trees, sing vigorously and perch further apart than usual. Simultaneously, for the first time since the previous summer, they relinquish their dominance over the hens and begin to court them. Adopting a special posture, a cock will approach a hen, hopping round her, keeping his distance, but reaching out and attempting to nibble or touch her bill with his. The form of the cock's approach differs between species. If the hen flees or takes no notice, the cock's display wanes. If she stretches her bill towards his and performs similar nibbling movements, an attachment might develop. Initially, the cock may court several hens, but gradually he spends more and more time with one particular hen, driving off other cocks from her vicinity, and it is with this bird that he will later breed.

As the pair are drawn together, the hen soon becomes dominant for much of the time, and will deliberately supplant the cock at food. Nevertheless, strong aggressive components persist in the cock's early displays. In the Greenfinch and in the *Serinus* species, in particular, the cocks often threaten and chase their mates with a special 'wings-raised display' (Fig. 43a). The Greenfinch also has a less aggressive form of this display, in which he points his bill upwards and lowers his wings, exposing the yellow rump (Fig. 43b). In most species, the pairs also perform vigorous sexual chases, in which the cock supplants the hen while in the flock, and the two then dash headlong zig-zagging through the trees, sometimes followed by other birds. These flights leave both participants exhausted, and are usually followed by bill-wiping, preening or, nearer the time of egg-laying, by unsuccessful attempts at rape.

The birds do not of course switch suddenly from non-reproductive to reproductive behaviour. The two forms merge gradually and overlap to a great extent. Even when most birds are paired, a sudden cold snap will bring courtship to a halt and a reversal to winter behaviour. Also, not all birds reach breeding condition at the same date, and since each cock might approach several hens before being accepted, birds at a similar stage of development tend to pair together.

As the days pass, the pair spend increasing periods on their own. The cock's displays become less aggressive and more elaborate; and billing develops into courtship feeding, in which the cock regurgitates food into the open beak of the hen. The birds begin to hop about on the ground, as though seeking nest material, but without picking any up. Later they pick up small fragments, carry them for a while and drop them. Then, some days before nest-building starts, the pair begin to visit potential nest-sites. The hen takes the lead, moving from site to site, crouching and moving round and round in each, while the cock waits near by, continually singing and calling. Normally the hen builds alone, though the

FIG. 43. Two courtship displays of the Greenfinch. A, 'sleeked wing-raised' posture, shown by the cock chasing his mate; B, less aggressive form of the sleeked wing-raised posture.

cock accompanies her as she fetches material. He may also carry some material himself, and in species like the Greenfinch, may occasionally help to build (Hinde 1954).

Territories and colonies

Having chosen a nest-site, the pair start to defend the surroundings against others of their species, though building may not begin for another day or two. The cock defends the territory mainly by making himself conspicuous, sitting on the tops of bushes and occasionally singing, but adopting no special postures. This alone is enough to deter most rivals, but if one approaches too closely, the owner flies nearer and sings loudly, and if this does not deter the intruder, the owner attacks. The European and the various New World goldfinches are especially aggressive at this time and sometimes engage in fierce tumble fights, in which the opponents peck and claw one another until one gives way. After a battle, the territory owner returns to his perch and sings, or performs a display flight over the breeding area (p. 164). Both sexes defend the territory, but the cock attacks from a greater distance than the hen, and whereas he attacks only other cocks, she attacks intruders of both sexes. For example, in the American Goldfinch, according to Stokes (1950), the cock attacks other cocks at ten metres, but the hen attacks both cocks and hens at five metres. Birds feeding within the territory often go unmolested, but are attacked the moment they take up a prominent position.

The size of territories in the carduelines cannot be estimated simply by counting the number of pairs in a given area, for even in uniform habitat, gaps often separate the territories of neighbouring pairs. Nor can territory-size be easily assessed by measuring the distance between nests, because the area defended shrinks after the eggs have been laid, enabling two pairs to nest closer if they start at slightly different dates than if they begin together. In a few (mostly American) species, however, the size of the territories has been assessed when defence is strongest by watching the fights between adjacent cocks or the response of birds to stuffed dummies placed at different distances from their nest:

Species	Average size of territory* (square metres)
European Goldfinch (*Carduelis carduelis*)	240
American Goldfinch (*Spinus tristis*)	250
Lesser Goldfinch (*Spinus psaltria*)	680
Lawrence's Goldfinch (*Spinus lawrencei*)	310
House Finch (*Carpodacus mexicanus*)	64

The carduelines clearly hold much smaller territories than the Chaffinch, at most a few hundred square metres, compared with several thousand. To put it another way, about thirty pairs of European Goldfinches could breed simultaneously in the area occupied by the average Chaffinch pair (though they would need other areas in which to feed). Also, while each Goldfinch pair might defend about 240 square metres to begin with, this would decline to less than 12 square metres after the eggs had been laid, which explains why two pairs can sometimes nest together in the same large tree (Conder 1948). I have no idea why, at the time of maximum

* Calculated from details given by Conder (1948), Coutlee (1968), Stokes (1950), and Thomson (1960).

defence, the territory varies so much in size between species – from 64 to 680 square metres in those studied.

The territories seem to remain intact, even though the cock is absent for much of the time after the eggs have been laid. He continues the defence whenever he visits the nest and, after feeding his mate, he often remains for a time and sings. The territory apparently provides little for the birds except privacy, for most of the food and some of the nest materials are obtained elsewhere. Its functions may be to isolate the pair and enable them to display and mate without disturbance, and to deter other cocks from attempting to court the hen when her mate is absent. The territories also help to space the pairs within a colony so as to lessen the chances of predation on eggs and nestlings.

The grouping of cardueline territories into 'loose colonies' is not due to lack of nest sites, but to the mutual attraction between individuals. It is true that a small scrub patch in open country might be replete with several finch-species because cover is lacking elsewhere, but even in an expanse of habitat most of the territories are grouped, with vacant spaces left between groups. Goldfinches, Siskins, Serins and Crossbills nest mostly in groups of 2–3 pairs; and Greenfinches, Linnets, Twites and Redpolls in groups of 4–6. In all species, however, larger numbers sometimes nest together, in the Linnet up to 40 pairs within two hectares (five acres). Conversely, in all species some pairs nest in apparent isolation.

The advantages of group-nesting are probably the pooling of information on food sources (p. 131), and an increased awareness of approaching enemies. Colonially nesting Hawfinches have been seen to join forces to mob a predator, and according to Mountfort (1957), their nesting success is one-third greater than that of Hawfinches nesting alone. Within the colony, as mentioned, the spacing of nests probably reduces further the chance of predation.

Colonies of carduelines change in size and location during the course of the breeding season, partly because some pairs raise their successive broods in different places. This is difficult to detect by ringing, because the same marked pair have to be caught at more than one nest. In a colony of American Goldfinches, three ringed hens built their second nests in the same territories as the first, and four others established new territories, up to 150 metres from the first (Stokes 1950). But any birds moving outside the study area would not of course have been found. Near Oxford, I caught the same pair of Greenfinches twice in the same season at nests one kilometre apart, but this seems to be the only relevant recovery for European finches. (Many ringed Linnets are known to have moved tens of kilometres in a breeding season (Retz 1966, 1968), but the records are not based on birds ringed and subsequently recaptured at nest-sites.)

The best evidence for movements between broods comes from the marked changes during the breeding season in the finch populations of particular areas. Anyone working a regular beat will be familiar with the fact that cardueline finches may appear at any stage in the breeding season, raise a brood, leave, and not reappear. An influx near the end of the season strongly suggests that this is not the birds' first attempt to breed that year, and that they have already nested elsewhere. Sometimes local movements can be related to changes in the availability of nest-sites. Linnets, for example, nest mostly in gorse at the start of the season, and mostly in deciduous shrubs near the end (p. 255). Goldfinches in northern Europe nest first in conifers on the edges of woods, and then in deciduous trees in parks and orchards (Hildén 1964). At other times the movements are probably linked with changes in food-supplies. In large pasture near Oxford, at least ten pairs of Linnets regularly moved in to nest at the end of the season, when thistles began to seed, whereas previously the area had held little suitable food and only one or two pairs of Linnets.

The most striking movements between broods, linked with changes in food, occur among Redpolls in Fenno-Scandia. Most individuals normally breed on the fjeld, the zone of birch scrub that separates forest from tundra. But in years when the spruce forests to the south hold a good seed crop many birds halt there on their northward migration and raise an early brood. Then, when the seeds have fallen from the cones, the birds continue north to the fjeld, arriving about a fortnight later than usual, and raise another brood. For some birds this entails moving several hundred kilometres. These movements have not been proved by ringing, but have been deduced from the simultaneous changes in the population of the two regions, and in particular, from the late arrival in these years of birds on the field with their young. They were recorded in 1932, 1955, 1965 and 1968 (Swanberg 1936, Peiponen 1957, 1962, 1967, Hildén 1969). Hence in contrast to the Chaffinch which normally keeps to the same territory in successive years, the carduelines are to some extent nomadic within a breeding season, perhaps most only locally, but settling wherever conditions are suitable. This is yet another adaptation to a food-supply which is constantly changing in distribution through the summer.

Courtship

The courtship of finches, like that of other birds, consists of displays and vocalisations, some by one sex to the other, and some mutual. The main function of courtship is to suppress those feelings of aggression and fear, which normally result from the physical closeness of individuals, and ensure that the partners can achieve the close proximity necessary for copulation and parental care. It also helps to synchronise the sexual cycles of the pair, both in the long term, where display by the cock accelerates ovulation in the hen (Hinde 1967), and in the short term, where display by the cock induces the hen to copulate at an appropriate moment. The displays also function as 'isolating mechanisms', that is, they help to ensure that each bird mates with a partner of its own rather than of another species, for each bird reacts most strongly to the appropriate displays.

The courtship displays of birds are thought to be derived chiefly from the threat and submissive postures which appear during everyday fights for food. This is evident partly from the components of the displays, which include wing-raising, feather-sleeking and other movements associated with threat, and feather-raising and other movements associated with fear. The display given at any moment is supposed to depend on the outcome of the three conflicting tendencies, to attack, to flee and to behave sexually, and its form changes during the season. When the cocks first approach the hens in spring, their displays contain many aggressive components, and differ from outright threat chiefly in the oblique or lateral orientation of the birds' body in respect to that of the hen. Later in the season, when submissive or sexual components predominate, the displays may take a different form. During the courtship period, the cock passes through three stages in which aggressive, submissive and then sexual components predominate in his displays, though these stages largely overlap.

The various components of the aggressive and submissive postures do not always appear in sexual displays in unmodified form. During evolution, some of the movements have become exaggerated, reduced or lost altogether when they occur in a sexual context. Also, certain movements have become associated with particular markings and colour patches so as to make them more striking.

The displays of the individual species are given in Table 13, and their components discussed below:

1. *Wing movements.* Wing-raising, normally associated with aggression, occurs in the early displays of all species except the Bullfinch. It is especially marked in *Carduelis* and *Serinus* species. Wing-drooping, in which the wings are lowered down the side of the body and the primaries are slightly separated, likewise occurs in all species, and shows the wing-markings and rump colouration to good effect. In some species, like the Twite, the primaries are continually opened and closed during display. Wing-shivering movements are given by the hens of all species during courtship feeding and solicitation; they also appear in the display of the cock Redpoll.

2. *Tail movements.* Most species spread their tails to some extent during courtship and singing, thereby exposing the markings. This is most pronounced in the Goldfinch, Siskin and Greenfinch. In the Bullfinch, which has no marks on its tail, the tail is instead turned to one side during courtship.

3. *Body movements.* All displays in which aggression is strong involve crouching. In addition, the hen crouches during copulation and courtship feeding, whereas in this last act the cock stands erect. A peculiar form of

Table 13. The main displays of some cardueline finches.

	Main display postures	Main display flight
Greenfinch	(a) Cock chases hen, with wings raised, tail spread and body-feathers sleeked. (b) In less aggressive display, cock points his bill upwards and lowers his wings, showing the yellow on the rump, wings and tail.	Flies with slow, deep wing-beats, weaving erratically among the tree-tops, calling and singing.
Goldfinch	Both sexes crouch, then swing from side to side, using their legs as pivots. The wings are lowered to show more yellow, the tail spread and the red 'blaze' expanded. The birds utter a 'tuleep' or 'tu-wee-oo' call.	Flies hesitantly, with slow, deep wing-beats, plumage fluffed and tail spread, singing and calling.
Siskin	Cock raises his black crown and yellow rump feathers, droops his wings, fluffs his breast, spreads his tail, sings and utters a prolonged creaking note.	More or less as in Goldfinch, perching and singing on tree-tops between flights.
Linnet	Cock raises his red crown feathers, droops his wings and spreads his tail to show the white marks; he usually sings.	Flies up to about ten metres or to a tree-top, then descends on rigid wings to the bushes below, singing.
Twite	Cock crouches, lowers and shuffles his wings, raises the red rump feathers, and spreads his tail to show the white marks.	More or less as in Linnet.
Redpoll	Cock, facing hen, spreads his tail and flutters his wings above his back, tilting his head back to show the black bib.	Flies high with hesitant bounding flight, calling loudly.
Serin	(a) Cock chases hen, crouching with wings out, body feathers sleeked, and head and throat feathers raised. (b) In less aggressive display, the body is more upright and the wings held in while the bird sings, hopping from one foot to the other.	Cock rises vertically and descends in circles, singing all the while.
Scarlet Rosefinch	Cock droops his wings to expose the rump feathers, slightly raises his tail, and fluffs his throat feathers while singing.	Flutters from bush-top to bush-top, singing, or weaves erratically through the bushes.
Crossbills	Cock crouches and lowers his wings to show the rump feathers which are raised.	Flies in circles over trees with slowly-beating wings, singing and calling.

body movement is pivoting, in which the body itself is held rigid, but swung from side to side about the legs. Incipient pivoting movements are evident in the displays of all species, but have become highly elaborated in the Goldfinch. In this species, the performing bird crouches, droops its wings to show more yellow, spreads and slightly lowers its tail, and expands the red blaze on its face. The colours are thus shown to their best advantage, and the bird swings from side to side about its legs, uttering a

PLATE 13. The Twite breeds mainly on arctic and alpine tundras, but in Britain is found on windswept coasts and moorlands. It is commonest in the northern and western Isles of Scotland, especially in places where the Linnet, its closest relative, is absent. The birds shown are hens, the lower at its nest in heather.

PLATE 14. Redpolls breed in the northern forests and scrub-tundras of Eurasia and North America, spreading south in winter. Their numbers and movements vary from year to year according to the abundance of birch seeds which form their main food. The British 'Lesser Redpoll' (*above*) is smaller and browner than the 'Mealy Redpoll', shown *below* at a nest in Swedish Lapland.

characteristic 'tuleep' or 'tu-wee-oo' call. The more excited the bird, the more exaggerated the posture (Fig. 44).

4. *Sleeking and fluffing the feathers.* Feather sleeking, ordinarily associated with threat, appears in the early displays of all species, though usually only part of the plumage is involved. Thus, when a cock Serin or Canary chases its mate, the feathers of the head and throat are raised. Fluffing of the entire plumage, normally associated with submission, is shown during copulation, but in other displays again only part of the plumage is involved, and often this is associated with particular colour patches. The Twite raises its rump feathers, which are reddish, whereas other species like the Linnet and Siskin, which have distinct head markings, raise their crown feathers. But the Goldfinch in contrast to other species, performs sexual chases and attacks with its entire plumage fluffed.

FIG. 44. The pivoting display of the Goldfinch. The performing bird crouches, droops its wings slightly, spreads its tail, and swings from side to side about its legs.

The main point of contrast between the cardueline and the fringilline finches is not in the postures adopted, but in the extent to which the hen participates in the displays. In the Chaffinch, except during sexual chases and copulation, the hen plays a mainly passive role in courtship; but in the carduelines many displays involve the active participation of the hen, who in some species adopts the same postures as the cock – for example, pivoting in the Goldfinch. It has long been thought that mutual displays serve to strengthen and maintain the pair-bond, and the most important of these in the carduelines is courtship feeding, which the Chaffinch lacks.

But nearly all the activities of the breeding pair, not just the displays, are performed at least occasionally by both sexes. The cock cardueline finch is much more active in parental care than is the cock Chaffinch, in part possible because of the reduced territorial behaviour. Also, he often carries nest material, and in some species, occasionally helps to build

(Hinde 1954). The hen, on the other hand, helps with the territorial defence, sometimes takes part in display flights, and in some species occasionally sings (though less well and less consistently than her mate). Hence, although most activities are carried out more by one sex than the other, there is less division of labour in the carduelines than in the Chaffinch.

Courtship feeding

The billing movements, important in the pair-formation of the carduelines, soon develop into courtship feeding. In this the hen crouches, flutters her wings and opens her bill, uttering faint begging calls, while the cock stands upright beside her, and reaches down with his bill to push food into her mouth with his tongue (Fig. 45). The act may be initiated

FIG. 45. Courtship feeding. The cock, standing upright, passes food to the hen, who crouches and shivers her wings.

either by the cock approaching the hen and pecking at her beak or by the hen begging; it lasts only a few seconds, during which three or four beakfuls of food are passed. This behaviour clearly involves the reappearance in the adult hen of the infantile begging behaviour. She plays the part of the dependent young and the cock that of the parent who feeds her. He exaggerates his part by stretching up and feeding the food from above (Nicolai 1956).

Courtship feeding develops just before nest-building, but is most frequent during the incubation and early brooding periods, when the hen gets nearly all her food from the cock. She does not then have to leave the eggs for long periods in order to procure her own food, which would often entail lengthy flights. (The hen Chaffinch, it may be recalled, feeds herself during incubation, but she always has food available near the nest.)

That courtship feeding also helps to strengthen the pair-bond is suggested by the great excitement shown by the hen when the cock comes to feed her, for she often begins to flutter her wings and beg before he has reached the nest. The act is probably also important in getting the pair used to being close to one another, which later facilitates their close co-operation while they are feeding young.

Song

In the Chaffinch and Brambling, the song is given only in the breeding season by the cocks on their territories: it serves to repel other cocks and to attract hens (p. 146–7). To these ends, it is loud, clear and stereotyped, but nonetheless in the Chaffinch it is sufficiently variable to enable neighbouring cocks to recognise one another. In the carduelines, although the song is most frequent and vigorous during breeding, it is not restricted to this time, nor to the territory, but occurs at all seasons except during the autumn moult. It is quieter and individually more variable than in the Chaffinch. Typically it consists of a jumble of notes, including most of the everyday calls of the species, and resembles in many ways the subsong of the Chaffinch. Its function, moreover, is less obvious, as it is uttered in social, as well as in aggressive and sexual contexts.

In winter, groups of cocks sometimes sit in the tree-tops and sing softly, in warm afternoons or in evenings prior to roosting. At these times song seems to result from the social stimulation of the group. It is also used at this season by an isolated bird wishing to gain contact with a flock, and thus serves as a 'long-distance contact call' (p. 125).

In the breeding season, the cocks sing on their territories, while sitting in conspicuous places where they can see one another. In this context, the song serves to discourage encroachment by other cocks, as in the Chaffinch. It is not certain whether, in carduelines, the song also serves to attract hens, since most birds form pairs while they are still in flocks. Yet any cocks which fail to get a mate sit and sing on the breeding grounds, so might get a mate in this way, even though normally they would not.

The song certainly serves to stimulate the hen sexually, however, and thus to synchronise the breeding of the pair. Uttered loudly and vigorously, it forms an integral part of the courtship displays of all carduelines. It acts on the hen in two ways. First, it has an immediate effect, like the visual components of the display, and sometimes leads to copulation. Indeed, a hen will sometimes solicit just on hearing the song of the cock. It is common practice among bird-fanciers, when trying to breed hybrids between two cardueline species, to use a cock bird in a separate cage to 'sing down' the hen, so that she solicits and can be mounted by the cock of another species kept in the same cage with her. Second, the song has a long-term influence on the hen, helping to stimulate ovulation, at least in the domestic canary, in which lone hens which can hear cocks singing lay eggs sooner than do lone hens which cannot (Hinde 1967). Thus, in its effect on the hen, the song is probably a much more important part of courtship in the carduelines than it is in the Chaffinch.

Display flights

Display flights comprise two main types: the 'moth flight', involving rapid wing-beats of small amplitude, and the 'butterfly flight', involving slow wing-beats of large amplitude. The former is given by the cock in the presence of the hen, who may also participate, and is usually performed in cover over distances of only a few metres. In some species, like the Redpoll, it consists of little more than the cock hovering over the hen's back, but in others, like the Goldfinch, it forms a longer and more elaborate ceremony involving both sexes. Either way, 'moth flights' usually precede copulation, and thus occur for only a few days in each nesting cycle. (They should not be confused with the moth flight of the Chaffinch (p. 138) which has a different function.)

Conspicuous 'butterfly flights' are likewise performed primarily by the cocks, but in the open over the breeding areas; they are accompanied by continual calling and singing, hence the alternative name 'song-flights'. They occur over more of the breeding cycle than do moth flights, from the establishment of territories until after the start of incubation. In many species, they involve a curious hesitant flight, in which a series of slow deliberate wing-strokes are interspersed with long glides, with plumage fluffed and tail spread. But the exact form of the flight varies from species to species. In some, the butterfly strokes are most pronounced; in others the glide (Table 13). The Greenfinch in its so-called 'bat-flight' weaves erratically among the tree-tops, singing and calling; the Linnet rises to about ten metres then plummets down like a paper dart on to the bushes below; the Redpoll bounces along at great height calling incessantly; while the Serin rises almost vertically then descends in circles singing all the while. In all species, the flights often end beside the hen, and in some the hens also participate.

This type of display, which has no equivalent in the Chaffinch, seems to be associated primarily with advertisement, but may extend beyond the territorial boundaries. It is often given by the cock on sight of a rival, or after a fight with one; and is most frequent during the early stages of nesting, and wanes during incubation. Also, the flights are given most frequently by cocks nesting close together and starting at the same time. Over large colonies, several cocks are often in the air at once, performing independently except that they may sometimes chase one another. But whereas some species like the American Goldfinch, Linnet and Twite, perform over their immediate nesting areas, others like the Greenfinch and Redpoll, range over a much larger area than they would defend on the ground. The flights may function not so much in territorialism or courtship, but to attract others to the breeding colony, with the resulting advantage for all of improved food-finding.

To conclude, the typical cardueline finch may be described as a noisy, sociable, colonial-nesting, flock-feeding, seed-eater, which feeds its young by regurgitation. Its displays include song-flights, courtship feeding, billing and other mutual actions. These and other differences from the fringilline finches are summarised in Table 14.

TABLE 14. Differences in breeding behaviour between the fringilline and cardueline finches.

	FRINGILLINAE	CARDUELINAE
	Chaffinch and Brambling (*Fringilla*)	Goldfinches, siskins, linnets, redpolls, serins, rosefinches and crossbills (*Carduelis, Acanthis, Serinus, Carpodacus, Loxia*)
Food of young	Insects, fed frequently from parent's bill.	Mainly seeds, fed infrequently by regurgitation.
Nesting dispersion	Large territories. Elaborate fighting involving special postures.	Small territories, grouped into colonies.
Food obtained	Within territories, solitarily.	Outside territories, in flocks.
Sequence of behaviour	(1) establishment of territory. (2) pair-formation. (3) selection of nest site.	(1) pair-formation. (2) selection of nest site. (3) establishment of territory.
Type of song	Stereotyped, short, loud and clear.	Less stereotyped, prolonged and less loud.
Sexual behaviour	Inside territory.	Inside and outside territory.
Pair-formation	Sudden, hen attracted by song of cock in territory.	Prolonged, cock approaches hen in flock; courtship involves 'bill-scissoring'.
Nature of display	Aggressive elements strong. Hen's role mainly passive.	Aggressive elements strong. Some displays mutual.
Courtship feeding	Absent.	Present.
Display flights over breeding area.	Absent.	Present.
Incubation	By hen, feeds herself.	By hen, mainly fed by cock.

Deviations from the typical cardueline pattern of behaviour

Despite minor variations, the above behaviour is typical of *Carduelis*, *Acanthis*, *Serinus*, *Loxia* and *Carpodacus* finches, and confirms the close relationship between these genera. The Hawfinch and Bullfinch, however, differ in some important respects both from other carduelines and from one another. But these deviations are less clearly related to ecological factors than are those between the Chaffinch and the typical carduelines. Thus, both the Hawfinch and Bullfinch are secretive while breeding and have soft unimpressive songs; they build distinct two-layered nests of twigs and roots and, unlike other carduelines, keep the nest clean throughout the nestling period; linked with this, the faeces of the young are always enclosed in a gelatinous sac, so that they can be easily carried away (not just in the first few days). Also, both species have extremely elaborate displays, which in the Hawfinch seem to be associated with reducing the tension between two extremely aggressive and well-armed mates, and in the Bullfinch with strengthening the pair-bond to a degree not met with in other finches. During courtship feeding, the hens of these species pivot from side to side between accepting beakfuls of food from the cock, instead of pumping back and forth like other cardueline species. These similarities do not necessarily imply a close relationship between the two species, however, since they differ in other respects.

1. *The Hawfinch.* To begin with, this bird seems to have two systems of territorialism (Mountfort 1956). Some pairs, like other carduelines, breed colonially and defend a small area round their nests until the eggs have been laid, while others breed solitarily and drive off other birds from a wide area round their nests throughout the breeding period. I do not know the reason for the dual system, but either way, the birds forage largely outside their territories. (Of course other carduelines sometimes nest solitarily but in these this is not obviously associated with increased aggression.) Hawfinch colonies usually contain 3–6 pairs, but more than 20 pairs have been found nesting in less than two hectares (five acres), and 7 within 200 metres of hedgerow. The nests of different pairs may be as close as four metres, sometimes in adjacent trees or even in the same tree (Mountfort 1957).

As a rule the same parts of a wood are used year after year (records extend up to 30 years), and probably individual pairs return in successive years. Each March after pair-formation, individual cocks leave the feeding flocks for long periods and sit quietly in the breeding places, often in trees that have previously held nests. This may be a way of staking a claim but only after the arrival of the hens, some days or weeks later, does each cock begin to actively defend his nest-tree against other Hawfinches.

Later the cock chooses the nest site. He first tests suitable places by crouching in them; then he breaks the first few twigs and lays the foundation of a nest. He attracts the hen to this by lying in it, raising his head and offering to feed her by opening and closing his bill. The hen then takes over the rest of the building (Wallin 1966). When the young arrive, the parents use two methods of conveying food to them, regurgitating seeds and carrying insects, up to a dozen at a time, in their bills. Hawfinches also feed their young more frequently than do other carduelines, every eight minutes on average (Robertson 1954, Mountfort 1957).

It is in its courtship, however, that the Hawfinch is most peculiar (Fig. 46). The species is not only more aggressive than other carduelines, but it also has a stronger bill. Perhaps linked with this aggressiveness, the cock's initial approaches to the hen are often hesitant and indirect, and have developed into highly ritualised displays in which appeasing and sub-

FIG. 46. Courtship postures of the Hawfinch. (From Mountfort 1957.) A, body upright, head withdraw, feathers of throat and nape fluffed; B, the 'penguin' walk; C, the bow; D, frontal approach with dragged wing-tips; E, cock (left) approaching the hen in the bill-touching ceremony.

missive gestures prevail (Hinde 1955–56, Mountfort 1957). Also the bill
nibbling movements, which appear early in the courtship of other
carduelines, are in the Hawfinch cautiously preceded by 'bill-touching',
in which two birds reach out to touch just the very tips of their bills,
standing as far apart as possible, almost overbalancing while doing so.

Although the cock Hawfinch uses more displays in his approach to the
hen than do other finches, he often gets a hostile reception. In early spring,
with the plumage of the head, neck and chest puffed out, he may approach cautiously, zig-zagging from side to side, with a pattering walk, and
only gradually edging towards her. He stands almost erect with his wings
drooped loosely forward (like a penguin) and his tail spread. At the same
time the hen crouches, sleeks her feathers, and follows his every movement
with the point of her bill. Often she attacks or flees. But if she simply hops
to one side, the cock may follow, face her, and make a deep bow tucking
his bill right under his belly and exposing to her the grey nape patch – a
submissive gesture in which the offensive weapon is turned away. This is
followed by another display in which the cock lowers one wing, allowing
the tip to scrape the ground in a stiff semi-circle in front of the hen, showing the wing-bars and modified flight feathers. In a frontal approach,
both wings are dragged. The cock might then reach forward and attempt
to touch the tip of the hen's bill with his own.

Later in the season, in a more confident approach, the cock advances
in a series of long deliberate hops, and swings from side to side with each
hop, so that first one side and then the other is turned towards the hen,
thus showing the shoulder patches. This is accompanied by 'tick-tick'
calls. At first the cock's body is horizontal, but later it is raised upright,
the bill is pointed downwards, the neck feathers raised and the primaries
lowered. The display might then develop into the 'spread-wing dance' in
which the body is still held almost upright and pivoted from side to side,
but the wings are stretched out at right angles to the body and quivered
slightly. The head feathers are then raised and the tail spread, as the cock
patters to and fro in front of the hen, uttering a curious braying call.
Often the hen responds likewise and the two 'dance' together for several
seconds. Variations occur on all these themes, but the basic pattern of
fluffing the neck feathers, waddling in upright attitudes, bowing, drooping
the wings and bill-touching, remains. Other displays, which occur only
between mated birds, include 'head-flicking', in which the partners,
perched side by side, flick up their beaks, exposing their black bibs; a
moth display in which the cock makes short fluttering flights above the
hen; and sexual chases, as in other carduelines. All these displays, except
possibly the wing-dragging, bowing and moth flights, also occur in the
hen. The song consists of a mixture of call notes and other creaky sounds;
it is uttered rather rarely and is so soft that it carries only a few metres. It
varies greatly between individuals and, though uttered after disputes
with neighbouring cocks, it is used less in territorial defence than in other

carduelines. Also, the Hawfinch has no conspicuous song-flight over the breeding grounds.

TABLE 15. Differences in the breeding behaviour of the Hawfinch from that of the typical cardueline finches.

1. General	(a)	The two systems of territorialism, some pairs defending small territories in colonies, and others large territories outside colonies.
	(b)	The cocks visit their territories, several weeks before nesting begins.
	(c)	Soft quiet song, highly variable between individuals.
2. Displays	(d)	During pair-formation, 'bill-scissoring' is preceded by a special 'bill-touching' ceremony.
	(e)	Elaborate displays involving wing-spreading and bowing, which have no equivalents in other carduelines.
	(f)	While begging for food, the hen and young pivot from side to side.
3. Nesting	(g)	The cock chooses the site and builds the foundation of the nest.
	(h)	Distinct two-layered nest of twigs and roots.
4. Parental	(i)	Two methods of bringing food to the young: seeds regurgitated and insects carried, up to a dozen at a time, in the bill.
	(j)	Young fed frequently, on average every 7–8 minutes.
	(k)	The nest is kept clean throughout the nestling period, and linked with this, the faeces of the young are enclosed in a gelatinous sac.

NOTE. In addition to these behavioural differences, there are also pronounced morphological ones, including the distinct palate structure and powerful skull, and the presence of bars, rather than streaks, in the juvenile plumage. The eggs are also distinct from those of other carduelines.

To summarise, the major points of contrast between the Hawfinch and other carduelines include the two systems of territorialism, the site-selection by the cock, the two means of carrying food to the nestlings and the elaborate bowing and wing-spreading displays. These and other differences are listed in Table 15.

2. *The Bullfinch.* This species differs in even more respects than does the Hawfinch from the other carduelines (Table 16). First, it does not nest in colonies. Odd records exist of two pairs nesting together in the same small bush (e.g. Snow 1953), but almost certainly these result from chance, for if colonial nesting were the rule, it would have been noted more often. At the same time, the Bullfinch is not obviously territorial. Even when leading his mate to the nest, or flying in with food, the cock will often ignore a caged bird placed near the nest, and this holds throughout the breeding cycle, not just in the late stages as in other carduelines. In fact, each pair

nests and behaves generally as though it were oblivious of all other Bull-finches.

TABLE 16. Differences in the breeding behaviour of the Bullfinch from that of the typical cardueline finches.

1. General	(a)	Sexual behaviour persists through the year, hens dominant to cocks throughout.
	(b)	Unusually intimate relationship between the pair, and the apparent persistence of the pair-bond from one breeding season to the next.
	(c)	Inconspicuousness while breeding.
	(d)	Absence of both colonial nesting and obvious territorial be-behaviour, nests solitarily.
	(e)	No display flights.
	(f)	Soft quiet song, highly variable between individuals, and having no aggressive function, voice distinct, with piping sounds and hoarse notes, but devoid of any form of twittering which characterises other carduelines.
	(g)	Lack of flocking and other social behaviour in the breeding season.
2. Displays	(h)	Pair-formation typically involves a ritual attack by the hen on the cock.
	(i)	Thereafter, the almost complete lack of aggression between the pair.
	(j)	No sexual chases and no attempts at rape.
	(k)	All courtship displays mutual and highly ritualised.
	(l)	All displays involve the tail being turned to one side, an action lacking in other carduelines.
	(m)	While begging for food, the hen and young pivot from side to side, the former without calling.
3. Nesting	(n)	The cock leads the hen to various sites, directing her attention to them with a special call.
	(o)	Distinct two-layered nest of twigs and roots.
4. Parental care	(p)	The nest is kept clean throughout the nestling period, and linked with this, the faeces of the young are enclosed in a gelatinous sac.

NOTE. In addition to these behavioural differences, there are also pronounced morphological ones, including the distinct palate structure, the lack of any form of streaking in both adult and juvenile plumages, and the presence of special pouches for holding food for the young (though these last are shared with some other species), and no difference in size between the sexes.

In contrast to the noisy display flights, singing and calling found in other carduelines on their breeding areas, Bullfinches at this time are remarkably quiet and inconspicuous. They have no display flights. The cock does not sit conspicuously near the nest and, except during building and when bringing food, keeps well away. The song has no aggressive function, but it does play a part in the cock's displays to his mate, chiefly in the early stages of courtship. It is so soft that it carries only a few metres, and is highly variable between individuals.

Social behaviour is almost non-existent in the breeding season. Pairs feeding at the same place usually ignore one another, but if two lone cocks or two lone hens meet by chance, they fight fiercely for a moment and then separate. All this behaviour, which is thoroughly atypical for carduelines as a whole, reduces the contact of each pair with other Bullfinches to a remarkable degree.

On the other hand, those types of behaviour which serve to strengthen the pair-bond are greatly elaborated in the Bullfinch. All the displays are mutual, for example, the hen playing as active a part as the cock. They are also highly ritualised, and in most of them similar postures are adopted by both sexes (Nicolai 1956). When two unacquainted birds of opposite sex meet, a strict 'introduction ceremony' takes place, in which the hen flies at the cock, threatening him with open beak and uttering a hoarse 'hweh hweh'. If the cock is disinterested he flies away, but if he is sexually disposed, he flies in a peculiar tense attitude, puffs out the feathers of his abdomen, and turns his tail towards her. The more confident the cock, the more quickly does the ritual attack of the hen collapse. If the birds are unmated, this soon develops into 'beak-caressing', in which the cock hops towards the hen, in the same postures as before, touching her beak for a moment with his; he then turns away and hops a little to one side, whereupon he at once repeats the procedure, the hen responding likewise (Fig. 47a). During bill-caressing, Bullfinches nibble in silence, unlike other carduelines, which make soft pleasing sounds. Above all, however, the actions of turning the tail to one side and of hopping straight towards one another and turning away, which are characteristic of the Bullfinch during courtship, are absent in other species. Bill-caressing later develops into courtship feeding, in which the cock stretches up and places the regurgitated food into the open beak of the hen, who crouches and pivots from side to side.

As the time of nest-building approaches, the pair also perform the 'twig-display' (Fig. 47b). The cock, in the same puffed posture as before, picks up a root or a short dry twig in his bill and offers it to the hen. Thereupon the hen often picks up a twig herself and they both fly off, one behind the other, with the material in their beaks. Mating itself is largely stimulated by the partners showing nest material to one another. Hens wishing to copulate purposely go in search of such material and, having found some, seem to gain extra stimulation. The cocks show the same behaviour, and often both birds keep hold of the material while mating. In other carduelines nest material has no such significance.

These elaborate mutual displays of the Bullfinch serve to strengthen the attachment of the sexes to a degree not met with in other species. Aggression between the partners is virtually non-existent, and sexual chases and

FIG. 47. Courtship displays
of the Bullfinch. A, bill cares-
sing; B, the twig display.

attempts at rape, which are common in other carduelines, are lacking.
The cock, moreover, is exceptional among finches in refusing to mate with
any other species in captivity, though the hen will do so.

As in the Hawfinch, the cock takes the initiative in choosing a nest-site.
He leads the hen from site to site, crouching in suitable spots and uttering
a special call, to draw the hen's attention to it. The cock sometimes gives
the same call when standing in the half-completed nest, and it is probably
this which has given rise to the mistaken idea that he helps to incubate.

Another peculiar feature of the Bullfinch is that some degree of sexual
behaviour persists through the year, except during moult, so that courtship may be seen in almost every month and hens are always dominant to
cocks. The statement that Bullfinches pair for life is frequent in orni-
thological textbooks, and seems to be based on the fact that pairs are often
seen together in winter. The persistence of sexual behaviour through the
year might anyway result in early pair-formation each year, but this behaviour would be difficult to explain if its function was not to keep the
same pair together between breeding seasons. In captivity, moreover, two
partners will certainly remain attached from year to year, and will also
recognise one another instantly after many months of separation (Nicolai
1956). Still, however, proof by ringing for the persistence of pairs in the
wild for more than one year is needed.

In his study of captive Bullfinches, Dr Nicolai found that each young
bird formed an intimate association with one of its siblings, when only
6–7 weeks old and still in juvenile plumage. The birds caressed each other

with their beaks, fed each other and invited each other to mate; but none of their actions were proficient, and no mating took place. At this stage, there was no colour difference between sexes, and two cocks or two hens often paired together. Such pairs remained together, billing and courting throughout the autumn and winter, but broke up in the following spring when each bird formed a normal relationship with an unrelated bird of the opposite sex. This probably represented the early appearance, in incomplete form, of behaviour which would keep the pair together in later life.

Concluding, the almost complete lack of social behaviour, the inconspicuousness while breeding, the lack of display flights, the suppression of calling, the soft song and the highly ritualised mutual displays of the Bullfinch all serve to reduce the social contacts with other individuals, yet strengthen and maintain the bond between the pair. The continuance of sexual behaviour through the year, and the tendency of even young birds to form intimate relationships with another individual, suggests a strong advantage to the Bullfinch in life in pairs – one sufficiently important to make it drop the advantages of social food-finding and colonial nesting found in other carduelines. If this peculiar behaviour has an ecological basis, it has escaped me.

Phylogenetic relationships

It remains to draw conclusions on the phylogenetic relationships of different species. Like other birds, the finches were initially classified on morphological and anatomical features, but the courtship and breeding behaviour provide further evidence on which species are closely related and which more distant. In general, the behavioural evidence confirms the current generic groupings based on morphology, but also suggests that some genera are closer than others. It confirms, for example, that the Greenfinch is very close to the Goldfinch and is best grouped in *Carduelis*, rather than in a distinct genus, as formerly. There are no consistent differences between *Serinus*, *Carduelis* and *Acanthis* in behaviour. The information available also suggests that *Carpodacus* is very close to these genera, though more evidence is required. The crossbills *Loxia*, too, are very close to the main genera, as shown not only by their general behaviour and displays, but also by their calls. The Hawfinch is clearly more divergent than the other genera, and the Bullfinch even more so. These last two species also have a distinct juvenile plumage, the Hawfinch having crossbars instead of streaks, and the Bullfinch lacking either.

To summarise this chapter, the main differences in breeding behaviour between the cardueline and fringilline finches can be related to the difference in nesting dispersion and this in turn to their feeding habits. Typical carduelines nest in loose colonies and forage at a distance in flocks. They feed their young at long intervals by regurgitation, on a diet consisting primarily of seeds. Pair-formation occurs while the birds are in flocks, and involves 'bill-nibbling' movements, which later develop into courtship feeding. While the hen is brooding, she depends on the cock for food. Most carduelines perform display flights over their breeding areas. The Hawfinch and Bullfinch are divergent in several respects, particularly in their elaborate courtship displays. A classification of European finches based on behaviour would fit the current one based on morphology.

CHAPTER 10

THE BREEDING ECOLOGY OF THE CARDUELINE FINCHES

THIS chapter deals with the nests, eggs and parental care of the cardueline finches. Most of the European species build their nests in trees or shrubs, only the Linnet and Twite occasionally in a tussock on the ground. The nest of each species is distinct and can be recognised from its position, size and shape, and from the materials of which it is made. Grasses, roots, moss and fur are common ingredients, but the lining is always of finer materials than the outer part. Three types of nest predominate within the group. The commonest type is rather bulky and made of various flexible materials, often with a base of fine twigs and bents, a main structure of grass and moss, and a lining of hairs and rootlets. This type is built by most shrub-nesting species, including the Greenfinch, Linnet, Twite and Redpoll, and is usually placed in a fork. The second type consists of a shallow platform of twigs, on which is placed a pad of thin roots and grasses, which is easily separable from the base. The twigs tend to be dead and inflexible, and project on all sides, and often the whole structure is so thin that the eggs can be seen from below. This type is built by the Hawfinch, Pine Grosbeak and Bullfinch. Usually it is placed on a flat branch or on a flat tangle of twigs, rather than in a fork, but in a comparatively stable situation. The third type of nest is neat, small and compact, made chiefly of mosses and lichens, and lined with the down of thistles and other plants. This type is built by those *Carduelis* species, such as the Goldfinch, which nest high on the branches of trees. Such nests are deep, so as to retain the eggs in windy weather, and are bound to twigs with the help of spider silk. The birds do this by dropping a loose end over a branch and picking it up the other side. This is another adaptation to make such nests safe in wind, for the other types, in more stable sites, are secured only by the adherence of the material to the supporting twigs. Finally, the Scarlet Rosefinch's nest is a deep, grassy structure, placed low in a clump of vegetation, which looks more like the work of a warbler than of a finch.

In all species, building occurs in spates lasting 10–40 minutes, during which time several lots of material are brought and fixed, but each spate may be followed by hours or even days when nothing is added. The time taken to complete a nest varies considerably within each species. It probably depends partly on the reproductive condition of the hen, and generally the first nests of the season take longer to build than do later ones. In the American Goldfinch, for example, periods of 2–27 days have been recorded between the start of a nest and the laying of the first egg but, on average, the first nests take 13 days to build and the last 6 days (Walkinshaw 1938, 1939, Stokes 1950). Likewise the completed nests may remain empty for longer at the start of the season – periods of up to three weeks have been recorded in the Greenfinch – than near the end (Boase 1948). Periods of 3–12 days have been recorded for Hawfinches to build their nests (Mountfort 1957), 9–11 days for Parrot Crossbills (Valeur, in Bannerman 1953), 3-6 days for Scarlet Rosefinches (Risberg 1970), and 2–4 days for Mealy Redpolls nesting in the Arctic, where the summer is short (Hildén 1969).

The eggs

The eggs of most species have a whitish background, usually tinged with blue or green, and are spotted with reddish or brown, especially near the blunt end. Exceptions include the Hawfinch, in which the eggs are buffish or grey-green, with dark brown spots and streaks, and the Scarlet Rosefinch, in which they are vivid blue, with dark brown spots. Most carduelines lay 3–6 eggs per nest, but usually 4 or 5, producing one each day. The seasonal trends in clutch-size have been examined in at least five species (Appendix 5). In the Greenfinch and Linnet in Britain the clutches tend to be slightly larger in mid-season than at other times, so that the largest broods are in the nest when days are longest and the opportunities for feeding are greatest. In the Bullfinch, on the other hand, which breeds in Britain in the same months, the mean clutch-size declines through the season. This trend is more difficult to explain, unless food is so much more plentiful early in the summer as to offset the advantage of longer days in mid-summer. Evidently the trend is adaptive, because Bullfinches which produce broods of five or six early in the season rear them easily, but the few birds which produce so many young in late season rarely rear them all: at this time broods of four and fewer are most successful (Newton 1964c). A seasonal decline in the average clutch-size also occurs in the Mealy Redpoll in Finland and in the Goldfinch in Wisconsin, but these species do not start till June and July respectively, so all their young are produced during a period when daylength is decreasing (Hildén 1969, Stokes 1950).

Within each species, clutches also tend to be larger at higher latitudes, where summer days are longer. For example, the Goldfinch mostly lays 4 eggs in North Africa, 4–5 in Britain, and 5–6 in Scandinavia. Moreover, in arid parts of New South Wales, Australia, where the species was introduced only a century ago, the average clutch is 3.7 eggs per nest, significantly lower than anywhere in Europe (Frith 1957).

Trends in clutch-size similar to these are well known and have been thoroughly studied in other song-birds. In general, the number of eggs laid in each nest corresponds with the maximum number of young that the parents can rear successfully (Lack 1954). If they have fewer young, the

PLATE 15. The Serin was once restricted to the Mediterranean wood-lands of southern Europe, but for more than 150 years it has been spread-ing north and now breeds over at least two-thirds of the continent. *Above*, a cock feeding its young. *Below*, hen brooding.

PLATE 16. The Citril Finch (cock, *above*) is the only bird-species which is endemic to the mountains of central and southwest Europe. It breeds among conifers near the tree-line, but spreads to lower ground in winter.

parents do not work to full capacity, and if they have more, they do not raise them all successfully. It is assumed that birds from each population inherit a tendency to produce clutches of a certain size-range, together with an ability to vary their clutches within this range according to the prevailing conditions. Subsidiary factors, such as the food available to the laying hen, may also influence the number of eggs, but this aspect has not been studied in finches.

In all finches, each egg usually weighs around one tenth of the weight of the hen. The variation in egg-size, however, has been examined in only one species, the American Goldfinch, in which the eggs range between 0.8 and 1.8 grams (Holcomb 1968). In each clutch, successive eggs tend to be larger than the one before, except that the second is usually smaller than the first. Also, 3-egg clutches tend to have a larger second egg than do 4-egg clutches, but the significance of these trends is not known.

Incubation

Incubation usually begins with the last egg or the last but one, so that the eggs hatch over one or two days. It is often difficult to decide how much the eggs have been incubated during the laying period and, for this reason, incubation periods are best calculated from the laying of the last egg to the hatching of the last young. Only those calculated in this way are given in Appendix 6, from which it may be seen that the eggs of most species take a fortnight or less to hatch. Within each species, however, the periods recorded vary by 1–3 days, because of variation in the rate the embryo develops, which in other birds has been found to depend mainly on temperature. (In the Greenfinch the incubation period is, on average, slightly shorter in mid-season, when outside temperatures are higher – Monk 1954.) Each egg takes several hours to hatch and, when the young is dry, the shell is eaten or carried away by the hen.

During incubation the hen cardueline sits day and night. Three Goldfinches were found to spend 98%, 97% and 87% of their incubation periods on the nest (Conder 1948), and an American Goldfinch 97% (Linsdale 1950). Likewise, a Crossbill watched for a 15-hour day left only six times for periods of one, one, three, three, five and thirteen minutes respectively; she was fed eight times by the cock, sometimes on the nest and sometimes off (Snyder & Cassell 1951). In all the carduelines studied, daytime incubation stints of two hours are common, and in the Linnet daytime stints exceeding five hours have been recorded (Steinfatt 1938). The hen uses the breaks between stints to defecate, preen, exercise vigorously and sometimes to bathe.

In at least two species which nest under cold climates, the eggs are kept warm from the start to prevent them from freezing. Incubation then begins with the first egg and the young hatch asynchronously over several days, so that for a time they vary greatly in size. A Redpoll nest found by

Watson (1957) on Baffin Island contained five young at various stages of development, from one which had a tail only a centimetre long and could barely flutter more than a metre, to another which had a tail nearly full-grown and could fly straight for 200 metres. In such diverse broods, the parents have difficulty for a time in keeping the young together. I have also found asynchronous hatching in the Common Crossbill (p. 79).

The nestling period

While collecting food for their young, adult carduelines husk seeds and crush insects, in the same way as they would do for themselves. When their crops are full, they take a few sips of water and a few particles of grit, then fly to the nest and regurgitate the whole mass into the open mouths of the young. The food is neither predigested, nor supplemented with any special secretion (as it is in pigeons), but is bound together with mucus, which might provide some extra protein and water for the young. Each nestling stores the food for a time in its gullet, which, when full, appears as a large yellowish mass on the side of the neck. The various items can be seen through the transparent skin, so the food can be easily studied without harming the young.* I used to find several nests close together, and examine the young every hour or so for most of the nestling period (Newton 1967b).

Nestlings of the Greenfinch, Goldfinch and Bullfinch normally receive a mixture of seeds and insects from their parents, but the exact composition of the diet changes with seasonal and local variations in the abundance of insects. Broods raised early in the season get more insects than do broods raised later, and broods near woodland get more than do those in open country. Also, whatever the season or habitat, the young get fewer insects with increasing age, so that by the time they leave the nest, they are getting seeds alone. Throughout the season, moreover, the adults of these species feed themselves almost entirely on seeds, so are selecting a special diet for their young. Caterpillars and aphids are taken by all three species, and spiders and small snails by the Bullfinch.

These various points are shown in Appendices 7 and 8 from studies near Oxford. As may be seen, young Greenfinches hatched in May and June received an average of 10% animal-material to the fifth day, falling to 1% by the ninth; whereas those hatched in July and August received an average of 3% for the first three days, only 1% by the sixth, and none thereafter. The diet of broods in the nest at the same time varied greatly, however, and some late broods were probably fed on seeds alone. Differences in diet dependent on habitat were most marked in the Bullfinch. Broods in woodland, where invertebrates were plentiful, received 40%

* Nestling fringilline finches also possess an expandable gullet (Harrison 1970), but normally receive small meals which pass straight through to the gizzard, so the method cannot be used on them.

for the first five days, declining to 1% by the twelfth; but at the same time broods in farmland got only 5% for the first three days, declining to 1% by the sixth. Again, the variation between broods was considerable, and some late ones were apparently fed on seeds alone.

If the protein requirements of a nestling are set by the composition of its own tissues, then these should be better supplied by animal than by vegetable matter, which might explain the addition of insects to a diet which is already rich in plant-protein. Also, for the first few days, the young digest insects more efficiently than seeds, many of which are passed through whole. But these are not wasted, for at this stage the nestlings' faeces are eaten by their parents, whereas later, when digestion improves, the faeces are carried away and wiped on a twig, or near the fledging date, allowed to accumulate on the nest-rim. The young of some carduelines are none the less regularly raised on seeds alone, and sometimes on those of a single plant-species. This is true of the various crossbills, the Siskin and the Redpoll, all of which raise some young early in the year on seeds from cones, but these same species feed insects to later broods, raised in summer. The Linnet, on the other hand, regularly rears its young entirely on plant-material, whatever the month. In two years, I made repeated visits to 62 broods near Oxford, and found insects in only two of them: one brood was given some caterpillars and aphids until the ninth day, and the second was once given a few small beetle larvae. The remaining 60 broods were apparently fed on seeds alone. Unlike the fringilline finches, therefore, the cardueline finches are not restricted to breeding at seasons when insects are plentiful. An ability to raise their young on vegetable matter alone is rare among birds, and most species which are vegetarian as adults give at least some insects to their young.

In most carduelines, the young stay in the nest for about a fortnight, in some for a few days less, in others for a few days more, though within each species the variation is great. In the Greenfinch, for example, the young leave any time between the 11th and 17th days, usually on the 14th or 15th. Also the young of all species are liable to leave the nest prematurely if they are disturbed, which might account for some of the short nestling periods recorded. Much of the remaining variation in the nestling periods of each species is due to differences in the rate at which the nestlings grow and this in turn depends partly on how much food they get. Young Greenfinches stay in the nest for a slightly shorter period in mid-summer than at other times, even though there are more of them per brood, reflecting presumably the fact that the feeding is so much better in mid-summer (Monk 1954). If food is short, the weight of the young is affected long before the growth of their feathers, and underfed young are always underweight, but their feathers continue to grow at a rate which is nearly normal. This ensures that a deprived young can fly as well as its larger siblings and, when the time comes, is ready to leave the nest with them, thus having at least a chance of surviving. On the whole, however, the growth rate of young finches can be varied only within fairly restricted limits and extreme food-shortage soon results in death, though this is rare (cf. crossbills discussed later).

The nestling period of each species depends not only on the growth rate of the young, but also on the stage at which they leave the nest. The *Acanthis* and *Carpodacus* species, which nest in low bushes, are especially vulnerable from predators, and their young tend to leave the nest at a comparatively early stage and sit separately on twigs a slight distance from the nest. A predator is then less likely to get all the young than if they had stayed in the nest together. In the remaining species, which nest either in tall shrubs or in trees, the young leave at a later stage. This is probably because they are less vulnerable in the nest than are the young of the previous species, but also, in the case of the tree-nesters, because it helps to be able to fly when they leave. A second difference is that the young of the species which build low are more likely than are the young of the other species to leave the nest prematurely if they are disturbed (as every ringer knows), which is perhaps another adaptation in the former to reduce predation. The difference can be illustrated by two species, whose young develop at a similar rate. In the Linnet, which builds low, the young usually leave at 11–12 days, but as early as the ninth if disturbed, and flutter only a few metres to hide in cover. But in the Goldfinch, which builds in trees, the young usually leave at 13–16 days, and are difficult to flush even on the 12th. On leaving, they can fly vertically upwards to the tree-tops, and in another few days can follow their parents. The few extra days in the nest adds more than a centimetre to the length of the flight feathers.

The post-fledging period

At the time young carduelines leave the nest their feathers are between half and two-thirds grown, depending on the stage at which they leave, and in most species the fledglings weigh much less than their parents. Young Bullfinches, for example, weigh 16–18 grams at fledging, but adults at this season weigh 22–26 grams. The young lose a little weight while learning to feed themselves, but gain thereafter. In most species, feather growth is completed at 4–5 weeks of age, but the young do not reach adult weight until near the end of their first moult in the autumn.

It is not known how long the young of most carduelines are fed by their parents after leaving the nest in the wild, but it is at least ten days in the Goldfinch, in which the young leave at a late stage of growth, and at least 15 days in the Linnet and Twite, in which the young leave at an early stage. In all three the young begin to follow their parents at about three weeks of age. Only in the Bullfinch are precise details on development available for several broods of captive birds (Nicolai 1956). Such young leave the nest on the 16th or 17th day, begin to peck at food on the 20th,

PLATE 17. Bullfinches, in contrast to most cardueline finches, are quiet and secretive while breeding. The cock (*above right*) has his throat pouch swollen with food, shortly to be regurgitated to the young. The juvenile (*below*) is eating honeysuckle fruits. In this plumage it lacks the black cap and bib of the adults.

PLATE 18. Two vagrants to Britain. The Pine Grosbeak (*above*), at 9 inches long, is the largest of the European finches, and in its general shape and behaviour resembles the Bullfinch. This cock, at a nest in Swedish Lapland, has his throat pouch distended with food for the young.

The Scarlet Rosefinch (hen, *below*) breeds mainly in Asia, but is increasing and spreading from its strongholds in eastern Europe, hence the rising occurrence of the species in Britain.

make shelling movements by the 22nd, can fly after their parents by the 24th (when the body feathers are full grown), and are fully independent by the 35th day (when their flight and tail feathers are full grown). Thus, half the five-week period of parental dependence is spent in the nest and half out, more or less the same as in the Chaffinch (p. 144).

The development of crossbills

To the foregoing generalisations, the crossbills provide some exceptions. They lay 2–5 eggs, usually 3–4, so their mean clutch is slightly smaller than that of other European finches. Their incubation takes slightly longer (Table 22) and, in my experience with the Common Crossbill, sometimes begins with the first egg, leading to asynchronous hatching (p. 79). In the young of this last species, moreover, each stage of development takes about half as long again as in other finches. The nestlings usually begin to open their eyes at 5 days, begin to grow their feathers at 7 days, and leave the nest at 18–22 days, compared to 3, 5, and 13–18 days in other tree-nesting carduelines (Appendix 9). The crossbills leave at an equivalent stage of development, however, with their wings and tail about three-fifths grown and, at 30–35 grams, around three-quarters of adult weight (Ternovskij 1954). The longest recorded nestling periods (25 days) are about 60% longer than the shortest (16 days), excluding extremes where the young either starved to death or left prematurely, which may be set against the 20% variation in other carduelines.

After leaving the nest, some young crossbills were seen to be fed by their parents for at least 33 days and, assuming they spent 20 days in the nest, the total period of dependence was at least 53 days (Bailey, Niedrach & Baily 1953). This figure may be compared with that of Ternovskij, who found that captive young could extract and shell seeds by the 45th day. It might be thought that parental care was prolonged in this species to enable the young to develop their bills and special feeding behaviour (p. 107–8), but this is not so, because every stage of body growth is extended, both in the nest and out. The slow growth might instead be linked with the fact that most young are raised at seasons when days are short and cold, while the ability of the young to vary their growth so much is probably an adaptation to a food-supply which fluctuates unpredictably from day to day, as cones open and close with changing weather. Both the longest and shortest nestling periods recorded were from winter nests.

Predation on eggs and nestlings

Many finch nests are unsuccessful because predators take the eggs and nestlings. In my experience, species which nest in low bushes suffer most, probably because they fall prey to the greatest number of predators, including Stoats (*Mustela erminea*), Weasels (*M. nivalis*), various mice and voles, rats (*Rattus*), squirrels (*Sciurus*), Foxes (*Vulpes vulpes*), Crows (*Corvus corone*), Magpies (*Pica pica*), Jays (*Garrulus glandarius*), cats and small boys. Species which nest high are vulnerable chiefly from squirrels and the crow-family, but on the other hand, are more at the mercy of the wind, which sometimes tilts the nests and spills the contents. In addition, whatever the site, a few nests are deserted, and occasional eggs fail to hatch, either because they are infertile or because the embryo dies.

Some idea of the extent of predation on the eggs and young of three species which nest in bushes may be gained from Appendix 10. At the start of the season, 56–85% of all clutches started are taken, but the proportion declines as the season progresses. This is probably due to the gradual thickening of the vegetation in summer, which makes the nests more difficult for the predators to find. When these finches start nesting in spring the leaves are barely out, but later in summer the bushes themselves have thickened and also a dense stand of herbaceous plants secludes the site. One result of this seasonal decline in predation is that the recruitment of young into the population is slow during the early part of the season, but increases abruptly towards the end. The greater vulnerability of the Linnet compared to the Greenfinch nests, which is shown in Appendix 10, is probably because the former are at all times lower and less well hidden. In the Bullfinch the nests are throughout the season more successful in farmland than in woodland. This is probably because the nesting bushes are thicker in farmland, as a result of clipping, and also because one of the main predators, the Jay, is less numerous there. In all three species, more clutches than broods are taken, presumably because the most conspicuous nests are found quickly, so that those which escape till hatching have a good chance of surviving further.

Some readers might have seen Crows and Magpies robbing nests in their gardens. These predators find nests either by watching from some vantage point until the parents come or by systematically searching hedges and bushes. Outside gardens, predators are rarely seen in action, though much can be deduced from the signs they leave behind. In the Oxford district, three types of predation occurred on the eggs of the three species mentioned (Newton 1964c). Sometimes the eggs disappeared whole; at other times a few broken pieces of shell were left in the nest; and at others the shells were broken into tiny fragments and mixed up with the material lining the nest. The first type was often attributable to Jays, which often left some of their feathers behind; the second to Weasels, for I sometimes saw them in action; while the third was possibly due to rodents; though in all types other predators might also have been involved. Nestlings were also taken whole, again sometimes by Jays, and occasionally their remains were left in the nest, though with no hint of the culprits.

Weasels evidently search from the ground, because nests lost to them were always easily visible from below. Jays, on the other hand, search from above, and could often be seen hopping and hovering over the surface of bushes. Sometimes a Jay would force its way through thick bramble, and some of the best hidden nests were lost in this way when they held young, so perhaps the Jay had either seen the parents visiting the nest or heard the young calling.

Since so many nests fail to produce young, it is easy to overrate the importance of predation in limiting breeding success. But a repeat nest is usually started a few days after the loss of a previous one, so that a pair might lose several nests and still have a large part of the season left in which to rear successful broods. The Bullfinches studied by Nicolai (1956) in Germany usually reared two broods each year, but laid up to five clutches to get them. In captivity, if the eggs were taken away, the number sometimes rose to seven clutches a year. One bird, whose successive clutches were destroyed on completion, built seven nests and laid 32 eggs within 70 days (Newton 1964c). Either way, the number of young raised by each pair does not seem to be limited by the number of eggs that the hen can lay.

To summarise this chapter, most carduelines in Britain lay 3–6 eggs per nest, usually 4–5, but the crossbills lay 3–4. In some species the mean clutch-size declines through the season, in others it shows a mid-season peak. Incubation begins with the last egg or the last but one, except in crossbills and arctic-nesting Redpolls in which it sometimes begins with the first, so that the young hatch over several days. In four species which nest in low shrubs, the young leave at 12 days or less, in those which nest in tall bushes or trees at 13 days or more, the difference probably being linked with the greater vulnerability to predators of young in low nests. Young Bullfinches in captivity are fed by their parents for 35 days, the first 16–17 in the nest and the rest out. The growth of young Common Crossbills is much more variable than that of other carduelines, but usually takes half as long again, both in the nest and out. In three species which nest in shrubs, 56–85% of the early nests in one study were robbed by predators, but the proportion declined as the season progressed and cover thickened.

CHAPTER II

BREEDING SEASONS

THE lives of most finches, like those of many other birds, revolve around a regular succession of events which recur at about the same time every year: migration to summer quarters, breeding, moult, and migration to winter quarters. The timing of these events is geared to seasonal changes in food-supplies, breeding occurring at the favourable season, and other events around it (Lack 1954). Some species raise only one brood each year, others regularly raise two or even more successive broods; and those which raise only one will usually lay again if their first attempt is destroyed early in the season. The breeding season of a species appears to be the longest possible in the region in question, but the evidence for this view is circumstantial. First, in any one region the breeding seasons of the individual species coincide with the period in which their respective foods are most readily available. Second, in each species the breeding season is shorter towards the north where the growing season is itself shorter. Third, in some species the number of broods raised each year varies in accordance with annual variations in the food-supplies.

To take the first point, concerning the correlation between breeding and food, the Chaffinch and Brambling have short breeding seasons coinciding with the time the insects, on which they feed their young, are at a peak of abundance. In southern England, Chaffinches lay mainly over six weeks each year, and their young are in the nest when defoliating caterpillars are plentiful. Most pairs raise only one brood. On the other hand, the cardueline finches, which feed their young mainly on seeds, breed over more of the year than the preceding species, presumably because their food remains plentiful for longer. The Greenfinch, Linnet and Bullfinch eat a great variety of seeds and breed for almost the whole growing season, continually changing their diet as different plants come into seed. In southern England, they begin laying from late April, when fresh seeds first become available, and continue at least until mid-August, so that by the time their last young leave the nest, some five weeks later, plant-growth has almost stopped. In this period individual pairs would have time to raise four broods, but few (if any) breed for the full season and most lose at least one nest to predators. The European Goldfinch also has a long breeding season, but starts about a fortnight later than the others, reaching a peak in June and July, when most Compositae are seeding. The American Goldfinch has a more restricted diet than the European. It breeds mainly from July to September, when the seeds of thistles are plentiful, and raises 1–2 broods each year. It breeds later than almost all other birds in North America.

The shortening of the breeding season towards the north of the range occurs in most finches. To choose as examples two of the most widespread species, the Greenfinch and Linnet breed for seven months each year in southern Europe, for five months in middle Europe and Britain, and for three in northern Europe.

The tendency to breed for different periods each year, according to variations in food, is marked among the Siskins and Redpolls of northern Europe. Both species eat spruce seeds and, when the crop is good, start nesting soon after the cones have opened in early spring, but when it is poor the birds wait up to another two months until other foods have become plentiful. The same has been noted among Siskins and Citril Finches in the Alps. But the most striking correlations between the food-supply and the breeding season occur among crossbills, which reverse the usual trend in birds and nest mainly in late winter and early spring before the seeds have fallen from the cones. (Unlike the previous species, cross-bills can open closed cones.) They also breed at other seasons if food is plentiful and, in one region or another, have nested in every month (p. 76–8). On the other hand, they do not breed at all if their special foods are scarce. Taking these facts together, there is good circumstantial evidence that finches, like other birds, breed when their food is most abundant, and that the differences between species are linked with the differences in their diets.

The timing of breeding seasons

It seems reasonable to suppose that, within each species, only those indi-viduals which nest at a time when suitable food is readily available will manage to raise young and perpetuate themselves, whereas those which nest at other times will not. Hence, the availability of food for the young is probably the major factor through which the breeding season of each species has been evolved. Subsidiary factors are concerned at times, however, so that the birds may not always breed for the full period each year that young could be raised. At the start of the season, the hen may be unable to get enough food to form eggs early enough to allow her to produce young at the earliest time they could be raised. At the end of the season most species moult, and breeding is perhaps timed to cease before the period of abundant food has ended, thus enabling the birds to grow their feathers while food is still easy to get. If an individual breeds later than usual, however, its moult is delayed accordingly (p. 199).

In the past, confusion over the timing of breeding seasons has arisen through a failure to distinguish between the 'ultimate' and 'proximate' factors involved. Thus a bird may be said to breed in summer either because its food is most plentiful then or because its gonads are stimulated to develop under the lengthening and warming days of spring. All these factors may be involved, but the food-supply is the 'ultimate reason' for breeding at a certain time, while the daylength and temperature changes are the 'proximate' factors which bring the bird into breeding condition at an appropriate date (Baker 1938). Through natural selection, the seasonal maturation of the gonads will tend to become linked with whatever environmental factors provide the most reliable indication that breeding will shortly become practicable (Lack 1954). Hence, the proximate factors may differ from species to species and, in any one species, several proximate factors may be used, some of which, such as daylength, provide the long-term stimulus, while others, such as temperature or food, may facilitate minor adjustments to the prevailing conditions. Some proximate factors may have no direct importance to breeding except that the birds use them as cues to anticipate the season when nesting is likely to succeed. Other examples of 'ultimate' and 'proximate' regulating factors will be given later in this book in connection with moult and migration.

At most latitudes, daylength gives the best clue to date, because it is the only obvious environmental factor which changes in a regular and consistent manner from year to year. And there is ample evidence that birds react to it. About 60 species of wild birds have now been brought into breeding condition prematurely by exposing them to artificially long days in winter, and none has failed to respond (Lofts & Murton 1968). However, only the cocks can be brought into full breeding condition in this way: the hens also react, but their ovaries rarely develop more than a small amount, other stimuli, such as a mate and a nest, being needed to induce egg-laying.

The start of breeding

(a) *The influence of daylength*

Under natural conditions the gonads of finches begin to develop several months before nesting begins. Some change is evident in the testes of most British species as early as January, but the birds do not breed until April or May. The steady enlargement of the gonads during the intervening months is accompanied by other outward signs of reproductive development, such as a change in bill-colour and the beginnings of courtship. Normally the cocks reach full breeding condition first, and their testes contain sperm several weeks before the hens are ready to lay their eggs. Considering the demands of laying, the development of the hens probably depends more on food-supplies, at least in the late stages.

The effect of daylength on the breeding condition of finches has long been known from the Dutch practice of 'mewing', whereby captive birds were brought into breeding condition in autumn. The aim was to get them into full song and use them as decoys to catch the finches which migrate through Holland in October. About mid-May, when the birds had already reached breeding condition on natural daylengths, they were placed in almost complete darkness, which induced a premature regression of the gonads and an early moult. When the moult was complete around mid-August, the birds were again brought into the light, their gonads developed rapidly, and they began to sing strongly. But this continued only for the few weeks they were needed as decoys and then their gonads soon regressed as the autumn daylengths fell below the stimulatory level. This procedure was practised most commonly on Chaffinches, which were the main quarry of the bird-catchers, but also on cardueline finches. It has been repeated in the laboratory on Greenfinches, but here the traditional procedure was extended and after the gonads had regressed a second time in November, exposure to artificially long days in December caused the gonads to enlarge again in January/February. Thus, by appropriate treatment with light, three cycles of testes development were induced within one year (Damsté 1947).

In recent years, at least seven fringilline and cardueline species have been used in experiments involving light (Hinde 1965, King & Wales 1965, Hamner 1966). In at least three of these (Chaffinch, Brambling and Greenfinch), the early stages of testes development are influenced by light alone, and other factors, such as weather and food, operate at later stages, when the birds have reached their breeding areas. Furthermore, these same three species in Baltic Russia require different artificial daylengths to reach the same stage of gonad development. In the wild this would ensure that the Greenfinch was ready to breed before the Chaffinch, which lives in the same area, and that both species were ready before the migratory Brambling, which nests further north (Dolnik 1963). The same principle holds in different populations of the same species, northern Chaffinches for example requiring longer daylengths than southern ones to reach comparable gonad states (Koch & de Bont 1952). This explains why continental Chaffinches in Britain are still in flocks at a time when the local ones have taken up territories and started to nest. These differences are adaptive and ensure that birds from each population are brought into breeding condition at a date appropriate to the latitude at which they breed.

In the American House Finch (*Carpodacus mexicanus*) the response to light depends on stimulation being received during a sensitive stage of the day. Hamner (1963, 1964) gave these birds non-stimulatory six-hour light periods and alternated these with dark periods of different duration in different groups to give cycles of 12 (6l–6d), 24 (6l–18d), 36 (6l–30d), 48 (6l–42d), 60 (6l–54d) and 72 (6l–66d) hours' total duration. Testes growth occurred with cycles of 12, 36 and 60 hours, but not with the others, suggesting that there existed a 24-hour rhythmic sensitivity to light. He then kept more birds on the non-stimulatory 24, 48 and 72 hour cycles, and gave them an extra hour of light during the dark period. Providing this brief light period was given in appropriate relation to the underlying 24 hour rhythm of the bird, testes growth occurred. This was at 12 or 36 hours after the start of the main light period, but not 24 or 48 hours after. In this way, testes growth occurred in birds getting a total of only seven hours of light in every 24, 48 or 72 hours, whereas under natural conditions 10–12 hours of light per day are needed. Evidence for a circadian-based light response has also been found in some North American buntings, and in the European Greenfinch (Murton, Lofts & Westwood 1970).

(b) *The influence of temperature and food*

The pattern of egg-laying in Chaffinches through the season is strongly correlated with fluctuations in temperature, as shown by the nest-records of the British Trust for Ornithology (Newton 1964a). In most years in southern England these birds begin laying in the second week of April, but in the warm spring of 1957 they began three weeks earlier than usual and in the cold spring of 1960 one week later. The threshold temperature that has to be passed in early April before laying will begin then is about 45°F (7°C), but this threshold is higher for March and lower for late April. The subsequent pattern of laying varies considerably from year to year, again in accordance with temperature changes (Fig. 48). The sudden onset and narrow peak of egg-laying in 1952 was associated with a steep rise in spring warmth, and the steady onset and broad peak in 1956 with a slow rise. For much of the four seasons shown, each increase in laying was preceded by a rise in temperature and each decline in laying by a drop (see especially 1955). The birds evidently took about five days to react to a change, though once an egg had been laid, the clutch was completed regardless.

From information of this type, one cannot be certain whether the birds are responding directly to temperature as such, or to some other factor, such as the food-supply, which itself varies with temperature. Thus, the caterpillars on which the Chaffinches feed at this time also develop more rapidly in warm weather than in cold, as do the young leaves on which the caterpillars are in turn feeding, at least in the early part of the season. Also, warmth reduces the energy needs of the birds themselves, making more of the food they eat available for egg-production.

The start of nesting also varies by up to a month, according to weather, in certain cardueline finches, namely the Greenfinch, Linnet and Bullfinch. Like the Chaffinch in southern England, these species began unusually early in 1957 and unusually late in 1960. The variation was less marked in the Goldfinch, which does not anyway start until later in the season. Again, however, the birds might react directly to their food-supply, rather than to temperature as such, for the herbaceous plants from which they feed also fruit earlier in warm springs than in cold ones. In this case food would act as a proximate, as well as an ultimate timing factor.

PLATE 19. Bullfinches (*left*) are renowned in Britain for their attacks on buds, but some fruit varieties are sought more than others. 'Conference' pear (*below left*) is especially favoured, so in many springs bears fewer blossoms than the avoided 'Comice' variety (*below right*).

PLATE 20. An extreme example of Bullfinch damage to pear trees. *Above*, a normal 'Conference' tree in full blossom; *below*, a similar tree on the same day whose flower buds have nearly all been eaten.

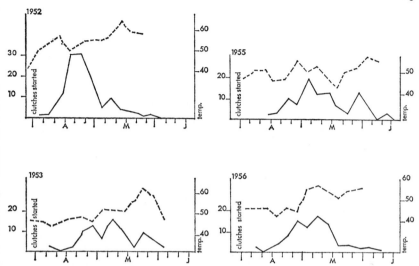

FIG. 48. Egg-laying in the Chaffinch in relation to air-temperatures (Fahrenheit) during different years in southern England (from Newton 1964a). Unbroken line: % clutches started; broken line: mean temperature.

No doubt exists in the Siskins and Redpolls of Fenno-Scandia as to whether food or temperature has the biggest effect on nesting dates, for as mentioned, if food is plentiful, they will start up to two months earlier than usual, whatever the weather. In one year, when the spruce crop was good, some Redpoll nests were found in March and April, when snow was half a metre deep and temperatures were down to −20°C (Witt-Strömer, Ingritz & Magnusson 1956). In most years, however, neither species begin before mid-May. Presumably, their gonads grow to a certain stage in early spring and complete their development only when food becomes sufficiently plentiful, though whether this applies to both sexes or just to the hen is not known. In crossbills, which nest in any month if food is plentiful, and hence under a wide range of temperatures and daylengths, food has evidently assumed the major proximate control of breeding, though the gonads of these birds are not completely unresponsive to change in daylength (Tordoff & Dawson 1965).

Abundant food might be expected to influence finches in at least two ways, either directly by enabling the hen to form her eggs, or indirectly by enabling both sexes to spend less time on feeding and more on courtship. Work on canaries has shown that those hens which get a lot of stimulation from their mates lay earlier than others (Hinde 1967). By both means therefore, the date of laying could be brought into closer synchrony with the food-supply, but this is speculative.

The interval between successive nests

In most finches about five weeks elapse between the date a clutch is started and the young are ready to leave. In captivity, cardueline finches normally begin their second nest a few days after the young have left the first, and the cock takes over most of the feeding of the first brood. The same has been noted in a few species in the wild. In one study of American Goldfinches, the interval between the first egg of successive clutches was remarkably uniform. In ten cases it varied from 32 to 36 days, the first egg in the second nest usually appearing 5–6 days (range 3–10) after the young had left the first. The interval was 6–14 days when a second nest followed the failure of the first (Stokes 1950). Likewise, in a pair of Bullfinches which raised three broods, the first eggs in successive clutches were laid 33 and 35 days apart (Newton 1964c).

Sometimes there is more overlap between broods. One pair of Linnets started a second nest when the young in the first were only four days old, and when these young flew on 24 June, the second nest contained three eggs. The second brood flew on 24 July, so this pair had built two nests and reared two broods within 60 days (Oakes 1952). At the other extreme, Common Crossbills have been recorded nesting twice in one year in captivity, with a long interval between. One pair raised one brood in January and laid another infertile clutch in April, and a second pair raised one brood in January and another in June (Birch 1968). In the wild it would be difficult to record long intervals between successive nests of cardueline finches, especially if the nests were in widely different places, but from the details just given, nests usually seem to follow in swift succession.

The end of breeding

A good deal is known about what starts breeding in birds, but practically nothing about what stops it. Under experimental conditions, the gonads of many birds regress and the moult begins if daylength is reduced, either gradually or suddenly (Voitkevich 1966), but among the finches only the Greenfinch has been put to a test of this sort (Damsté 1947). The adaptive value in such a response in the wild is that the birds are prevented from starting another nest at a time of year when they have little chance of raising young. Chaffinches stop breeding before mid-summer while daylength is still increasing, and presumably each species has evolved a response to whichever daylengths end breeding at an ecologically appropriate time (Lofts & Murton 1968). Under natural conditions, however, daylength cannot be the only factor terminating the breeding of finches, for a species may finish on widely different dates in different years, with considerable individual variation. In all known cases where breeding was unusually prolonged, the food at the time was unusually plentiful. This is perhaps most marked in species which eat tree-seeds and raise extra broods in years when the crops are good. Thus, in most years Common Cross-bills in northern Europe finish breeding in April or May, when the seeds have fallen from the spruce cones, but in years when pine seeds (on which they next feed) are plentiful, the birds continue into June or July (p. 76–7). Likewise, in five out of six years, in the Oxford district, the last young Bullfinches of the year fledged in late August or early September, but in 1962 in early October. In this last year the birds fed in late summer mainly on the seeds of birch and privet, which were much more abundant than usual. Finally, during five years in Northumberland, Lesser Redpolls finished breeding ten days later, on average, in the best birch year than in the worst, and in other years on intermediate dates (Evans 1969).

Breeding is also extended occasionally in species which feed from herbaceous plants. In southern England, more Linnets and Goldfinches than usual breed into August and September in warm dry years, when their food-plants are more prolific. This was especially marked in the exceptional summer of 1959, and lead to huge populations of these species in the autumn of that year (Williamson & Spencer 1960). But in these species the abundance of food seems merely to increase the proportion of birds that breed late, without appreciably extending the season of the population as a whole. Either way it is clear that, while the end of breeding in individual finches might be controlled partly by daylength, food is also involved.

Breeding cycles at different latitudes

From the foregoing, it seems that in each species the timing and duration of breeding each year is closely correlated with the prevailing food-supply. When the season is long, however, few pairs breed for the maximum time possible, for individuals vary greatly in the dates they begin and end their breeding. Thus Greenfinches in southern England may lay eggs between mid-April and mid-August, so that the last young fledge around mid-September, giving time for four broods in all. But the onset of breeding is spread over at least six weeks and the end over at least thirteen, as may be deduced from the pattern of egg-laying, from analyses of gonads and analyses of moult. Clearly, different pairs must be widely out of phase with one another in their breeding cycles, but it is not known whether the first to start are also the first to finish. In captive Greenfinches, Hinde (1954) found that most pairs raised one or two broods each year, and that second broods were more frequent from pairs that started early; but one pair raised four broods.

So far, the American Goldfinch is the only species studied in detail in which the birds were marked so that they could be identified individually. Even in this species, in which the breeding season lasts only 12 weeks, there was apparently no time of year when the entire population was breeding at once, for the latest birds started after the earliest had finished. Both the start and end of breeding was spread over six weeks, and only 15% of the birds studied raised two broods and bred for the full season (Stokes 1950).

In places where breeding is possible for only a short period each year, the cycles of individual pairs are more closely synchronised. This is shown by the Redpolls breeding on the tundra of Baffin Island at ($66\frac{1}{2}°$N), which is free of snow for only ten weeks each year (Wynne-Edwards 1952, Watson 1957). The birds arrive in late May or early June, when less than one-tenth of the ground has cleared. Usually they are already paired and begin nesting immediately. To save time many birds add a lining to an old nest, rather than building a completely new one, and most have eggs within a week of arriving. Some nests fail as a result of predation and other causes, but nonetheless all the young of the season fledge within four weeks. After breeding, the birds moult and move south when the first heavy snow falls around mid-August. Hence, in this short season, the activities of different pairs are well synchronised.

In species with long breeding seasons, it is puzzling that many pairs breed for only a small part of the time that young could be raised, for in any environment, natural selection might be expected to favour those individuals which bred for as long as possible and raised most young. Perhaps, however, breeding in some way exhausts the birds to such an extent that this alone prevents most of them from raising as many young as the season would permit. If so, selection would not operate strongly in favour of all birds starting and finishing at the same time, and could explain the spread in individual cycles. Bullfinches lose weight while feeding young, and by the time they finish breeding in late summer, they are lighter than at any other time (p. 242). Thus, whether a pair started another nest might depend on how much weight they had lost after raising earlier broods. The fact that breeding is prolonged in years when seeds are plentiful means that food is involved, but whether this acts by slowing the weight-loss or protein-loss of breeding birds or in some other way is not known.

In this chapter, I have been concerned chiefly with the influence of the environment on breeding, but even in artificially constant conditions the gonads of some birds have shown autonomous cycles of activity, though these were shorter and less regular than normal (Marshall 1959). No experiments have been done to test the importance (or otherwise) of such an 'internal rhythm' in regulating the annual cycles of finches, but it is well to remember that environmental factors may be only part of the controlling influence.

To summarise this chapter, finches, like other birds, breed at those seasons when food suitable for rearing young is most readily available, and differences in breeding seasons between species are linked with differences in their food-supplies. The gonads of most finch-species begin to develop under the influence of increasing daylengths several weeks before nesting will begin. They complete their development mainly under the influence of other factors: in some species food is important, but in others it is not yet possible to tell whether food or temperature has the major influence. In the crossbills, food has assumed the main proximate control of breeding. In species with long breeding seasons, few (if any) pairs breed for the maximum time possible; different pairs start at different dates and breed for different periods of time. In species with short breeding seasons, all pairs start and end at about the same dates, and their individual nesting activities are well synchronised.

CHAPTER 12

THE MOULT

ONCE a year, after breeding, adult finches replace their feathers. The onset of moult is accompanied by striking changes in the birds' behaviour, and imposes on them a special way of life. All the various sexual activities which have dominated the birds' lives during the preceding months cease within a matter of days. The birds become silent, skulking and lethargic; they avoid long flights and spend large parts of each day resting in cover. At the same time the gonads regress, and the various sex hormones, which have controlled breeding, are largely replaced in the blood by other hormones, which are involved in moult. The thyroid hormone, in particular, raises the general metabolic rate of the bird and controls the growth of the new feathers. The latter are fed from the blood stream; and the skin, which for much of the year is thin and loose, becomes heavily vascularised. Gradually, and in regular sequence, the new feathers emerge, and the process of replacement continues over several weeks.

Regular moults are necessary in birds because, after a time, the feathers become worn and less effective for flight and insulation. (The alternative, of producing feathers that would last the life of the bird, would entail the incorporation of so much more material into their structure, that the flexibility and lightness essential for the proper functioning of the feathers, would be lost.) In all species of birds, the moult is seasonal, and in most it occurs outside the breeding and migration seasons, yet when food is still sufficiently plentiful to support the growth of feathers. The food-supply of the bird, and the other events in the annual cycle, are thus the 'ultimate' factors timing the moult, but 'proximate' factors, such as daylength, are again involved in initiating the growth of feathers at an appropriate date.

A bird's feathers are grouped into 'tracts' which, for the most part, run along the length of the body and are separated by areas of bare skin (Fig. 49). When fully grown, the feathers spread over the whole body, but the tracts can easily be seen in nestlings when the feathers have just emerged. At this age all the feathers grow at about the same time. At moults later in life, however, replacement begins at a slightly different time in different tracts, and within each tract the feathers are renewed in regular sequence. Typically, when one feather is partly grown, the next is shed and so on through the series. The moulting bird thus has patches of growing feathers at several points on its body. The advantage of such sequential replacement is that the bird is never left naked or flightless. New feathers will also grow out of season if existing ones are

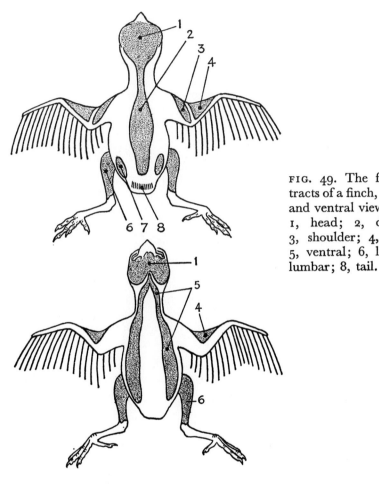

FIG. 49. The feather tracts of a finch, dorsal and ventral views.

1, head; 2, dorsal; 3, shoulder; 4, alar; 5, ventral; 6, leg; 7, lumbar; 8, tail.

knocked out accidentally, but the mere breakage of feathers will not result in fresh growth.

At first, each growing feather is encased in a protective sheath containing blood; but when about one-third grown the feather breaks through the tip of the sheath and, as growth continues, the sheath shrinks and finally comes away just after the feather has reached full length. Within a few days the new feather hardens, its connection with the blood-supply is severed, and from then on it is a 'dead' structure, held in place by muscles surrounding its base. Here it remains until the next moult, when the muscles relax and the growth of a new feather begins below.

In all the finches, the first feathers to be shed when the adults start moulting are the innermost primaries of the wings, and the last to complete their growth are either the outermost primaries or the innermost secondaries. All other feathers, both of the wings and the body, are replaced in the meantime (Table 17). The nine large primaries of each wing are moulted in order from the innermost out to the wing-tip; and when the first few have reached full-length, the moult of the six secondaries begins with the outermost (i.e. that one next to the innermost primary) and spreads inwards to the body. The two wings moult in phase. The twelve large tail feathers are replaced in pairs from the central pair outwards. And among the body feathers, moult begins along the centre of each feather tract and spreads out (Newton 1966a).

At the same season as the adult finches replace their feathers, the juveniles undergo a partial (post-juvenile) moult, replacing in the same sequence as the adults the feathers of the body and some small feathers of the wings and tail. The large flight and tail feathers, the primary coverts, some of the secondary coverts, and a few other feathers, acquired when the bird became fledged, are kept for another year. Hence, in the first year, the plumage consists of two generations of feathers, some acquired in the nest and others at the post-juvenile moult. The small wing-feathers that are retained through this moult are of characteristic colour, and provide a means of distinguishing in the hand first-year from older birds. This holds in all species. However, occasional Goldfinches hatched early in the season in Britain replace all their feathers, including the large wing and tail ones, and this appears to be regular among juveniles of this species in Spain, Sicily and some other parts of southern Europe.

The food-requirements of moult

Some captive Chaffinches were found to use more than 25% more oxygen during moult than at other times, which presumably reflected a corresponding change in their food-demand (Koch & de Bont 1944). The exact nutritional demands of moult have still not been assessed for any bird, however, though an attempt can now be made to define these needs. To begin with, the feathers themselves consist almost exclusively of keratins, which are proteins containing exceptionally large amounts of the sulphur amino-acids, cystine and methionine. It is chiefly these materials which make feathers so remarkably durable and resilient for their weight. But these two acids are much more concentrated in feather keratins than in other proteins, so a great deal more protein is needed by birds in moult than one might have thought, simply to get enough of these two limiting acids.

In the Bullfinch, which I have studied in detail, the adults produce about two grams of feathers during moult and the juveniles about 1.5 grams. As this is equivalent to 32% and 25% respectively of their total dry protein contents at the start of moult, the feathers cannot be formed merely by the degradation and redistribution of proteins already in the

Table 17. The sequence of moult in finches.
The solid line indicates that all birds caught at that stage can be expected to have the feathers concerned in moult, the dotted line only some of the birds. (From Newton 1966a, 1969b and unpublished.)

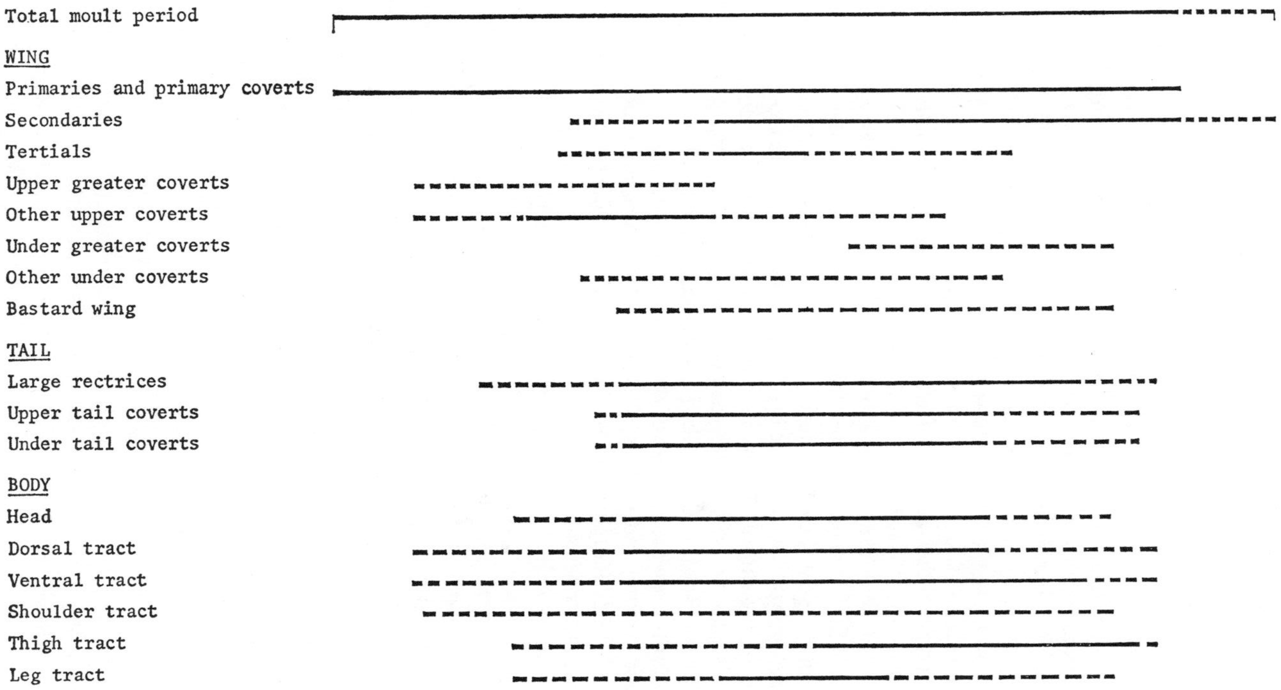

Total moult period

WING

Primaries and primary coverts

Secondaries

Tertials

Upper greater coverts

Other upper coverts

Under greater coverts

Other under coverts

Bastard wing

TAIL

Large rectrices

Upper tail coverts

Under tail coverts

BODY

Head

Dorsal tract

Ventral tract

Shoulder tract

Thigh tract

Leg tract

body, but must come chiefly from food eaten at the time. The moult in adults lasts about 12 weeks and in juveniles about eight, so the mean rate of feather synthesis in both is about 27 milligrams per day. It must at some times greatly exceed this, however, and at other times be almost negligible, according to the number of feathers in growth (Newton 1968c). And feather growth, like all chemical syntheses, also requires energy.

For a successful moult, moreover, food must be available continuously, because shortage on only one day is enough to cause the formation on the growing feathers of 'fault bars', where the rachis is pinched and the barbs on the vane are deficient in barbules. The feathers are later liable to break at such points, so that at worst even temporary food-shortage may be sufficient to impede the bird's flight for the next year. Fault bars occur rarely on the feathers of all species of finches, chiefly in birds moulting late.

The requirements of moult are not set merely by the needs of feather growth, however, for the birds also lose more heat than usual at this time. Not only do they have less insulation, but warm blood flows continuously through the bases of the growing feathers. Anyone who has handled birds in heavy moult might have noticed how hot they feel, and this results chiefly from the greater ease with which heat is lost from the body then. In the Bullfinch, the deep body-temperature also rises slightly during moult, from an average of 40.7°C to 41.7°C, though at all times the variation among individuals is considerable (Newton 1968c). To maintain a high body temperature with increased heat-loss requires a further increase in food consumption, unless the bird is to lose weight.

Nevertheless, the demands of moult are probably small compared to those of breeding. Whereas an adult Bullfinch has to collect during a moult of 12 weeks enough extra protein to grow two grams of feathers, a pair of birds when breeding must collect enough food in only five weeks to support the growth of a whole brood. This involves the production of about 60–80 grams of birds, of which 8–12 grams are feathers – and all this in addition to the needs of the adults themselves. Hence, Bullfinches could moult at levels of protein availability that would not permit them to raise young. The same holds for other finches, so it is no wonder that they breed at the most favourable season, when food is plentiful and days are long and warm, and that they moult later in the year when these conditions are deteriorating.

The timing of adult moult

Normally, individual adult finches start moulting at about the time that their last young of the year reach independence,* and after completing

---

* As judged by examining individual breeding pairs and by the dates that young appear in the population. In the European Goldfinch in Australia, however, Middleton (1969) has shown that some adults shed their first feathers at the laying stage of the last nest.

moult the migrant species begin their journeys. But because different individuals stop breeding on widely different dates, there is considerable overlap between the breeding and moulting seasons of the population as a whole, and later in the year between moult and migration (Newton 1968a). The moult of each finch is not triggered by the end of breeding alone, because birds that have not bred (unmated adults and juveniles) moult at the same season as adults that have bred. Evidently some environmental factor is involved in initiating moult at a particular season (though this may serve only to regulate an intrinsic rhythm within the bird – see p. 192).

In some bird-species this outside factor is daylength, the artificial manipulation of which will induce a moult at the wrong season (Stresemann & Stresemann 1966, Voitkevitch 1966). Experiments have suggested that different species have evolved a response to different daylengths, so as to begin their moult at the season which is ecologically best for them. Some species start to moult before mid-summer under an increasing daylength, others after mid-summer under a decreasing daylength, while others start around mid-summer, and are probably stimulated by long days as such. Furthermore, those species which normally moult after mid-summer will moult more quickly if the experimental daylengths are reduced rapidly than if they are reduced slowly (Voitkevitch 1966).

Among the finches, only the Greenfinch has been subjected to a test of this sort (Damsté 1947); but circumstantial evidence from field studies suggests that daylength regulates the moult of other species too. Thus, in all finches, the earliest birds to moult start on around the same date each year, despite pronounced annual differences in environmental conditions at the time. Such constancy of timing could be brought about only by daylength, since this is the only external factor which varies in a consistent manner from year to year. As mentioned, however, the effect of daylength in each individual is modified by the date it finishes breeding, the bird delaying its moult accordingly. Exceptions to this general rule include the Scarlet Rosefinch, which migrates soon after breeding and delays its moult until it has reached winter quarters, and the crossbills, discussed later.

(a) *Differences between species*

Under the moult enquiry of the British Trust for Ornithology, any ringer who catches a bird in moult can record the details on a standard card, which he then returns to a central collection. From these cards, the timing and duration of moult in different species can be calculated, as shown for the finches in Appendix 11 '(Newton 1968a, 1969b). The limits of the moulting season of each species seem to remain fairly constant from year to year, though regional and annual differences exist in the number of birds moulting at different dates within a season (cf. Bullfinch, discussed later). Also, for most species, it is possible to get from the cards only the average duration of moult in the adults, and not the range of variation, though the figures available are enough for comparisons.

The moulting seasons of all the British finches last longer than their respective breeding seasons. This is partly because individual birds take so long to moult, and partly because they vary so much in the date they start. In the Greenfinch, individual adults take an average of 12 weeks to replace their feathers and may begin any time during a 13-week period: as a result, moulting birds are present in the population for about 25 weeks each year, and the earliest to moult finish about a week before the latest begin. But the Greenfinch is extreme, and the moulting seasons of other finches are somewhat shorter.

Nearly all the British finches experience the same broad changes in the environment, with food abundant in summer and scarce in winter; and differences in the timing and duration of their moults are related chiefly to differences in their breeding and migratory habits. The Chaffinch has a short breeding season, finishes earlier than the carduelines, and also moults earlier, the majority of adults starting some time between late May and early July. Among the carduelines, the Greenfinch and Bullfinch, which are resident in Britain, start mainly in August and September and take about 12 weeks. The remaining species, which are partial migrants, start earlier than the residents or moult faster. On average, the Goldfinch takes 11 weeks to moult, the Siskin, Linnet and Twite 10 weeks, and the Lesser Redpoll 8 weeks. In consequence, most individuals of these migrant species finish their moults by late September or October and are ready to depart then, while most individuals of the resident species are still in moult.

The distinction between residents and migrants is true only as a general tendency, however, and in both groups more individuals prolong their breeding and delay moult in years when seeds are plentiful. This is especially marked in the Bullfinch (Newton 1966a). In five years near Oxford, the start of moult in the population I studied was spread over eight weeks from mid-July. But in 1962, when food was unusually abundant, some individuals continued breeding into October, and the start of moult in the population was then spread over 13 weeks from mid-July. Birds breeding later than mid-August sometimes started to moult a few days before their last young had left the nest. These parents, when caught in mist nets, could often be recognised by the presence of food in the throat pouches, and showed a different pattern of moult from adults without young. Not only were their primaries shed more slowly to begin with, but the growth of new body feathers was also delayed. Such birds provided a striking contrast to those apparently without young, in which the body moult began in turn in various tracts and proceeded at a steady rate. This overlap in late season between breeding and moult was comparatively slight, however, and the main finding was that a bird which was still breeding would normally postpone its moult, even though the start of the moulting season was well passed.

The figures in Appendix 11 give only the average duration of moult in different species and in those studied in detail the individual variation is considerable. Thus, adult Bullfinches in southern England take, on average, 12 weeks to moult, but periods of 10–13 weeks have been recorded for individuals, the shorter periods being mainly from birds moulting late in the season. Among captive birds, differences in the time taken to moult resulted from variations in the number of days between the shedding of successive feathers, rather than in the rates at which the feathers grew. In fact, equivalent flight feathers of different birds took about the same time to grow, whatever the total moult period, the outer ones always taking longer than the inner (Newton 1967a). The same trends have been found in some other species (Appendix 12).

(b) *Latitudinal differences*

Among song-birds in general, individuals tend to moult more rapidly and more in phase with one another as one moves northwards into arctic regions. Also, the moult in different body tracts bears a more fixed relationship to wing moult in the north than further south. These trends are associated with the shorter season and with the greater synchrony in the annual cycles of individuals at high latitudes (p. 192). What few data are available for finches support these general trends. Thus, House Finches resident at 38°N in California, take 13–17 weeks to moult, and start any time in an 18-week period (Michener & Michener 1940), which may be compared to 12 and 13 weeks respectively in the most extreme British species at 51–57°N. Moreover, the same trends are slightly evident in different populations of a single species, for Redpolls in Britain take, on average, a few days less to moult than do those in northern Norway (Evans, Elton & Sinclair 1967).

The timing of post-juvenile moult

While the young of all finches are known to moult at the same season as the adults, only the Bullfinch and Chaffinch have been studied in detail. In these species, the individual young take less time to moult than the adults, which is reasonable since the young replace fewer feathers. Also, the young which are raised late in the season moult at an earlier age and more rapidly than do young raised early. These are adaptations which help the late young to complete their moult before the winter sets in. To give the details, young Bullfinches raised in May and June start to moult at ten weeks of age and take nine weeks, young raised in July start at six weeks of age and take eight weeks, while young raised in August start at four weeks of age and take seven weeks. When these last young start to moult their body feathers, they are still being fed by their parents, and their first flight and tail feathers are still not fully grown. Likewise, in the Chaffinch in the Baltic region, the young from early nests start before mid-July at six weeks of age and take about six weeks to moult, whereas those from the latest nests start around mid-August at five weeks of age and take about five weeks to moult. Thus, despite a spread of about six weeks in date of onset, all the young finish within a period of less than three weeks (Dolnik & Blyumental 1967). Similar trends have been noted in other song-birds and probably hold in other finches.

The moult of crossbills

Since crossbills breed mainly in early spring, one might also expect them to moult earlier than other finches. This seems not usually to be so, however, for most birds moult within the period mid-July to mid-November, each adult taking at least 12 weeks. But just as these birds may breed outside the main breeding season, so they may moult outside the main moulting season. Adults replacing feathers have been found in every month except January–March, and juveniles in every month except January.

During the main moulting season, in late summer and autumn, adults may often be found breeding and moulting simultaneously. This occurred on a large scale after an invasion in Montana in 1954, when many birds shot in the first half of August were replacing feathers, yet had enlarged gonads, while the hens also had active oviducts and brood-patches (Kemper 1959). At other times of year I can find no instance of crossbills breeding and moulting concurrently. Indeed, in early summer, records exist of birds starting to moult at about the time the young leave the nest, as in other finches. Among some captive birds kept by Tordoff & Dawson (1965), some pairs finished breeding and started to moult in early summer, while others continued breeding till mid-summer and delayed their moult accordingly.

The relationship between moult and migration in the crossbills is also complicated (Newton 1970b). Usually, most movement on the regular range would have ceased by the time the birds began to moult, but irruptive movements outside the regular range, which occur in some years, may continue into October or even December, into and beyond the moult period. In some irrupting adults caught on Fair Isle in 1953, the moult of the flight feathers had apparently stopped, for the birds had some old feathers and some new but none in growth. Among 54 birds caught between 19 June and 14 September, 3 were moulting, 37 had not started and 14 showed arrested moult. Hence, under these circumstances, it seems that moult is sometimes suppressed, though more information is needed.

The post-juvenile moult is partial, as in other finches, so that first-year birds may be distinguished by the buff secondary coverts which are retained. Juveniles from the spring and summer broods normally moult in autumn, like the adults. But those from autumn broods may start to moult in February, and while some such birds finish in June, most take longer at this season than in autumn, at least to judge from the number of feathers in growth.

The variation in the colour of adult cock crossbills has attracted much comment. Most are predominantly reddish, but some are orange, bronze or yellowish-green, while others contain a mixture of feathers of different colours. Yellow plumage is more common among first-year than among older cocks (Ticehurst 1915), but particular individuals may change from red to yellow or vice versa, according partly to when they moult. Most cocks which moult before the start of July grow yellowish feathers; most which moult after this date grow red ones; while many of those whose moults overlap this period end up part yellow and part red, sometimes with both colours on individual feathers (Weber 1953, Newton, unpublished). This applies to all age-groups, and the more frequent occurrence of yellow among yearlings might be because more juveniles than adults moult in early summer. The transition occurs at the same time as the birds change from feeding on old cones to new, so perhaps diet is involved. In captivity, moreover, all cocks turn yellow whenever they moult, a trait which can be remedied by feeding them at this time the pigment rhodoxanthin (Völker 1957).

Feather wear

Some idea of the rate at which the feathers abrade can be gained by comparing the weight of the plumage of birds caught just after the moult in October with that of birds caught just before the next moult the following July, as is shown for the Bullfinch in Appendix 13. In this species, the large flight and tail feathers lose very little weight over the year, but the soft body plumage loses one-third in weight between the end of one moult and the start of the next.

In most finches the gradual abrasion of the feathers changes a bird's appearance towards the breeding season. When the feathers are first formed in autumn they have greyish or buff tips, which gradually wear off to expose the colour below, thus enabling the birds to don a special breeding dress without the need to moult. This is most pronounced in the cock Brambling, in which the head and back turn from buff to black in summer, and in the Linnet and other *Acanthis* finches in which the red patches become exposed or intensified. By the same process the colours of most other species become clearer and richer in summer, more so in the cocks than in the hens. The American Goldfinch is the only cardueline finch known to me to achieve a special breeding plumage by a spring moult of the body feathers, rather than by abrasion, though one American race of the Common Crossbill has been reported to replace the feathers of its head and throat in spring (Tordoff 1952).

To summarise this chapter, in each adult of most finch-species, breeding, moult and migration follow in swift succession. But different adults finish breeding on widely different dates, so that the breeding and moulting seasons of a population overlap by several weeks, as do moult and migration later in the year. Individuals of migrant species moult more rapidly (8–11 weeks in different species) than do individuals of resident species (12 weeks). In all the British finches (except crossbills), the moulting season of the population lasts longer than the breeding season, 14–25 weeks, according to species. The 'ultimate' factors timing the moult include the food-supply and the other events in the annual cycle. The main 'proximate' factor is probably daylength, but its effect is modified in the adults by the date that breeding ends, and in the juveniles by the date of hatching. In at least two species, those young born late in the season also moult later, but more rapidly and at an earlier age, than young born early. Crossbills moult mainly in late summer and autumn, but also at other times, and during the main moulting season individuals may also breed. In many species abrasion changes their colour towards the spring, allowing them to attain a special breeding dress without moulting.

CHAPTER 13

MIGRATION

FOR our purpose, migration can be defined as a large-scale seasonal movement of birds twice each year between their breeding and wintering areas. It is distinguished from purely local movements by the greater length of journey and the fact that it takes place in fixed directions. It has been studied chiefly by observations (made directly or with radar), by analyses of the recoveries of ringed birds, and by physiological studies in the laboratory. Migration may be seen in progress almost anywhere in Europe, but over low ground the birds are so spread out that it is often difficult to realise that it is taking place. Hence, the birds are best seen at coastal headlands, mountain passes, or other places where they are concentrated. Good places in Britain for watching the migrations of finches include Spurn Point in Yorkshire, where the birds are channelled along a narrow peninsula, the coast of Norfolk, and the various headlands on the south coast, such as Beachy Head or Dungeness. At all of these several thousands of birds may pass each hour at the height of the season. But much larger numbers than in Britain can be seen at some continental stations in autumn; for example, at the Swedish Observatory at Falsterbo, where up to half a million Chaffinches have been seen in a single morning. Movements can also be observed near the tops of high mountains, like the Alps or Pyrenees, where finches have been seen at over 2,500 metres altitude (Lack 1953).

Every species of European finch migrates in at least some parts of its range, and the longest movements are performed by those Chaffinches, Bramblings and Siskins which travel more than 3,500 kilometres each way between northern Europe and Iberia. As regards Britain, most of the Greenfinches and Bullfinches which breed here remain throughout the year; the majority of Goldfinches and Linnets move out to wintering grounds in France and Iberia; and the majority of Lesser Redpolls move from northern Britain into southern Britain and neighbouring parts of the continent. On the other hand, large numbers of Chaffinches, Bramblings and Siskins enter Britain each autumn, chiefly from Norway and Sweden.

Evolutionary aspects

It was once supposed that migration originated when northern birds were driven southwards in the last Ice Age and later returned through tradition or ancestral memory, and that present migration routes retrace the path of recolonisation from glacial refuges. But this view is too far-fetched to explain so fundamental and diverse a process extending from Poles to Tropics, and a more rational explanation must be sought.

To begin with, migration might be expected to occur in those species which survive better if they move out for the winter than if they stay in their breeding areas for the whole year (Lack 1954). The usual reason why the breeding areas become unsuitable during part of the year is lack of food. This is the 'ultimate' reason for migration. But it does not follow that food-shortage provides the immediate stimulus for the birds' departure. On the contrary, many birds react to 'proximate' environmental factors in such a way that they leave their breeding areas well before food becomes scarce there, and while it is still sufficiently plentiful for them to lay down fat for the journey. The situation presents obvious parallels with the timing of breeding and moult, discussed in Chapters 11 and 13.

In many bird populations some individuals migrate and the rest do not. Such 'partial' migration is usually attributed to a balance of advantages: in some years the birds that leave survive best and in other years those that stay, so that in the long term both types persist in the population (Lack 1954). This fits the fact that in many species the proportion of birds migrating is lower in areas where the winter is less severe. Thus many finch-species are completely resident in the south of their range and completely migratory in the north, but in between are partial migrants. Among the birds from a single population, the strength of the migratory tendency is partly innate (p. 212), but other factors also influence the behaviour of individuals. In some finches, for example, particular birds are more likely to migrate in their first than in later years, while in other species the hens leave in greater numbers or move further than the cocks (p. 24).

The location of the wintering areas, like the migratory habit itself, can also be explained by natural selection, the birds from each population wintering wherever they can reach and survive best. Imagine that the birds from a certain breeding area have innate tendencies to fly in particular directions at migration time and back again in spring, but that these directions differ from bird to bird. Some birds will then reach suitable areas and survive to breed again in large numbers, others will reach less suitable areas and survive in small numbers, and yet others will reach unsuitable areas and die. Thus only those with appropriate migratory habits will perpetuate themselves, and in this way the wintering area of a population will be determined. The suitability of an area in turn depends both on the environmental conditions there and on the distribution of other populations, for birds of the same species from different breeding areas tend to segregate in winter quarters. The ringing recoveries of Goldfinches and Linnets, for example, show that different breeding stocks winter in different parts of Iberia, those from the western parts of Europe mainly in the west of the peninsula and vice versa.

The south and west of Europe, where the climate is mild or oceanic, provide the chief wintering areas for finches breeding over the whole continent. Hence the main direction of migration is more or less southwesterly in autumn and the reverse in spring, with two exceptions. First, the Scarlet Rosefinch, which has colonised Europe from the east, has retained its old migration route southeast to Asia. Second, most of the Redpolls of Fenno-Scandia also move southeast in autumn, probably because they find more birch seed in this direction than by moving south or southwest. They also find lower temperatures than if they had remained on their breeding range, so here is a clear case in which food is more important than climate in determining a wintering area. But whether they move east or west, all migrant finches winter in latitudes to the south of their breeding areas. They thus gain longer and usually warmer days, shorter nights and milder winters, where plant-growth and seed-production stop for a shorter period.

Migration over the sea

Finches which migrate wholly overland normally take a more or less straight course, as shown by plots of ringing recoveries (p. 226). But when a sea-crossing is involved, the migration is often indirect, for some birds take the shortest crossing, even though their journey is thereby lengthened. Thus, British Goldfinches and Linnets winter south and southwest of Britain, yet many start by flying east or southeast, reaching the continent by the shortest sea-route and avoiding the risk of having to cross the Bay of Biscay. But later they must correct for this and change direction over France. It seems reasonable to suppose that birds inherit whatever directional tendencies get them to their winter quarters by the safest route, even though this might entail a change of heading during the journey, and that any birds taking less safe routes are in the long term eliminated.

The Norwegian Chaffinches which winter in Britain seem exceptional among birds in the extent to which they change direction during the course of their migration (Van Dobben 1953, Lack 1962, Perdeck 1961). Some Chaffinches cross the southern North Sea direct, but the route by which many reach Britain in autumn is as follows. They leave Norway rather east of south, change to south-southwest in Denmark, and eventually to west-southwest as they move down the east side of the North Sea. After they have reached Holland, some take off west-southwest for England, some continue along the coast to Cap Gris-Nez, from which many depart west-northwest, while others follow the coast south and west beyond Cap Gris-Nez and later turn north or northwest into England. These last can be seen arriving, for instance, at Portland Bill in October. From England, some birds pass on west to Ireland. Many individuals thus change their flight direction through 180° from southeast to northwest during the course of their journey.

It is not certain to what extent this particular route is inherited as such, or is the effect of the birds' inclination to follow the coast on a basic south-west tendency. If the birds somehow 'know' the whereabouts of their wintering areas, and can correct for being off course, then it matters little if the route they take is indirect, for they still should not get lost. The birds sometimes migrate at such a height that they could see land across the sea. They fly over Holland higher with following easterly winds than with opposed southwesterly ones, and tend to put out to sea with easterly winds, but to turn along the coast with southwesterly ones (Van Dobben 1953). The survival value in this behaviour presumably lies in deterring the migrants from setting out to sea in less favourable weather, which is yet good enough to allow migration over land (Lack 1959). But a consequence is that the weather also influences the route the birds take, and particularly where they cross the sea. By following the coast all the way, Chaffinches avoid long sea-crossings, but their resulting journey is at least three times longer than it need be.

Some Bramblings and Siskins take the same coastal route to Britain as do the majority of Chaffinches, as shown by observations and by ringing recoveries, but the appearance of all three species on Shetland, Fair Isle and the Isle of May each autumn and spring shows that others of their kind take crossings which span more than 450 kilometres. The same flight is performed by the three crossbills and the Mealy Redpoll, for on irruptions the former appear in the Northern Isles and are sometimes seen at sea between Norway and Scotland (Murray 1928, Davis 1963), while the latter turn up annually on the east coast of Scotland, and came in especially large numbers in 1910 (Evans 1911). Long sea-crossings are also obligatory for those Redpolls (*C.f. rostrata*) which fly the 500 kilometres from Greenland to Iceland in autumn, and even longer ones for the few that fly the further 750 kilometres from Iceland to Scotland. Also, several species of finches winter in large numbers just south of the Mediterranean, and Chaffinches and Serins have been seen over the sea at places requiring more than 600 kilometres of continuous flight (Moreau 1953). Finally, many species regularly cross the Gulf of Bothnia (50–200 kilometres), the Skagerrak (120 kilometres) and the Irish Sea (30–200 kilometres). And all these distances must of course be lengthened in case of drift by wind. It thus seems safe to conclude that, while finches often avoid long sea-crossings where possible, some species nonetheless regularly fly 500–600 kilometres over water. This applies at least to the Chaffinch, Brambling, Goldfinch, Siskin, Linnet, Serin and Redpoll, and during irruptions to the crossbills.

The preparation for migration

A bird about to migrate must clearly be in a different behavioural and physiological state from one which is breeding or moulting. The beha-

PLATE 21. Crossbills occur sporadically in conifer forests throughout the northern hemisphere, and extract the seeds from cones using their specially adapted bills. In Eurasia, the Common Crossbill (*above*) feeds mainly from spruce, and the attacked cones (*below left*) can be readily distinguished from those eaten by squirrels (*centre*) and from intact cones (*right*).

PLATE 22. Juvenile Common Crossbills just out of the nest, with their bills still uncrossed.

vioural changes necessary for migration involve an urge to depart given suitable weather, and a tendency to fly in one particular direction rather than in any other. The symptoms of this state are easily noticed in captive birds, which at appropriate times of year develop 'migratory restlessness', when they hop and flutter round their cages. The chief physiological change necessary for migration involves the accumulation of reserves of fat to make the flight possible. The symptoms of this change include an increase in the food-intake and the weight of the bird, and the appearance of a yellow colour (due to fat) beneath the skin, which can be seen when the feathers are blown aside. Fat also accumulates in other sites around the body, mainly in the tracheal pit (at the base of the neck) and among the viscera (p. 254). It is by far the most economical fuel available to the bird, for the use of one gram will yield 9.2 kilocalories of energy, compared with only 4.2 kilocalories from the same weight of carbohydrate or protein. Weight for weight, fat is an even more efficient fuel than high octane petrol, and also has the advantage for birds that its oxidation yields water equal in weight to the fat used.

The weights of migrant finches usually increase by around 15% at migration time, both in spring and in autumn, but in occasional individuals by as much as 30% (Appendix 14). The relationship between weight and fat-content has been studied in particular detail in some Chaffinches that were killed in autumn as they flew along the Baltic coast (Dolnik & Blyumental 1967). Some were migrating at around 26 grams, of which about 5 grams was fat, but most were migrating at 23 grams, of which around 2 grams was fat. (In Britain, individuals have been caught at more than 30 grams, but their fat-contents have not been determined.) Migrating Siskins and Lesser Redpolls weighing around 14 grams usually carry about 2 grams of fat, while exceptionally heavy birds of both species weighing say 16 grams, might carry up to 4 grams of fat (Newton 1969b and unpublished, Evans 1969). The Redpolls put on more fat in autumn than their weights indicate, for the birds also lose some water at this time. In general, however, the migratory reserves of European finches are smaller than those of other types of birds which winter in the tropics and fly non-stop over the Mediterranean and Sahara. Some small warblers, for example, take on so much fuel for this flight that their weights nearly double (Fry *et al.* 1970, Moreau & Dolp 1970). Natural selection has presumably determined which system each species has evolved. Thus if food is available en route, it will pay a bird to migrate in short stages, and carry little surplus fat, but if food is not available, the bird has no option but to put on a lot of fat and make long flights.

To judge from their behaviour in captivity, finches normally reach a behavioural state in which they are most ready to depart at around the time that their fat stores reach a maximum. However, the food-intake of captive Bramblings can be restricted to such an extent that little or no fat can be stored, yet they still show migratory restlessness in the normal way (Lofts & Marshall 1961). This suggests that the regulation of fat-deposition on the one hand, and migratory behaviour on the other are controlled independently. Usually, however, the two must develop together and vary in parallel during the course of a migration, ensuring that the bird will stop and feed when its fat is low and fly when its fat is high.

At Rossitten on the Baltic coast, Chaffinches usually break their autumn journey for periods of 2–4 days (Dolnik & Blyumental 1967). As expected, lean birds stop more often and for longer than do fat ones. Also, whereas lean birds feed and replenish their fat during stops, fat birds usually do not feed and may even lose some fat. Apparently a Chaffinch's appetite during the migration season is controlled partly by how fat it is. This species can replenish its fat at 0.5 to 1.0 gram per day.

Once migrant finches have achieved a migratory state, the date on which they leave depends partly on the weather. Like other birds, they are most likely to leave under clear skies, which facilitate navigation, and with light following winds, which speed the flight. But whether an individual migrates at a given time probably depends both on its migratory state and on the weather. If the migratory state is well advanced, the bird might well proceed under weather that would at other times inhibit flight. This is especially true in late season, when migration more often takes place under heavy cloud, mist or rain, or into strongly opposed winds. This makes analysis of the various influences on migration difficult, for it means that the birds may react differently at different times to the same meteorological situation. In general, however, spring migration occurs mainly with the passage of warm fronts, which bring northward winds, and autumn migration with the passage of cold fronts, which bring southward winds.

Except on long sea-crossings, finches normally migrate by a series of flights, as mentioned, each lasting a few hours and thereby covering perhaps 100–200 kilometres. The birds move chiefly in the mornings, hardly at all in the afternoons, and to a small extent in the evenings, but settle before dark. It is not obvious to me why most finches move by day, when so many other birds, both long- and short-range migrants, move by night. Finches can probably choose the place they settle more carefully by day, but if they travelled by night, they would gain more daytime feeding. The Brambling is exceptional among the group in departing mainly in the first two hours after dark and migrating mainly at night, though it also moves by day.

Having discussed what is meant by the migratory state itself, I shall now consider the factors that induce a bird to reach this state at the appropriate times of year. As with breeding and moult, environmental factors largely control the timing of migration, though again they may serve chiefly to regulate an internal rhythm already operating within the bird (p. 192). Different factors induce the migratory state in spring and autumn, and since the movements at these seasons differ in other respects, they are best considered separately.

The spring migration to the breeding area

Probably the ultimate factor timing the spring migration is the need for the birds to reach their breeding areas in time to take advantage of the most favourable season (Lack 1960, Preston 1966). Usually, the first birds arrive as soon as conditions improve enough for them to survive there, though this may be weeks before nesting begins. They can then not only claim the best breeding places, but are also better able to appreciate local conditions and start as soon as these permit. This is strikingly illustrated by certain American rosy finches (*Leucosticte*), which leave their winter quarters in March, arrive near their mountaintop breeding areas before June, and then wait until enough snow has melted for them to move up and make full use of the short season (King & Wales 1965).

Increase in daylength is apparently the major proximate factor inducing birds to reach a migratory state at the correct date in spring. This has been shown by experiments on many species of birds kept in cages, including several finches, all of which have deposited fat, or shown migratory restlessness, in response to an artificial lengthening of winter days. Some Bramblings, for example, which were switched suddenly from days of 8 hours (English mid-winter daylength) to 14.5 hours (April daylength), developed large fat stores and migratory restlessness within eight days, while others kept on winter daylengths through the normal migration season showed no such changes (Lofts & Marshall 1960). Likewise, some Chaffinches, kept under daylengths that were steadily increased for 20 days in winter increased their food consumption and weight; one bird put on 36% in ten days, including five grams in only six days, which is consistent with the gains among wild birds in spring (Koch & de Bont 1952).

Hence, the same main factor (daylength) induces the migratory state in finches in spring as later brings on breeding condition. Indeed, spring migration was formerly thought to depend on gonad development, to be stimulated by sex hormones, and thus to form part of the breeding cycle (Rowan 1926, 1929, 1932). However, experiments on Bramblings and other birds have since shown that even castrated cocks achieve a migratory state, though a few days later than normal (Lofts & Marshall 1961). The evidence from other song-birds is still conflicting, and suggests that gonadal hormones may modify both the timing and extent of fattening, but not prevent it (Weise 1967).

Under natural conditions, the effect of daylength is in some species modified by other factors. The American White-crowned Sparrow (*Zonotrichia leucophrys*) begins to fatten 10–12 days earlier in warm, dry springs than in cold, damp ones (King & Farner 1965). In the laboratory, too, high temperatures will advance the timing of fat-deposition in several species, though here fairly large increases are required, and to my knowledge no fringilline or cardueline finch has yet been tested. Sex also influences the start or progress of migration. In the Chaffinch, for example, hens pass through Belgium a few days later in spring than do cocks and the reverse is true in autumn (Verheyen 1960).

Once a finch migration has begun, the weather largely controls its progress, either by influencing the migratory state itself, or by permitting or inhibiting the flights of birds already in this state. That the migratory state itself fluctuates en route is indicated by the fact that the northward journey of certain finches in Europe takes up to several weeks, which is too long to be due just to shortage of suitable flying weather. Probably the migratory state is influenced by warmth, as found for other birds in the laboratory, but the field evidence in spring is inconclusive. Granted, waves of finches and other migrant birds often appear in Britain following warm spells, but since these spells normally coincide with clear skies and favourable northward winds, it is seldom possible to tell which weather factor(s) the migrants have reacted to (Lack 1960). Likewise, although cold snaps in spring seem to inhibit movement, the migrants may occasionally be responding to associated weather. Either way, the date they arrive on their breeding areas is influenced more by conditions encountered en route than by those in winter quarters. The birds' continued response to the weather ensures, among other things, that they do not arrive at successive latitudes too early for food.

Different populations wintering in the same area often react differently to the same environmental conditions. Those which induce British Goldfinches to migrate out of Iberia each spring induce the local Goldfinches to breed; and the same is true of the Scandinavian and local Chaffinches that winter in Britain. Furthermore, experiments show that, whereas migratory Chaffinches accumulate fat in response to artificially long days in winter, resident ones do not (Koch & de Bont 1952); also, the most northern migrant Chaffinches need longer days to induce fattening than do more southern migrant ones (Dolnik & Blyumental 1967). These differences are adaptive and in nature ensure that the birds from each population are brought into migratory or breeding condition at a date appropriate to the latitude at which they nest.

The autumn migration to the wintering area

The ultimate factor timing the autumn migration is the need for the birds to leave their breeding areas before their continued survival there becomes precarious (Lack 1960). Among finches, particular individuals normally depart soon after finishing moult, and well before food becomes scarce. The earlier they leave, the easier it is to accumulate the necessary fat, and the longer the days in which to move and feed.

While increasing daylengths induce a migratory state in spring, decreasing daylengths have often been assumed to induce the same state in autumn. This idea has not been proved experimentally, but field data suggest that at least some environmental factor operates in finches. In the Lesser Redpoll, those juveniles which finish their moult early in September wait till the last third of the month before leaving, whereas the adults and juveniles which finish after this time leave immediately (Evans 1966). The same probably holds for other finches in Britain. Hence, it seems that some environmental factor controls the start of the moulting season in each species, and that the few birds finishing moult before this time wait to leave, whereas those finishing after this time leave as soon as their feathers are grown. Thus, the period during which the three main migrant species leave Britain in autumn coincides almost exactly with the period during which the adults are completing moult (Table 18). But in any one autumn, the bulk of the birds may leave on only a few days within this period, if adverse weather renders the rest of it unsuitable.

Table 18. The migration seasons of finches in southeast England. Thick line, heavy passage; thin line, light passage; broken line, irregular passage, not every year. (Mainly from Harris & Scott 1964.)

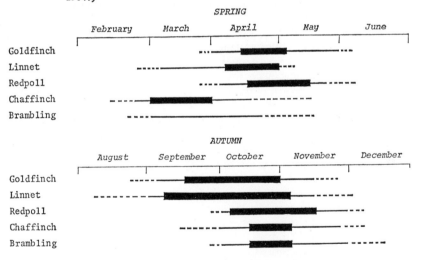

The advantage of waiting till moult is complete is that flight would be inefficient before this time. However, individual finches which moult especially late in the season occasionally set off before their flight feathers are fully grown, which further implies some environmental influence on migration dates. I have noted this in migrant Goldfinches, Linnets and Redpolls in Britain. Also, the precise relationship between the end of moult and the timing of fattening and departure differs in different populations of the same species (Dolnik & Blyumental 1967). Those Chaffinches which breed in Russia around 55°N usually wait a few days between finishing moult and depositing fat for departure; those at 60°N deposit fat towards the end of wing moult, so that they are ready to leave as soon as their feathers are grown; while those at 62°N regularly leave their breeding grounds before completing moult. These last birds, which breed where the summer is shortest, provide the only example of regular overlap between moult and migration in finches, except perhaps for crossbills (p. 202).

In contrast to the movements in spring, those in autumn are often heaviest after a pronounced fall in temperature, but again it is often difficult to tell whether the birds are reacting to cooling as such, or to associated weather factors that favour flight. However, Svärdson (1953) showed that nearly all the big autumn movements of finches and other birds through Sweden occurred with a drop in temperature in the area from which the migrants were presumed to have come. Indeed, this was the only factor common to all observed movements, so here at least the migrants had probably reacted directly to a change in temperature. This conflicts with recent findings in North America which suggest that the southward winds, prevailing with the passage of cold fronts, have more influence on the strength of migration than does the cooling itself.

The migration in autumn is often leisurely, but birds with a long way to go usually make faster progress than those which have only a short journey. Through analyses of ringing recoveries, Dolnik & Blyumental (1967) found that two Chaffinch populations took the same time to complete their journey, even though one had twice as far to go. They worked out the progress of Finnish Chaffinches on migration from the dates ringed birds occur in different places. The birds leave northern Finland in the first half of September, and reach their wintering grounds in France and Iberia around mid-October, the complete journey taking five weeks. The birds thus cover 3,000 kilometres at an average of 90 kilometres per day. The Goldfinches that leave Britain in autumn make a shorter journey but take as long, for ringing returns show that the birds reach Iberia, on the average, about a month later than they pass through Belgium. The birds thus cover about 1,200 kilometres, at an average of only 40 kilometres per day. These figures may be compared with rates of 70–100 kilometres per day found for Mealy Redpolls moving 1,000–1,500 kilometres from Fenno-Scandia to central Russia in autumn (Eriksson 1970b). But all three species probably make no progress on many days within this migration period because of adverse weather or the need to replenish their fat.

In conclusion, the spring migration is best viewed as an attempt by the birds to push their way northwards as quickly as improving conditions permit. It is the weather which mainly sets the pace and times each stage of the journey. In autumn, in contrast, food is generally plentiful, weather is for the most part favourable, and the pace can be set primarily by the birds themselves.

While the development of the migratory state has been studied in detail, the way it is suppressed, once the birds have reached their destination, is not known. The mere exhaustion of the fat is not sufficient, for the reserve is used and replaced several times during each journey. The birds must presumably respond to the particular conditions of the breeding or wintering grounds in such a way that their migratory state wanes, but it is not known how they 'know' they have arrived.

Also, the two migrations are less distinct in time than might be thought, and in some species individual birds may be migrating on and off for most of the time between leaving their breeding areas in one year and returning there the next. Those Twites, for example, which breed in Lapland, depart in August and September and do not reach the south of their wintering range in Poland until December or January, after which the majority stay for only a week or two before starting back (Tomialojć 1967). Furthermore, many finches move long distances in winter if there is a sudden cold spell or a fall of snow. It is mainly those species which feed on or near the ground which participate in 'hard-weather' movements, namely the Chaffinch, Brambling, Greenfinch, Goldfinch, Linnet and Twite.

The pattern of migration

In finches and other small birds, a few days of heavy migration are often followed by days with little or no movement, and these in turn by another wave. These waves have usually been interpreted in terms of the weather and, as discussed above, a heavy movement often follows a marked temperature change. Once started, however, a movement may continue in less suitable weather, and furthermore on many apparently ideal days little or no movement occurs. Some recent Russian work by Dolnik & Blyumental (1967) suggested that the behavioural and physiological state of the birds themselves have a much greater influence on the volume and timing of movement than was formerly envisaged. At the Kerusche Nehrung on the Baltic coast, Chaffinches were collected at different stages of a migratory wave and their carcasses were examined to determine the fat-content and the amount of food in the gut. These results were then related to the volume of migration, and a consistent pattern emerged.

On the first day of the wave only very fat birds fly: they begin their movement before sunrise, without feeding beforehand, and continue for about four hours. There is then a pause of between one and three hours, after which the movement is resumed and continues for two hours in the evening. On the first day of a wave all the birds are of about equal fatness. On the second day, the volume of migration reaches a peak; again the movement begins at sunrise and at first only fat birds participate. As the day progresses, however, the migrating flocks contain increasing numbers of lean birds, which unlike the fat ones, normally have fresh food in their stomachs, showing that they begin their flight later in the day than fat birds and only after feeding. During the day, the lean birds stop to feed again: at the same time they attract down some fat birds, though on this day the latter do not normally feed. In the afternoon, all the lean birds have stopped to feed, and by evening the fat birds are the only ones left flying. On the last day of the wave, the migration does not begin at sunrise, but only after the birds have had time to feed. Fewer birds participate, they fly with frequent stops and at lower altitude. On this day, almost all the flying birds contain little fat, some feeding occurs throughout the day, and the movement does not reach a peak in the evening. Some flocks fly in the reverse direction. Each migratory wave usually lasts three days, but varies from one to seven. After it is over, the pause usually lasts three days but varies from one to eight, depending partly on the weather. One migratory wave, lasting up to three days, may cover up to 500 kilometres, during which individual birds may expend 2–3 grams of fat.

In their explanation of this pattern, Dolnik & Blyumental (1967) attached great importance to the pull flying birds have on others which at that time are physiologically less ready to migrate. Since the first birds to fly are the very fat ones, it is presumably the presence of many fat birds, which start to fly under a common stimulus (such as an improvement in the weather) which begins each wave. Once started, however, the stream of flying birds stimulates others to participate, and the larger the stream of flying birds, the greater the pull. The expenditure of fat by the fat birds, and the frequent stops by the lean ones, explains the picture which is observed in the suceeding days of the wave. After most of the fat birds have depleted their fat, their stopping pulls the rest down, and the wave is brought to a standstill. Movement is resumed after the birds have had time to build up their reserves again, though inclement weather will delay departure.

The frequency with which the migratory waves appear is thus dependent primarily on the time needed for spent birds to replace their fat, but is modified by variations in the weather, which also affect the tendency to leave. It is the movement of the fat birds, and their stimulating effect on others less fat, which causes a large part of the population to move together and produce the wave-like pattern. Although birds move at various stages of fatness, the amount of fat carried by a bird affects the timing and duration of its flights; and in general the fattest birds make the fastest progress.

At the time of writing, this work in the Baltic is unique, and further work elsewhere is needed to show how generally applicable this pattern is. The birds concerned were making a diurnal overland journey (along the coast), in a region where short-term variations in weather are less extreme than further west in Europe. Possibly around Britain and other parts of western Europe, the more variable weather has so much influence on the movements as completely to obscure any underlying pattern in the behaviour and physiology of the birds themselves. This work does, however, help to explain why movement does not occur on all days when conditions are apparently ideal, and why it sometimes occurs on days when the weather is less good. The advantage to the birds in this behaviour is not obvious to me.

Watching finch migration

Anyone wishing to watch finches on migration could go to one of the coastal sites mentioned at the start of this chapter, or look for others not yet known. For carduelines in autumn, almost any projecting headland in the southern two-thirds of Britain could be tried, but those on the east and south coasts are more likely to be productive. Anyone wishing to interpret their observations, however, should bear in mind that the numbers and directions of birds flying within the range of low-power field-glasses may be totally unrepresentative of what is passing higher up. This was shown, for example, for Goldfinches, Linnets and other birds on the East Anglian coast, by Axell *et al.* (1963), who compared visual with radar observations obtained over the same period. From visual observations alone, the authors could only conclude that these finches coast south in autumn chiefly when the wind is northward and opposed, and that the few that migrate when the wind is southward and apparently favourable, fly mainly northwards back towards their breeding areas. Radar, however, revealed that high, broad-front, southward movements, which are probably the main departures, occur either with a following wind or an extremely light head wind. The difference is that, with a following wind, the birds migrate high and spread out on a broad front, and on reaching the coast they put straight out to sea, and so are not normally seen by an observer using ordinary field-glasses; on the other hand, with a moderate or strong head-wind, the birds fly too low over the ground to be detected by radar, and on reaching the coast they turn along it, to pass in a concentrated stream within easy view of the observer. With a light head wind, the position is intermediate: some birds fly high and out to sea on a broad front, so are detected by radar, and others fly low, turn and follow the coast, so are visible. The puzzle remains why, with northerly winds, any Goldfinches and Linnets should coast northward in autumn, when their fellows are simultaneously proceeding southward high above them. 'Wrong-way' movements are commoner in autumn than in spring, and occur on a broad-front inland, as well as along the coast. They are perhaps connected with the physiological state of the birds themselves, as mentioned above for the Chaffinch.

In general, all finches fly progressively lower as wind-speed increases, and lower in opposed than in following winds. Also, the lower the birds fly, the more they incline to follow coastlines and to fly round hills instead of over them. In some conditions, the tendency to coast is so strong in Chaffinches that they fly for a time in a direction markedly different from where they are supposed to be going (Lack 1957). This is not always from a reluctance to put out to sea, moreover, for it also occurs in birds which have just crossed the sea. Some arrivals were seen to fly first north, then west, then south, as they rounded the Norfolk coast one autumn, and this odd behaviour is still unexplained (Lack 1960). In fine weather, Chaffinches arriving in Britain usually push straight inland, however, where their migration may appear more pronounced than on the coast, because the birds lose height at about the time they leave the sea (Lack 1960). Also, departing Chaffinches tend to fly high and almost out of sight early in the morning and lower along the coast later in the day, even when the weather remains the same, as seen, for example, in Cornwall by Lack (1952). Clearly, many aspects of the behaviour of migrating birds remain unexplained.

To summarise this chapter, every species of European finch migrates in at least parts of its range. The main direction of migration is more or less southwest in autumn; the longest regular journeys span more than 3,500 kilometres each way, and the longest sea-crossings more than 500 kilometres. The migratory habit itself, the wintering areas of different populations, and hence the directional tendencies, can all be explained in terms of natural selection. Before migration, the weights of finches increase by more than 15% through fat-deposition; movements overland proceed by a series of short flights, each up to about 200 kilometres, between which the fat is replenished. In spring, increasing daylength, and probably also warmth, promote the migratory state at an appropriate date. The flights themselves take place mostly under clear skies and more or less following winds. These conditions are usually associated with a rise in temperature and on any one occasion it is often difficult to tell to which of these various factors the migrants are responding. In autumn, birds usually leave their breeding areas before food becomes scarce there, and soon after finishing moult. The flights themselves often follow a drop in temperature, but again this may be because the birds are responding to wind-direction or other associated weather factors. The familiar wave-like pattern of migration is associated in the Chaffinch with changes in the fat-contents of the migrating birds. Radar has shown that the numbers and directions of birds migrating within visual range are usually unrepresentative of what is passing overhead.

CHAPTER 14

IRRUPTIONS

THOSE finches which depend mainly on the seeds of trees differ in migratory habits from those that depend on the seeds of herbaceous plants. This is because, whereas the herbaceous plants in an area provide a regular and dependable food-supply from year to year, the trees do not. As every countryman knows, the woods and hedgerows are in some years laden with fruits and berries of various kinds, but in other years bear almost none. The cropping depends partly on the natural rhythm of the trees themselves and partly on the weather. Most tree-species require more than one year to accumulate the reserves necessary to produce fruit, and they crop at longer intervals towards the north, where the growing seasons are shorter. Spruce, for example, tends to crop well every 2–3 years on the mountains of central Europe, every 3–4 years in the southern boreal forest, and every 4–5 years in the north. For a good crop, the weather must also be fine and warm in the preceding autumn, when the fruit buds form, and again in the spring when the flowers set: otherwise the crop is delayed for another year. In any one area, most of the trees of a species crop in phase with one another because they come under the same weather, and often those of different species also crop in phase.

Of course the trees in widely separated areas may be on different cropping régimes, partly because of regional variations in the weather, so good crops in some areas may coincide with poor ones in others. Usually each productive area extends over hundreds or thousands of square kilometres, and is separated from the next by terrain which, in that year, is almost devoid of seeds. In some years, moreover, the productive patches are plentiful and widespread, and in others few and far between, so that the total production of seeds over Europe varies greatly from year to year.

The finches that depend on such tree-seeds always concentrate wherever their food is plentiful at the time. The majority of individuals migrate regularly in spring and autumn, but may breed and winter in different areas in successive years. An influx is usually termed an 'irruption' and an outmovement an 'eruption'. The species involved and their main food-plants are listed on p. 220, but the crossbills, which differ in some respects, are left till the next chapter.

All these birds breed in northern or mountain regions and, at one season or another, depend on the seeds of only one or two tree-species. Four such finches depend on tree-seeds and show 'irruptive behaviour' only in winter, and the remaining two in summer as well. The different species occur abundantly in the same area in the same years only when their

	Main food* in spring and summer	Main food* in autumn and winter
Siskin	spruce and pine	birch and alder
Mealy Redpoll	spruce and dwarf birch (B. nana)	birches (B. verrucosa and B. pubescens)
Lesser Redpoll	herbaceous plants	birch (B. alba) and alder
Northern Bullfinch	various plants	rowan and others
Pine Grosbeak	various plants	rowan and others
Brambling	insects	beech

*Unless otherwise stated, seeds are implied

particular food-plants fruit together. Also, since most of them feed directly from trees in winter, they are almost immune from the effects of snow. Only the Brambling feeds from the ground, and the movements of even this species depend more on the occurrence of beechmast than on hard weather (Richters 1952). Perhaps the easiest way to understand the irruptive finches is to compare their behaviour with that of the remaining species, which feed mostly from herbaceous plants, namely the Greenfinch, Goldfinch, Linnet, Chaffinch and others. The supply of food for these last species is influenced by farming operations, by snow-cover and by other factors, but its fluctuations are small from year to year compared to those of tree-seeds.

Population trends

To begin with, most experienced bird-watchers would agree that the breeding populations of irruptive finches fluctuate much more from year to year than do those of other species. This is difficult to prove conclusively from the few published figures, which were collected in various ways for different reasons, but these are nonetheless suggestive. Thus, under the national census scheme of the British Trust for Ornithology, four 'non-irruptive' finches have been monitored for eight years by a method which provides an index of their breeding populations. These years contained an exceptionally hard winter, when mortality was heavy, so the fluctuations which occurred over this period were probably as great as they ever are. During this time, the largest population found in any one of these species on farmland was only twice the smallest, and the most a population increased from one year to the next was by one half (Fig. 50). Even smaller fluctuations occurred in the numbers of these same species breeding in open woodland, though the areas sampled were fewer. These figures reflect the trends over the whole of southern Britain, however, and swamp the local variations. Some studies of the Chaffinch in restricted areas show that the numbers remain more stable from year to year in preferred than in other habitats. During ten years in a mixed wood in Holland, the largest number of breeding pairs observed was only one-third greater

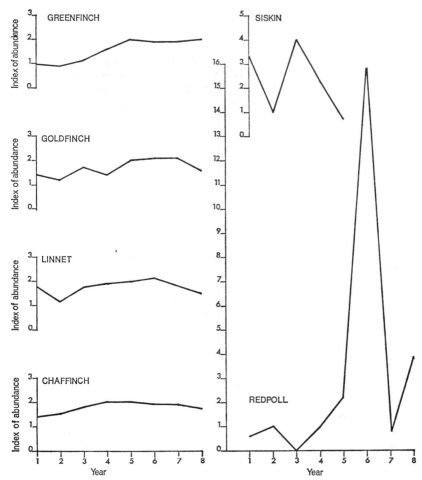

FIG. 50. Fluctuations in the populations of four 'non-irruptive' finches (left) in southern Britain compared with those of two irruptive species (right) in northern Europe. Different authors expressed their results in different ways, so an index of abundance was calculated to enable the comparison to be made. (From Bailey 1967, Batten 1969, Haapanen 1966, Enemar 1969 and *in litt*.)

than the smallest, but in a nearby pine wood it was three times greater. Changes of this order have also been noted from year to year in spruce woods in Finland, but in no type of wood in either country did the numbers increase by more than one-half from one year to the next (p. 20). Hence, insofar as one can judge from such limited data, the largest population of a 'non-irruptive' species that can be expected in an area is no more than

2–3 times the smallest, and a 50% increase is the most that can be expected from one year to the next. An increase of this order could result primarily from the good survival of the local adults and young from the previous year, and need not depend on immigration.

In the two irruptive species that have been studied in detail, much greater variations in numbers have been noted, which parallel changes in food (Figs. 50 and 51). In one year, Siskins were found in spruce forests in Finland at between 12 and 70 pairs per square kilometre, according to

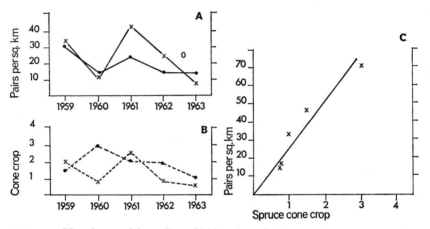

FIG. 51. Numbers of breeding Siskins in relation to the cone-crop in Finland. Fluctuations in the Siskin population follow the spruce (x), but not the pine (●) crop. Cone crops classified in four categories. (From Haapanen 1966.)

the local abundance of cones; and as the crops changed from year to year in the same locality, so did the number of birds. Over five years, the greatest number of breeding pairs in one area was seven times the lowest (6–41 pairs per square kilometre), and the population increased by four-fold (10–41 pairs) from one year to the next (Haapanen 1966). A similar relationship was found in one year between the numbers of Mealy Red-polls and the local abundance of birch seeds in Lapland (Taylor 1954). Also, over six years, the number of Redpolls in a single area of birch varied in different years between 0 and 79 pairs per square kilometre, and showed a 16-fold increase in one year compared to the average over the preceding five years (Enemar 1969). Hence, the breeding populations of the two irruptive finches studied fluctuated more markedly from year to year than did those of the 'non-irruptive' species. Sometimes the increases which occurred from one year to the next were so great that they must have been due mainly or entirely to immigration. Such local changes in numbers depend at least partly on local food-supplies and need not of course reflect the trends over a wide area.

In winter quarters, even greater fluctuations can be seen in the numbers of irruptive finches, ranging from total absence in years when the appropriate tree-seeds are lacking, to hundreds or thousands of birds per square kilometre in years when such seeds are plentiful. Any bird-watcher can see this for himself. But the most striking concentration documented was in the winter of 1950/51, when millions of Bramblings, equivalent to the number breeding over the whole of northern Europe, assembled in a small part of Switzerland where beechmast was abundant (p. 30).

As well as the local changes in numbers, irruptive finches undergo long-term changes, and sometimes a species reaches a peak over the whole of northern Europe simultaneously. Siskins were unusually plentiful in 1949 and 1953; Mealy Redpolls in 1932, 1955, 1965 and 1968; Northern Bullfinches in 1961 and 1966; and Lesser Redpolls in Britain in 1959, 1964 and 1969. In such peak years, some species breed well outside their usual range, and also spread to less favoured habitats. The Siskin, for example, breeds much further north than usual then, and in birch as well as in conifer woods (Svärdson 1957). Such widespread peaks in population probably result from an abundance of food in the preceding years, which leads to good breeding and good survival. The Siskin and Mealy Redpoll, in particular, breed for twice as long as normal, and increase accordingly, in summers when spruce seeds are unusually plentiful. Also, the number of adults available to breed each year depends partly on their survival during the preceding months, and this in turn on seed-stocks on the winter range (Perrins 1966).

Almost certainly the widespread peaks in the breeding populations of irruptive finches occur at irregular intervals, but, in the absence of special studies, the trends are hard to discern. Some authors have extrapolated to the breeding populations from changes in the numbers visiting particular wintering areas, but this can be misleading, because, apart from the local effects just discussed, a given wintering area may receive birds from different breeding areas in different years. For example, most irruptions of the Pine Grosbeak into Germany have come from the north and the birds belonged to the European subspecies, but in 1892 another subspecies invaded from Siberia (Grote 1937). Nor is it safe to infer the trends in breeding numbers from changes in the strength of the autumn migration, because it is not usually possible to tell what proportion of the total a given migration represents. A heavy movement might represent only a small part of a very large population, or a large part of a small population, the remainder in each case staying behind. In short, trends in breeding populations can be properly studied only on the breeding areas themselves, a difficult task because of the inaccessibility of much of the north.

In the Siskin, the strength and timing of the autumn migration has been linked with the prevailing food-supply, which in autumn is birch seeds. For nine years, ornithologists counted the number of migrants passing each day over a bird-observatory off southern Sweden, and Svärdson (1957) later related the annual totals to the size of the birch crop further north (Appendix 15). The birds tended to pass in largest numbers in years when the birch crop was poor. The bulk also passed up to one month earlier in the poor birch years than in the good ones. Svärdson thought that the birds began to migrate on about the same date every year, but stayed in larger numbers in southern Sweden, or interrupted their migration for longer, in years when the birch crop there was good. He was not able to relate the size of the passage to the size of the total population, however, because each year an unknown proportion remained on the breeding range. In the Mealy Redpoll, too, the strength and timing of the autumn migration varies greatly from year to year, and more birds remain in northern Europe in winters when the birch crop there is above average (Eriksson 1970b).

Siskins, Redpolls and other irruptive species seem to move each autumn only until they find areas rich in food, then settle there. The value of this behaviour is that the birds do not pass over such areas when the chances of their finding others are not certain. In consequence, however, the distance travelled by the bulk of the migrants varies from year to year according to where the crops are good, and only when the migrants are exceptionally numerous, or their food is generally scarce, do they reach the furthest part of their wintering range. Thus, Lesser Redpolls migrate each year from northern to southern Britain, and then many pass on to the continent. In years when the birch crop is poor in Britain, more birds than usual cross the channel, but only rarely do they reach Iberia (p. 56). Likewise, only in exceptional years, do large numbers of Bramblings reach southernmost Europe, and Pine Grosbeaks central Europe. It is chiefly at the extremities of the wintering range, which the birds reach only at irregular intervals, that the movements of irruptive species have been studied.

The food-shortage, which leads to a long and heavy migration, is accentuated if the birds are especially numerous at the time. This situation is frequent because good seed-crops are usually followed by poor ones. The good crops in the first year lead to high survival among the birds over winter and to a large breeding population the next summer, and these same birds and their young then encounter the widespread poor crops in the next autumn, so have to move further than usual then (Perrins 1966).

How far irruptive species move northward in spring also depends partly on how much food they meet on the way. The Mealy Redpoll provides the most striking example, for this species curtails its migration by up to several hundred kilometres to breed in southern Fenno-Scandia in years when the spruce crop there is good (p. 158). Irruptive species also tend to

PLATE 23. The different species and races of crossbills vary in size of body and bill according to the types of cones they have to deal with. In Eurasia, the large, heavy-billed Parrot Crossbill (*below*) feeds mainly from hard pine cones, while the small, slender-billed Two-barred Crossbill (*left*) feeds mainly from soft larch cones.

PLATE 24. A cock Scottish Crossbill feeding its hen on the nest. This race of crossbill is restricted to northern Scotland and has developed a fairly large bill through long association with pine. It breeds mainly in early spring before the cones open and lose their seeds.

breed south of their usual range in years after a large exodus. Recent records of Lesser Redpolls nesting in Holland followed the exceptional emigrations from Britain in 1959 and 1964 (p. 56), and records of Northern Bullfinches nesting in Denmark have likewise followed large invasions from the north (Svärdson 1957).

Ringing recoveries

Among the finches that feed from herbaceous plants, the birds from particular breeding areas tend to have fixed migration routes and restricted wintering areas. Look at the maps of ringing recoveries of British Goldfinches and Linnets, and of the Scandinavian Chaffinches which winter in Britain (p. 40, 47, 25). Although the movements of all these birds are complicated by a sea-crossing, the recoveries all come from a relatively restricted part of Europe, and from the same places year after year. Where these species migrate wholly overland, their route is even more direct. The Linnets which move through Belgium, whether local breeders or passage birds, move strictly northeast–southwest, and 99% of the recoveries lie within a narrow corridor across Europe, only 370 kilometres wide (Fig. 52). The recoveries of Greenfinches ringed in Belgium are fewer, but show the same pattern (Verheyen 1955b).

The adults of such species usually return to breed in the same general area each year, and the young often return to the same area in which they themselves were raised. Examples may be found among the recoveries of migrant Goldfinches and Linnets ringed in Britain, and of Scarlet Rosefinches and Chaffinches ringed in Fenno-Scandia. These last birds usually return to exactly the same territories year after year (p. 26, 135). For the Linnet, a large list of recoveries from central Europe mentions several dozen birds which bred in the same place in successive summers, nine which bred within ten kilometres, two within 50, and none at greater distances (Retz 1966, 1968). Goldfinches, Linnets and Chaffinches also return either to the same place in successive winters or, if to a different place, on the same migration route (p. 39, 48, 24). Hence, in these species, the tendency to return to the same breeding area is strong, the tendency to return to the same wintering place is less so, but nonetheless an individual normally moves each year in the same restricted direction.

To these tendencies, the irruptive species show some strong contrasts. To begin with, the birds from a particular breeding area may spread over a large part of Europe on migration. Bullfinches ringed in Fenno-Scandia have been recovered the following winter anywhere between southwest, through south, to east of their breeding place in the previous summer, and similar, but less marked, trends have been noted in others species (p. 28 for Brambling). This is partly because irruptive migrants show more spread in their departure directions than do other migrants (as often noted by Scandinavian bird-watchers), and also a greater tendency to

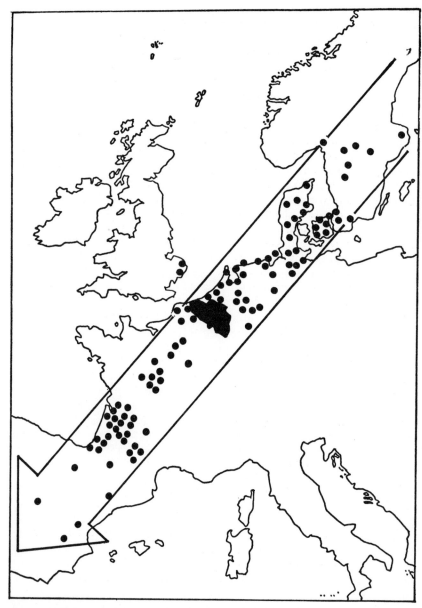

FIG. 52. The recoveries of Linnets ringed in Belgium as breeders or passage migrants. 99% of the 703 recoveries lie within a narrow corridor only 370 kilometres wide, running strictly northeast-southwest. (From Verheyen 1955a.)

change direction inconsistently during their journey. Thus many Siskins and Bramblings from northern Europe are ringed each autumn on migration through Belgium. The subsequent recoveries show that, while some of these birds continue southwest into France and Iberia, others turn west and northwest into Britain, and yet others east and southeast into central Europe and Italy. Moreover, the same individual may take different routes in successive years. The birds presumably behave in this way because they are as likely to find food in one direction as in another, so natural selection has not fixed their directional preferences as rigidly as those of other finches.

Very few ringed birds of irruptive species have been reported on their breeding range in more than one year, partly because there are few people to come across them there. In the ringing reports of Fenno-Scandia, I have found only one recovery of a Siskin in successive breeding seasons, at places 120 kilometres apart, and two of Mealy Redpolls, at places 280 and 550 kilometres apart. In neither species were any birds found at the same place in different years. Four Bullfinches had moved up to several hundred kilometres between breeding areas, and three others had remained at the same place. The six relevant recoveries of Lesser Redpolls in Britain were all from the same place in different summers, but these resulted from a local study, so if any birds had moved elsewhere the chances of finding them were smaller (Evans 1969). Also, Lesser Redpolls feed mainly from herbaceous plants at this time, so might not be expected to change their breeding place from year to year.

On the winter range, the ringing recoveries of irruptive finches are more numerous. They confirm that individuals may winter in widely separated areas in successive years, and not just along the same migration route. The Siskins and Bramblings, which were caught in Britain in one winter and on the continent the next, were mentioned earlier (p. 43), but even bigger movements have been noted elsewhere. Individuals of these same species have been caught in Belgium one winter and as far east as Turkey or the Balkans in a later one. Another Siskin was ringed in Germany one February and recovered 2,200 kilometres to the east in Russia the next, and a Bullfinch was recovered one winter in Russia 2,000 kilometres to the west of where it had been ringed in the previous year. Three Mealy Redpolls are known to have wintered in different years at places 1,300, 1,500 and 1,800 kilometres apart (Eriksson 1970b). Presumably all these birds had returned to the breeding range in the meantime, and took quite different directions in the two years. On the other hand, I can find no records of individual Siskins, Mealy Redpolls or Bramblings wintering in the same place in more than one year. Among the Lesser Redpolls from northern Britain, at least six were found in England in one winter and on the continent the following autumn, but at least two visited the same place in Germany for two years running (Evans 1969, Mohr 1967).

The extent to which an irruptive species will wander for food is best shown by the North American Evening Grosbeak (*Hesperiphona vespertina*), which breeds in conifer forests and moves south or southeast in autumn. This species feeds mainly on large, hard tree-fruits, but also visits feeding trays for sunflower seeds, a habit which makes it easy to catch. Over 14 winters, 17,000 Grosbeaks were ringed at a site in Pennsylvania. Of these, only 48 were recovered at the same place in subsequent winters, yet 451 others were scattered among 17 American States and four Canadian Provinces. Another 348 birds that had been ringed elsewhere were caught at this same locality, and these had come from 14 different States and four Provinces (D. H. Speirs, *in litt.*). These recoveries show both how widely individual Grosbeaks range and how weak is their tendency to return to the same place in later years.

The wide wintering range, less rigid directional tendencies, and the poor homing shown by irruptive species are all ways of coping with a sporadic food-supply. They enable such species to wander widely until they find their food and, having found it, to stop. They contrast with the marked directional tendencies, narrow migration routes and strong homing shown by species which feed from herbaceous plants. Both systems are adaptive, the first to an erratic and unpredictable food-supply, and the second to a dependable one. The distinction is not clear-cut, however, and at times all finches show some irruptive tendencies, whatever their diet. Also, parallels in the behaviour of both groups may be found among other birds – Waxwings (*Bombicilla garrulus*), titmice, Redwings (*Turdus musicus*) and other species which feed from tree-fruits behave like the irruptive finches (Lack 1954, Cornwallis 1961, Ulfstrand 1963).

To summarise this chapter, the finch-species which depend mainly on the seeds of herbaceous plants occupy practically the whole of their breeding and wintering ranges each year; and their numbers, it seems, change relatively little from one year to the next. Typically, the birds from particular breeding areas have fixed migration routes and restricted wintering areas. Individuals tend to return to the same breeding areas each year, and sometimes to the same wintering areas, or at least to another place on the same migration route. In contrast, finches which depend on the seeds of a limited number of trees normally occupy only parts of their breeding and wintering range each year, and always concentrate wherever their food is plentiful at the time. Their numbers fluctuate markedly from year to year, both locally and over wide areas. Individuals often breed or winter in widely separated areas in different years. The migratory habits of the first group are adapted to a regular and predictable food-supply, and those of the second group to a sporadic food-supply.

CHAPTER 15

THE MOVEMENTS OF CROSSBILLS

WHEREAS most irruptive migrants leave their breeding range every year, but in greatly varying numbers, crossbills leave only in exceptional years. At these times they often reach areas devoid of conifers and have to eat unusual foods. '*In the course of this year, about the fruit season, there appeared, in the orchards chiefly, some remarkable birds which had never before been seen in England, somewhat larger than larks, which ate the kernel of the fruit and nothing else, whereby the trees were fruitless to the loss of many. The beaks of these birds were crossed, so that by this means they opened the fruit as if with pincers or a knife*' (Matthew Paris, St Albans, 1251). This is the earliest record of a crossbill invasion in Britain. Another occurred in 1593: '*there were greate plenty of strang birds, that shewed themselves at the time the apples were full rype, who fedde upon the kernells onely of those apples, and haveinge a bill with one beake wrythinge over the other, which would presently bore a greate hole in the apple, and make way to the kernells; they were of the bignesse of a Bullfinch, the henne right like the henne of the Bullfinch in coulour: the cock a very glorious bird, in a manner al redde or yellowe on the brest, backe and head. The oldest man living had never heard or reade of any such like bird; and the thinge most to be noted was, that it seemed they came out of some country not inhabited, for that they would at first abide shooting at them, either with pellet, bowe, or other engine, and not remove till they were stricken downe; moreover, they would abide the thoweing at them . . . with apples. They came when the apples were rype, and went away when the apples were cleane fallen. They were very good meate*' (Wats 1640, in Yarrell 1876-82).

To recapitulate, on the regular range the Common Crossbill lives primarily from spruce, the Two-barred from larch, and the Parrot from pine. Irruptions of these various species have recently been recorded from all their main centres, including North America (Griscom 1937), the Himalayas, eastern Asia and Japan (Vaurie 1959), but have been best documented in Europe. On this continent, between 1800 and 1965, Common Crossbills irrupted at least 67 times (Fig. 53). Sometimes they came in several successive years (probably from different areas), and at other times at intervals of up to 11 years. The two other species, despite their different foods, often came in the same years as the Common Crossbill, though less frequently. This was true at least 36 out of 47 invasions of the Two-barred, and 22 out of 27 invasions of the Parrot Crossbill. The latter might have overlapped even more frequently however, as it is so similar in appearance to the Common that it might often have been missed.

I shall return later to the problem of synchrony in invasions, but for the time being, will be concerned only with the Common Crossbill, since this

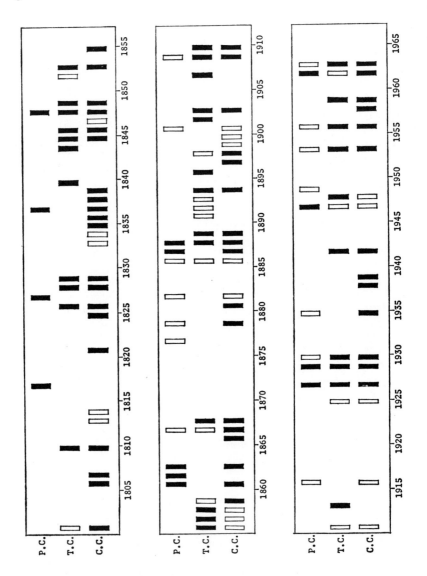

FIG. 53. The dates of crossbill invasions into southwest Europe. Filled blacks show large invasions, open blocks small ones. P.C., T.C. and C.C. refer to Parrot, Two-barred and Common Crossbills.

has been most studied (refs. in Newton 1970 a, b). Those individuals reaching southwest Europe originate from the northern forests between Norway and the Urals, and probably beyond. (The most easterly ringing recovery is from just this side of the Urals at 56° 40' east.) In some years (1927, 1930, 1958), however, the birds have come mainly from parts of Fenno-Scandia, and in others (1929, 1939, 1942) mainly from further east, as shown by comparing the migration at different places. But whatever the origin, the course of each invasion was much the same. The birds arrived in southwest Europe in summer and soon spread widely. Probably many perished, but some remained to breed in the following spring, and most then moved on again. To understand these movements, it is helpful first to examine the habits on the regular range (for further details see p. 73–81).

The annual cycle of Crossbills

Good seed-crops of conifers, like those of other trees, are sporadic. In any one year, the cone crops may be good over hundreds or thousands of square kilometres, but each productive area may be separated from the next by similar terrain in which the crop is poor. The next year the crops may be good in different areas, however, and Crossbills will move accordingly, always concentrating where cones are plentiful. An observer at any one place therefore sees enormous fluctuations in Crossbill numbers from year to year which parallel the changes in seeds. This was first shown by Reinikainen (1937) in northern Finland. He travelled over the same route by ski each Sunday in March for eleven years, counted the number of Crossbills met on his journeys and estimated the cone crops of spruce and pine. As shown in Figure 54, the number of breeding Crossbills seen each year was strongly correlated with the size of the spruce crop (though not

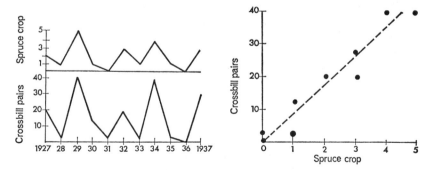

FIG. 54. Relation between the population density of the Crossbill and the cone crop of spruce (from Reinikainen 1937). Crossbills in number of pairs per 120km.; spruce crop classified in five categories.

with the pine crop), the highest number of birds being twenty times the lowest, with an increase of this order occurring from one year to the next. Even more pronounced fluctuations were noted by Formosov (1960) in northern Russia. In autumn 1935, when cones were scarce, he spent 21 days in spruce forests and saw Crossbills only three times. Then in 1952, when cones were plentiful, in a single day he saw more than 100 flocks.

In Northern Europe, the seeds of spruce, like those of most conifers, are formed from late June, remain in the cones over winter, and are shed the following April or May when the cones open. Crossbills can obtain seeds from cones at any stage of ripeness but, owing to their special bill-structure, cannot easily pick up fallen seeds from the ground. In the period (up to two months), between the falling of one spruce crop and the formation of the next, the birds feed chiefly from pine cones, which open later than those of spruce and shed their seeds more slowly. It is also while the new spruce cones are forming that the birds move, leaving areas where the new crop is poor and settling where it is good. They fly in various directions, and would usually need to cover at most a few hundred kilometres before finding a suitable area. If spruce cones are scarce over a wide area, however, Common Crossbills will feed from pine throughout the year, not just in summer. Typically, their annual cycle consists of successive periods of moult, breeding and movement, and they differ from other birds in making only a single major movement each year, between one good seed area and another. Broadly speaking, other species of crossbill follow a similar cycle, though centred on different food-plants.*

The foregoing describes the annual cycle in a normal year. In an invasion year, movement may begin earlier and end later than usual. Instead of dispersing in various directions, the birds move mainly in one direction; they also cover longer distances, appearing up to 4,000 kilometres from their previous home range. Before departing, they are unusually restless and excited, and once under way, do not always halt when they meet with abundant food, but appear within a few days over their whole invasion area, including the furthest sea-coasts and off-shore islands.

Accepting that some Crossbills move locally every year away from local scarcities, the key question is why large numbers leave the regular range in some years but not in most.

The cause of eruptions

Most authors agree in speculating that the adaptive value ('ultimate cause') of mass emigration is to avoid food-shortage on the regular range, but there is dispute over the proximate factors which might release the

*In North America, Crossbills move mainly in autumn and spring, like other birds, but there most conifer-species shed the bulk of their seed in autumn. On both continents, therefore, the timing of Crossbill movement is connected with the fruiting of their food-plants.

flight. On one view, eruptions result directly from widespread crop-failure and are a continuation of the normal movements (Svärdson 1957). On another view they can also result from 'overpopulation', and crowding presents the stimulus to leave (Lack 1954).

There is no doubt that some eruptions have occurred in years of widespread crop-failure. In 1909, 1930 and 1935 spruce cones were scarce over almost the whole of Fenno-Scandia and northern Russia, and in all three years Crossbills irrupted into southwest Europe. Two lines of evidence suggest, however, that eruptions cannot be attributed to crop-failure alone and that some other factor, probably the population level, is also involved. First, not all poor crops have resulted in eruptions; and second, in some years emigration has begun before the new crop is ready and hence before its size was manifest. To take these points in turn:

1. *Spruce crops and emigration.* In Sweden the spruce crop in different districts has been assessed annually for many years and the information obtained co-ordinated first at a regional and then at a national level (Svärdson 1957, Huss 1967). Over the country as a whole very small crops have occurred this century in 14 different years (1901, 1903, 1929, 1930, 1932, 1935, 1938, 1939, 1943, 1947, 1955, 1957, 1961, 1963). But mass emigration of Crossbills has occurred in at most six of these years (1903, 1929, 1930, 1935, 1938, 1939) and in three of these the birds were probably mainly from further east. In the remaining eight years of poor crops, there was no mass emigration. Further, big emigrations sometimes occurred in years of moderate crops (as in 1927, 1953, 1956, 1958, 1962); but never in years of exceptionally good crops (1913, 1915, 1921, 1928, 1931, 1934, 1942, 1945, 1954). In other words, eruptions from Sweden have occurred in years of various crop-sizes, except the largest, and less than half the poor crops have resulted in eruptions. Hence, while food has strong influence, it cannot be the only factor involved.

2. *The timing of emigration.* In those recent invasions that have been described in detail, most movement was in July and August, by which time the birds would be able to feed on the new spruce crop; and, to judge from the arrival dates in Britain, thirteen of these invasions began in late June or July, only after this crop became available (Appendix 16). However, another three started in May, so that in these the period of emigration spanned three successive crops (spruce – pine – spruce) and began before the new spruce crop was ready. Elsewhere, migration in all months between early April and late December has been recorded in invasion years. This again suggests that mass emigration is not linked simply with the failure of individual crops.

Turning now to the second hypothesis, that the flights might be stimulated by crowding, little quantitative information from the regular breeding range exists on Crossbill numbers in different years, except for that already given. But before their main eruptions, the birds are often

said to be exceptionally numerous over large areas. Further, where invasions of southwest Europe have occurred in successive years, they have
almost certainly originated from mainly different regions. This century,
emigration from Fenno-Scandia has often occurred in the same year, or
the preceding or the following year, as has emigration from further east,
thus showing that Crossbills have repeatedly reached an eruptive state
at about the same time in widely separated parts of the boreal forest.
Possibly the birds have repeatedly reached a population peak at about the
same time over the whole area.

The hypothesis that best fits these various observations is that high
numbers are necessary for eruptive movements, but that the size of the
spruce crop modifies this. Once the population is high, emigration probably
occurs in response to the first inadequate crop, and only an exceptionally
good crop over a wide area will delay the flight another year. The more
intense migratory state among erupting Crossbills, which is characterised
among other ways by a stronger directional tendency than usual, might
be explained if an additional factor (crowding) contributes to its development in these years. In this way, the views of Dr Lack, Dr Svärdson and
others are not incompatible. The problem remains, however, as to whether
crowding alone will stimulate emigration, irrespective of food. The earli-
ness of some irruptions suggests that it might, but none of these early
movements have preceded good crops (which is needed to test this view),
and it is possible that the birds can assess a developing crop before it is
ready.

To conclude, the normal annual movements of Crossbills are associated
with food-shortage and some eruptions have occurred in years of widespread crop-failure. However, not all poor crops have been followed by
eruptions, and high numbers may also be needed, though confirmation is
required. A small spruce crop (though reducing breeding) does not
necessarily mean that birds will starve, because alternative foods are
normally available. On the other hand, when numbers are unusually
high and all the birds remain, food-shortage will almost certainly accrue
(despite alternative foods), if not in one year, then in the next. There will
then be an advantage in emigration.

The fate of birds on irruptions

Since it reduces the population on the breeding grounds, mass emigration
is presumably useful to those birds that stay, providing food is available
there. The behaviour of the emigrants, in contrast, is frequently considered
suicidal because they often reach areas devoid of conifers. Indeed, mass
emigration is thought by some to be a means of population regulation
when numbers exceed the food supply, the 'doomed surplus' moving out
and wandering till death (e.g. Wynne-Edwards 1962). On the other
hand, others have postulated that the movements might be advantageous

for the participants, as well as the residents, but the problem was to find what happened to them.

In recent years ringing recoveries have provided the first concrete evidence that some Crossbills return successfully to their home range in a later year. These derive mostly from the 1,740 birds ringed during the irruptions of 1959 and 1963 at the Col de Bretolet, in the Swiss Alps (Fig. 55). All but one of the 17 caught again in the year after ringing were in latitudes to the south of Bretolet, whereas the four obtained in later years were far to the northeast in Russia (the direction from which the birds had come). This suggests that Crossbills in large irruptions do not return in the same year to their place of origin, but only in a later year. As is usual on the regular range, they apparently made only one movement each year. These results also show the long distances covered by migrating

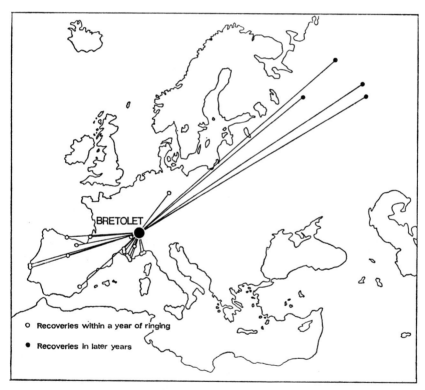

FIG. 55. Recoveries of Common Crossbills ringed in Switzerland (mostly at Col de Bretolet) during the invasions of 1959 and 1963, showing that some birds returned to the boreal forest in a later year. The four concerned were classed at ringing as juvenile, first-year cock, adult cock, and cock (unaged).

Crossbills, as the most distant recoveries in different years are nearly 4,000 kilometres apart.

If, after an irruption, Crossbills find areas of conifers, they often remain to breed. Mostly they move on after breeding once, but some irruptions have resulted in the colonisation of a new area. In Britain a stock of *curvirostra* has now lived in the Scots pine plantations of East Anglia since the invasion of 1909, and other colonies elsewhere since later invasions. These are all in areas planted by man, but presence of crossbills in the tropics (*L. curvirostra luzonensis* in northern Luzon, *L. c. meridionalis* in southern Annam, and *L. leucoptera megaplaga* on Hispaniola) suggests that the birds have occasionally established themselves in natural forests following invasions. Nevertheless, the formation of colonies may only be an incidental result of irruptions.

The directions and destinations of irrupting Crossbills

A few years ago it was not known whether irrupting Crossbills merely dispersed outwards in various directions from a centre or whether they moved mainly in one direction; and if the latter whether this direction was the same each time. However, the increased observation in recent years has shown that those Common Crossbills inhabiting the Russian forests irrupt in directions chiefly between west and southwest, and those from Fenno-Scandia between west and south. For Fenno-Scandia these directions have been confirmed by the recoveries of birds ringed on several irruptions, all of which lie in the western half of Europe. Hence, far from moving randomly, Crossbills irrupt in the same direction each time. Admittedly, they may move further in some years than in others, and their initial directional preference may disappear as the weeks pass and their migratory impulse wanes. (The appearance of odd vagrants in places like Iceland, Faeroes and Greenland is only to be expected, whatever the main directional tendency, as it occurs among other migrant birds.)

The return of the birds after an outward movement is analogous to the 'homing' of other migrants, but unlike other species, Crossbills often breed before returning. This means that, if they are to reach their ancestral home, young raised in invasion areas have to make their first migration in a direction opposite to the first migration of their parents and of all other individuals raised on the regular range. Experiments on other species of birds have shown that, if the young are displaced artificially, they set off in the direction normal for their population, even when this is wholly inappropriate under the experimental circumstances. Apparently, young birds are inherently 'programmed' for direction and distance, and can correct for displacement from a point they have previously experienced, but know nothing about the co-ordinates of areas which they have not yet visited (Matthews 1968 and *in litt.*). On these grounds, young Crossbills reared in invasion areas are unlikely to reach the boreal forest, except by chance. Normally, however, they leave the immediate breeding area at the same time as the adults, so much more ringing is needed to show their fate.

Fat deposition

The fact that some Crossbills move every summer raises the question of whether, like other migrants, they lay down body fat before migrating. During the irruption of 1963, the weights were taken of over a thousand birds caught while crossing the Col de Bretolet in the Swiss Alps. In both adults and young, the individual variation was considerable, some birds weighing up to 50% more than others (Fig. 56). Wing-length indicated that these birds came from a single population, and such a wide spread in the weights suggests that Crossbills do deposit migratory fat and that these birds were caught at different stages of fatness. This was confirmed by visual estimates of the fat present in the tracheal pit of each bird, which can be seen by blowing the feathers aside. Furthermore, ten more Crossbills caught at other times of year in Switzerland weighed much less, on average than those of birds caught on migration. The presence of abundant fat

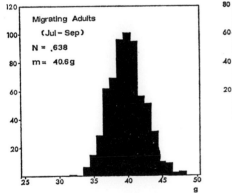 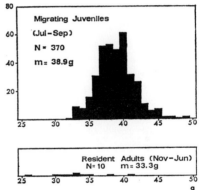

FIG. 56. Weights of Common Crossbills. Those on migration were obtained in 1963 at the Col de Bretolet, Swiss Alps, and those resident were obtained over several years elsewhere in Switzerland. Almost all the migrants were caught before mid-day, and most before 09.00. N=number, m=mean.

Note. Wing-length migrants (mm); juvenile cocks, range 89-102, mean 97.1; juvenile hens, range 89-100, mean 94.6; adult (yearling) cocks, range 90-102, mean 97.0; adult (yearling) hens, range 89-100, mean 94.5; adult (older) cocks, range 91-104, mean 97.5; adult (older) hens, range 89-100, mean 95.5; residents (7 birds), range 92-101, mean 96.

on the migrants also implies that irruptions should not be regarded as the death wanderings of starving birds, but as an event for which the birds are physiologically adapted.

The proportion of young in invasion flocks

In many irruptive species, the young predominate in invading flocks, and among the adults, hens outnumber cocks (refs. in Lack 1954). This has given rise to the ideas (a) that irruptions follow good breeding seasons, (b) that the young emigrate in greater proportion than the adults, and (c) that more adult hens than cocks leave. But recent information on the composition of the migrant flocks is conflicting. As may be seen from Appendix 17 the proportion of young in different samples has varied between 6% and 88%, and in any one invasion between 6% and 37%, all differences being significant statistically. Even the higher figure from this last invasion did not suggest that it had followed good breeding.

Among the adults, hens outnumbered cocks in the 1953 sample from Fair Isle, but in no other recent invasion did the sex ratio differ significantly from 1:1. However, many of the juveniles caught in 1963 at Bretolet could be sexed (because they had started to moult) and hen juveniles (99) were significantly more numerous than cocks (59); the same was true of migrant young examined in Finland in 1956 (Hildén 1960).

These recent observations on the Common Crossbill suggest that large-scale emigration does not always follow a good breeding season, and will occur in a population containing more adults than young. Except where the young are exceptionally numerous throughout an emigration, one cannot be certain that they are leaving in greater proportion than adults, without figures from the breeding grounds as well. If the different sex and age groups move at different dates, moreover, this would also influence the composition of the flocks.

Concluding remarks

Summarising, Crossbills normally move every year away from local shortages. They move in various directions, and over comparatively short distances, remaining within their regular range, wherever food is plentiful. Mass emigration from the regular range sometimes occurs in years of widespread crop-failure, but not in all such years, and probably high numbers are also needed. Irruptive movements take place chiefly in one direction and over long distances. Either way, the birds move mainly in summer.

Many problems remain. To begin with, it is hard to see how the normal annual movements of Crossbills, which apparently take place in various directions, become mainly unidirectional in an invasion year. But this is the sort of change occurring in all migrants at the migration season, so all that is needed to produce the change in Crossbills is that they reach a higher migratory state in some years than in others. Every year they move away from local shortages, so some additional factor is needed in invasion years. The evidence suggests that crowding is this factor. By responding in this way, the birds leave before food becomes really scarce and they are too weak to go. They at least then stand a chance of surviving elsewhere. The birds are now known to deposit extra fat in invasion years, but it would also be interesting to know whether they do so in other years.

It is also puzzling that the three species of Crossbills tend to erupt together. This cannot always be attributed to all their respective food-plants failing simultaneously, for even if they all flower poorly in the same year (as often happens) the cones of spruce and larch then take less than one year to mature, whereas those of pine take nearly two. Thus if eruptions depended only on the failure of the food supply, Parrot Cross-bills would normally be expected to erupt in the years after Common Crossbills, and not in the same years. Perhaps the most likely explanation of the synchronous eruptions is that the excited state, which appears in the birds beforehand, spreads from one species to the other, inducing them all to leave together. Since the three Crossbills overlap in diet, a shortage of food for one might affect them all in due course, in which case a tendency to respond in this way would be advantageous.

As the Two-barred Crossbill breeds mainly east of the Urals, only the tail-end of its irruptions reach Britain. Nevertheless, the number of these birds appearing among Common Crossbills in western Europe has varied greatly in different invasions. The species was especially numerous in 1845 and absent altogether in 1958. Presumably, this reflects the different origins of the irruptions, the greater the proportion of Two-barred, the further east the emigration.

As in the previous chapter, the term 'irruption' has been used by ornithologists to cover not only the irregular emigration of Crossbills, but also the occasional heavy migrations of regular migrants, such as the Redpoll, Siskin, Pine Grosbeak and Brambling. All these finches feed from trees whose seed-crops fluctuate greatly from year to year, and the birds concentrate wherever their food is plentiful. However, the three Crossbills are the only irruptive migrants which feed on the same type of food (conifer seeds) throughout the year, and migrate only once each year. The others depend on the critical seed-crop for only part of the year, and migrate twice each year, in spring and autumn. Further, whereas Crossbills leave their breeding range only in exceptional years, the others do so regularly every year, but in greatly varying numbers. The differences are linked with the ecological needs of the different species, the movements of the Crossbills being adapted to annual fluctuations in food, and the others to seasonal, as well as to annual, fluctuations.

CHAPTER 16

WEIGHTS AND BODY COMPOSITION

WEIGHT is not used as a taxonomic criterion because it is too changeable. In any one individual it varies with both time of day and time of year: between individuals it varies with overall body size (as judged by wing-length) and with physiological state. The weights of finches fluctuate like those of many northern song-birds, varying in individuals by up to 10% of the minimum during the course of each day, and by up to 25% during the course of a year. It is convenient to begin with the Bullfinch, which I was able to study in detail near Oxford by netting birds at their feeding places (Newton 1966b, 1968c, 1969a, Newton & Evans 1966). Also, being resident, this species does not put on the migratory fat which complicates the seasonal weight changes of some other finches.

Around Oxford, the daily light period changes from about 16 hours on 21 June to just under 8 hours on 21 December, and average temperatures are highest in July and lowest in January. Plants fruit almost entirely between May and September, during which months food for Bullfinches is abundant. In the colder months the birds live first on seeds remaining from the summer and then on buds (p. 119). Probably the most critical month is January because seeds are scarce by then and buds are still small. All individuals breed and begin to moult within the growing season and some individuals continue to moult into October or November, when seeds are no longer being produced but are still plentiful from the summer. The two most demanding activities thus occupy the most favourable season; and for the rest of the year the birds are free, if necessary, to feed all day for maintenance alone.

Summer Weights

The weights of Bullfinches do not vary in parallel with environmental conditions. The cocks are lightest in July, at around 22 grams, rise steadily to around 26 grams in January, and fall again to the next July (Fig. 57). Hence, they are lightest in summer when days are long and warmest and food is most readily available; and are heaviest in winter when days are short and coldest and food is least readily available. The weights of the hens fluctuate similarly, but rise again in the breeding season, to reach 26 grams or more when the eggs are due. Only in summer do the weights of the sexes differ significantly.

These are average trends for the population, however, and for much of the year the weight of an individual depends on the state of its breeding

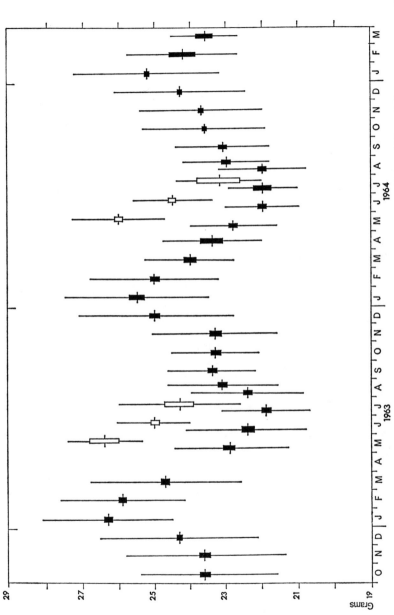

FIG. 57. Changes in the monthly weights of Bullfinches over two and a half years. The weights of the sexes are combined, except in the breeding season, when open boxes refer to hens. The vertical lines cover one standard deviation, and the boxes two standard errors, above and below the mean. Sample sizes range from 24 to 161 birds per month.

and moult. As may be recalled, the cock supplies all the food for the hen during incubation, and for her and the young during the first few days after hatching, a total of about three weeks. In the fourth week, when the young are larger, both sexes gather the food. For almost the whole season, therefore, the cock is collecting food, not only for himself, but also for the hen and then the young; and this is repeated for each successive nest. The hen, in contrast, has long inactive periods of brooding, separated by short active ones of feeding the young of different nests. But each cycle may be interrupted at any stage if the eggs and young are lost, and the birds have to start anew. In fact, predation on the eggs is initially so heavy that for six weeks few birds get beyond the laying or incubation stages, and only near the end of the season are the majority feeding young.

While the cock is feeding nestlings, his weight declines steadily. It recovers slightly between broods, when he has only the hen to feed, but the net result is a slow loss throughout the season. By the end, when he begins to moult, the cock reaches his lowest weight of the year. The hen is heavier than the cock throughout breeding, but the disparity is greatest at times of egg-laying. Her weight remains high during incubation but, like the cock's, falls while she is feeding young. On average, the cocks lose 6–7% of their weight during the nestling period, and the heavier hens lose up to 15% (Fig. 58). Hence, despite an abundance of food in summer, Bullfinches raise young partly at the expense of their own reserves. Their deteriorating condition might be partly responsible for terminating breeding each year, the birds failing to start another nest when their weight has fallen below a certain level. This view fits the fact that the birds breed longer than usual in years when food is uncommonly plentiful, when one might expect them to be under less strain (p. 191). But this is speculative, and suffice it to say that breeding, however prolonged, eventually reduces the cocks to their lowest weight of the year and the hens to one of their lowest.

The decline in weight while feeding young is easy to detect because the same individuals can be caught repeatedly in mist nets placed near their nests. But the rise in weight between broods is difficult to prove directly because the chance of catching the birds after the young have flown are small. It can be inferred, however, from the fact that birds which are feeding young are always lighter than the average weight of the population as a whole (based on birds caught at feeding places), the other (heavier) birds presumably being at earlier stages of a nesting cycle. The mean weight for the population falls between May and July partly because, as predation declines, more eggs hatch, and more birds are feeding young.

With the onset of the moult, the weights of the two sexes become equal again. In the population as a whole the start of moult is spread over more than two months and in each individual the process takes nearly three months to complete (p. 200). Average weight rises from start to finish, from 22 to 25 grams, and then declines slightly to 24.8 grams. Despite

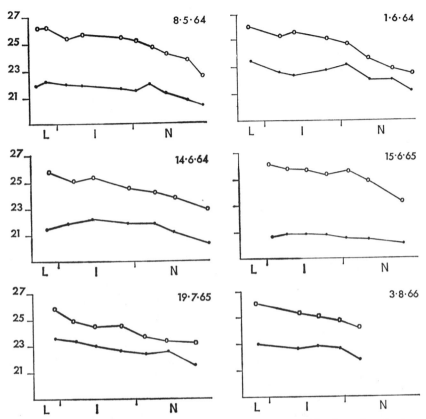

FIG. 58. The weight changes (in grams) of six Bullfinch pairs during the breeding cycle. Open circles hens, filled circles cocks. L=laying period, I=incubation period, N=nestling period.

variations in food and weather, these same weight changes occur among birds moulting in different years and at different dates in any one year. In other words, the weight of a Bullfinch at this time is correlated more closely with the stage of moult than with the environmental conditions. The mean weight for the population rises between August and October chiefly because the samples caught in later months contain more birds at late (heavier) stages of moult.

The young birds leave the nest at around 18 grams. They lose a little weight while they are learning to feed themselves, but soon recover and start to moult at around 22 grams, like their parents. They may begin to moult any time in a 2½-month period, depending on when they fledged, yet whatever the month or year they all show the same weight-changes.

Winter weights

Whereas for much of the year the weights of Bullfinches are closely correlated with particular stages of breeding and moult, and are thus determined primarily by the birds' own activities, for the rest of the year they are closely correlated with outside temperatures. From the end of moult in one year to the start of breeding in the next, the weights of different individuals fluctuate in parallel, being higher the colder the weather. The average monthly weight rises until January and falls thereafter, inversely with temperature, and is higher in cold winters than in mild ones – for example 26.3 grams in January 1963, when temperatures averaged −5°C, compared with 25.4 grams in January 1964 at +2°C.

The winter of 1962/63 was the coldest of the century at Oxford. For several weeks temperatures were below freezing, and on some nights down to − 20°C, yet the weights of Bullfinches were the highest recorded in six years, some over 30 grams. All the usual herbaceous food-plants were covered for several weeks by snow, and trees provided the food, especially the ashes (*Fraxinus*) which were laden with seeds. The birds maintained their high weights by feeding continuously from dawn to dusk, not as normally, mainly in the early morning and late afternoon.

Despite these trends, on any one cold day the weights of individuals of similar size may vary by up to 5 grams (25% of the lowest). Evidently not all birds achieve the weight appropriate to a given low temperature, perhaps because food-shortage and other factors prevent them. Thus, when seeds are scarce and the birds are eating buds, those individuals feeding in orchards (and getting larger buds) are consistently 1–2 grams heavier than are those in woodland. But birds are seldom caught in poor condition and markedly below average weight, which might seem surprising for many Bullfinches die each winter from food-shortage (Newton 1964b). Probably, however, they expire so quickly that the chances of catching them in the last stages of starvation are small.

Daylength has little or no direct influence on the weights of Bullfinches in winter, because the weights of birds caught on days of widely differing lengths but of similar temperature are the same (Fig. 59). On the other hand, over the range +12°C to −10°C, weight increases by about 0.14 grams for every degree of cooling (Fig. 60). But at any one temperature, the variation is considerable, showing that other factors influence weight. One already mentioned is the inability, through food-shortage, of some birds to reach the weight appropriate to a given temperature. The gain in weight, moreover, begins only when temperature falls below about 12°C. Above this so-called 'critical temperature', the birds are in the 'thermo-neutral zone', and lose no further weight as temperature rises. Otherwise, the birds respond rapidly to a marked temperature change, for within a day or two their weights have adjusted, or begun to adjust, to the new

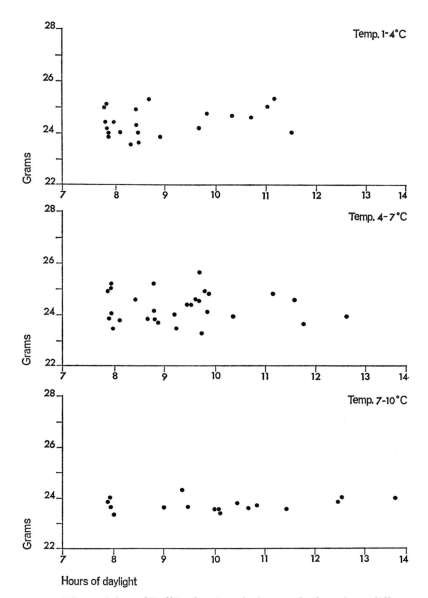

FIG. 59. The weights of Bullfinches in relation to daylength at different temperature ranges. Each point is the mean of at least ten weights obtained throughout a single day. The air temperature for each day was taken as the mean of the maximum and minimum.

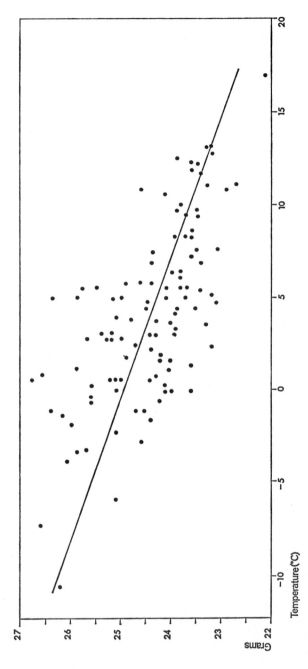

FIG. 60. The weights of Bullfinches in relation to air-temperatures. Each point is the mean of at least ten weights obtained throughout a single day. The air-temperature for each day was taken as the mean of the maximum and minimum.

level. Whether temperature acts directly on the birds, through its effects
on energy needs, or in some other way, is not known.

Body composition

The significance of the seasonal changes in weight can be better under-
stood by comparing the body-composition of birds at different times of
year. For this purpose, after removing any fresh food from the gullet and
gizzard, I analysed the carcasses of over 200 Bullfinches, most of which
had been killed on fruit farms. The aim was to find the proportions of
feathers, fat, water and lean dry material in each. The lean dry material
is the residue after the other components have been removed and consists
of muscle-protein, skeletal material and carbohydrate from the bird's
body, and dried food from the lower gut. Fluctuations in its weight are due
chiefly to changes in the muscle-protein.

In the course of a year the weight of each bird may change by up to
6 grams or more: 64% of this total change is of body water, 24% of protein
and 12% of fat. Stated otherwise, when the total weight changes by
6 grams, water changes by 4 grams, protein by 1.2 gram and fat by 0.8
gram. In addition, the feathers lose a little weight between the end of one
moult and the start of the next, as a result of wear (p. 203).

The three main body components vary according to a consistent pattern
and, under most conditions, no one component changes independently
(Fig. 61). This means that Bullfinches of a given weight and wing-length
nearly always have the same body composition, even breeding hens,
which have effectively the same make-up as birds of equivalent weight
in winter. The increase in their summer weights is due not merely to the
enlargement of their ovaries and other sex organs, but mainly to a heavy
deposition of protein and fat, as is evident on dissection. Their breast
muscles are especially large at this time compared to those of cocks. The
reserve is due not merely to the hen's inactivity while brooding, moreover,
for it is accumulated mainly before egg-laying, while the hen is still active,
and is maintained, but not increased, during the inactive phase on the
nest. At least it reduces the strain of feeding young and leaves the hen in
good condition to produce the next clutch.

The increase in the weights of all three body components during moult,
in both adults and juveniles, implies that this process is not such a strain
as feeding young. Any birds unable to meet the demands of moult by
extra feeding should have abnormally low fat or protein, but no such
birds were found, so if they exist, they must die without being caught, as in
winter. The weight of the plumage itself changes greatly during moult,
mainly because growing feathers contain blood whereas complete ones
do not. At the peak of feather-growth, the plumage of adults weighs 2.8
grams, nearly 70% more than at the start (1.7 grams), and in the juveniles
it doubles in weight (from 1.2 to 2.4 grams). It is the withdrawal and

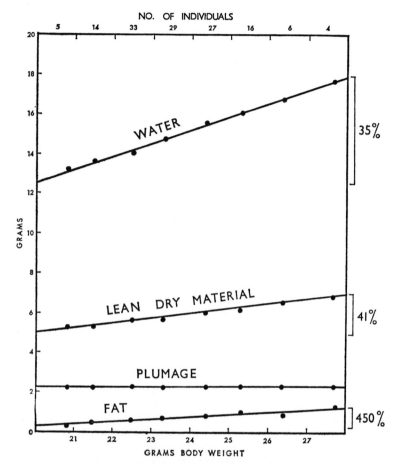

FIG. 61. The separate weight of different body components in relation to total body weight in the Bullfinch. The figures along the top show the sample sizes and the figures on the right show the increase of each component as a percentage of its initial value.

breakdown of blood and the loss of sheaths from the newly grown feathers that causes the total weight of the birds to drop slightly at the end of moult.

In addition to the seasonal changes in weight, there are also diurnal ones, the birds weighing 1–2 grams more at dusk than at dawn, but fluctuating around a higher level in winter than in summer. The weights of all three main components rise during the day and fall overnight. These changes result not merely from the filling and emptying of the gut, but mainly from the deposition of fat and other reserves during the day and their use overnight. The food digested overnight has been obtained in the few hours prior to roosting, but fat is laid down throughout the day. As shown in Figure 62, the later in the day the birds are taken the more fat they contain, and deposition begins in the morning, indicating an extremely rapid conversion of food to fat.

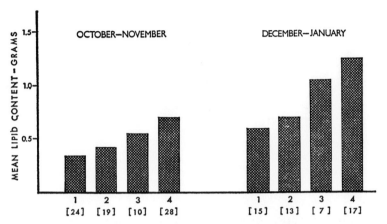

FIG. 62. Diurnal changes in the mean fat-content of Bullfinches. 1, first hour of daylight period; 2, first hour to mid-day; 3, mid-day to last hour; 4, last hour of daylight period. Figures in brackets show sample sizes.

The extent to which the stored fat is depleted overnight may be seen from Figure 63, which shows the fat-contents of some Bullfinches killed around dawn for comparison with those of others killed at dusk. At both times individuals varied considerably in their fat content, but it can be deduced that, on average, about half the fat present at dusk had been used by morning. The birds evidently lost about 0.4 grams of fat overnight in October/November, with nights of about 10 hours, and 0.66 grams in December/January with nights of about 16 hours, in both periods a mean rate of 0.04 grams per hour. The average amount of fat used overnight in autumn would yield 3.8 kilocalories of energy, and that used in winter 6.4 kilocalories. By comparison, any carbohydrate reserve, which is stored as glycogen in the liver and muscles, would yield at most 0.8 kilocalories (by analogy with other species), and any fresh food in the gut at most 1.6 kilocalories. Thus the stored fat is by far the most important source of energy for roosting Bullfinches. Probably it is not metabolised at a constant rate throughout the night, but is used most when the other, more immediate, reserves (food and glycogen) are nearing exhaustion.

On average, the fat remaining at dawn was more plentiful, and would have lasted longer, in winter than in autumn. But at both times some of the birds examined were starting the day with extremely little fat (0.1 gram),

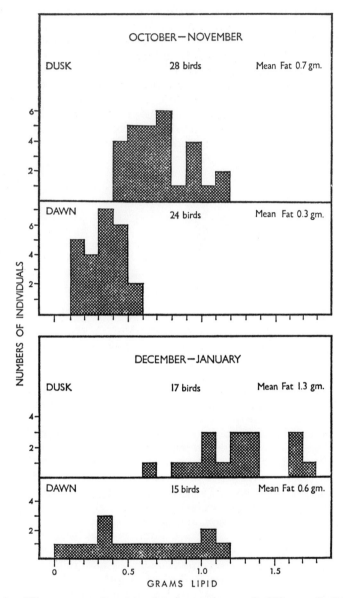

FIG. 63. Histograms, showing the fat-contents of different Bullfinches killed within one hour of dawn or dusk, at two times of year.

and even those with most would not have lasted another 24 hours without feeding. To survive, it seems, a Bullfinch must feed and replenish its fat every day. The reserves needed for roosting, and the ease with which they can be accumulated, vary greatly at different times of year. In mid-summer, the bird has a feeding day of 16 hours in which to prepare for an 8-hour night, but in mid-winter, it has only 8 hours to prepare for a 16-hour night. Hence, it is when feeding conditions are worst that the bird's require-ments are greatest. It is not now difficult to explain why Bullfinches often die of food-shortage in winter but are rarely caught in poor condition, for once their fat has been used, they can last only a few hours on the energy released from the further breakdown of muscle protein.

The adaptive value (ultimate cause) of the increase in weight and fat-content in winter is thus to ensure survival through long cold nights and to buffer the effects of temporary shortages in the daytime, rather than to serve as a long-term reserve, and as mentioned, the main proximate factor regulating the weight is probably temperature. This contrasts with mi-gratory fattening, which is apparently under the primary control of day-length, at least in spring, temperature having a secondary effect (p. 211).

The weights of water and lean dry material in the body, as well as fat, fluctuate over the 24 hours: for most of the year, their loss overnight is attributable mainly to the use of reserve carbohydrate and to the partial evacuation of the lower gut. During the moult, however, protein is also laid down in the body during the day and used overnight, presumably for feather growth, which continues at the same rate throughout the 24 hours. During the peak of moult, an average of 0.7 gram of lean dry material is lost each night and regained each day – more than 0.4 gram more than at other seasons (Newton 1968c).

The weights of other finches

The usual weights of some other British finches at different times of year are summarised in Appendix 18. The cocks of most species are slightly larger (as judged by wing-length), and for much of the year weigh slightly more than the hens, but the overlap in both measurements is great and in the breeding season hens weigh more than cocks. The Greenfinch is resident in Britain and shows similar weight changes to the Bullfinch. Both sexes are lightest in summer at the end of breeding, and heaviest in winter, with a minor peak during moult probably due to the presence of blood-filled feathers. Greenfinches also become heavier in cold winters than in mild ones. On average, their weights increase by about 0.16 gram for every degree of cooling, at least over the range $+3°$ to $-9°C$ (Lloyd-Evans & Nau 1965).

On any one cold day, however, weights may range from 22 to 40 grams, again implying wide differences between individuals in their ability to get enough food. From their appearance and behaviour, the lightest birds are clearly on the way out.

In my experience, the influence of food shortage on weight is even more marked in the Goldfinch and Linnet, only a few individuals of which manage to gain in cold weather. The general inability of these species to cope with the average British winter presumably explains why most individuals winter further south. These and other migrant species put on weight temporarily in spring and autumn, when depositing migratory fat (p. 209). In consequence, heavy individuals of the migrant species may be found in every month from September to May, as is evident from the weights of British (resident) compared to Scandinavian (migrant) Chaffinches (Appendix 18).

The weights of several North American song-birds are also correlated with temperature in winter, including, among the seed-eaters, the Purple Finch *Carpodacus purpureus* (Bartleson & Jensen 1955), the two forms of Redpolls (White 1966, Brooks 1968), and various buntings (King & Farner 1966). All these species are heaviest sometime between December and February, whichever month is coldest where they live. But they vary in the amount of fat they carry; and in some species in contrast to the British ones, the weight changes are due almost entirely to changes in fat, the rest of the carcass remaining stable. Also, the temperature below which extra fat is stored is usually lower for species living in colder climates. Redpolls in central Alaska begin to put on extra fat only below −12°C. For most of the year, they contain 5–6% fat, but this begins to increase in November and reaches 12% in January, when the average temperature falls to −23°C (White 1966). These birds remain further north and under colder weather in winter than any other song-birds. *C. hornemanni* has been seen in winter near the arctic coast of Alaska at 68°N, and both this form and *C. flammea* winter regularly in central Alaska at 65°N, where the night temperatures occasionally fall to −60°C. In adaptation, Redpolls have unusually long feathers, with fluffy tips, to trap the air efficiently for insulation. They also have unusually large gullets, which they pack with food before roosting. Their diet of dry birch seeds is exceptionally high in calories, and they digest these seeds better at lower temperatures. They burrow into the snow for shelter at night (Sulkava 1969), fly to and from their feeding places in near darkness, and feed at lower light intensities than most other birds. Moreover *C. hornemanni* has fluffier plumage, digests its food more efficiently at low temperatures, and remains active for at least 20 more minutes each day than does *C. flammea*. Any one of these advantages would count for little on its own, but together they enable the average *C. hornemanni*, on a 7-hour day and a diet of birch seeds, to survive temperatures down to −67°C, compared with −54°C for the average *C. flammea* in the same conditions (Brooks 1968).

Energy reserves

In general, birds accumulate reserves in preparation for any period in which their energy demand is likely to exceed their intake, whether during a winter night, a long flight, or some other regular period when food is not taken. But whereas large birds, such as geese, swans and certain raptors, can survive for days or even weeks on reduced rations, small birds live – literally – from day to day. Many, like the Bullfinch and Redpoll, must replenish their fat every day in winter to survive. Some, containing more fat, might last two days without food, but in none does the fat ensure survival through prolonged cold spells.

Most of the fat in lean birds is found in the muscles and liver. But as the total fat in the body increases, it accumulates in special 'fat-bodies', lumps of adipose tissue that on dissection separate easily from the rest of the carcass. They are found among the viscera and at several subcutaneous sites around the body (Fig. 64). In normal birds the latter can be easily seen through the skin after plucking, but in fat birds they coalesce to ensheath almost the whole body except the breast bone. Each fat-body consists of large cells, bound by connective tissue and supplied with nerves and blood vessels. The fat is deposited mainly in pre-existing cells, but as more fat is accumulated, more cells are formed to hold it (King 1967). Also, birds are selective in the type of fat they store. In the Junco (*Junco hyemalis*), a small American seed-eater, over nine-tenths of the total fat reserve consists of only four of the sixteen fatty acids present (linoleic, oleic, palmitic and stearic), which change in proportion through the year (Helms & Bower 1968). The composition of the fat apparently depends more on the physiological state of the bird than on the diet. Thus, captive Redpolls kept under constant daylengths and temperatures, but fed three different diets had fat of the same composition. Yet the fat of wild migrant Redpolls contained over 80% linoleic acid, three times as much as did the captive birds not in a migratory state, and twice as much as did wild birds that were breeding (West & Meng 1968).

To summarise this chapter, for much of the year the weights of individual Bullfinches are closely correlated with the stage of breeding or moult they are at, but for the rest of the year with outside temperatures, being heaviest on the coldest days. The 'ultimate' reason for the increase in weight and fat-content in winter is to ensure survival through long cold nights. The main proximate factor regulating weight is probably the outside temperature, though food-shortage sometimes prevents birds reaching the weight appropriate to a given temperature. The weights of other finches show similar changes to those of the Bullfinch, and are probably under similar control, but the migrant species also gain in weight, through fat-deposition, in spring and autumn. The laying down of migratory fat, in

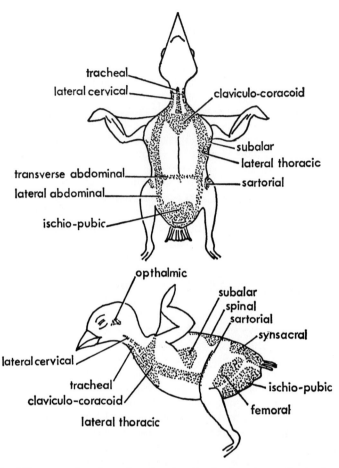

FIG. 64. Diagram showing the sites in the body where fat is deposited (modified from King & Farner 1965).

contrast to winter fat, is apparently controlled mainly by daylength, at least in spring. Either way, the fat is stored in concentrated form in special sites around the body. Particularly striking is the speed with which birds can accumulate and utilise fat. Imagine the impact of a slimming aid which could reduce fatness by half overnight.

Appendices

Appendix 1. The proportion of Linnet nests started in gorse or in deciduous shrubs in different months. (From the diaries of the late Arthur Whitaker, an egg-collector who operated in the Sheffield area and recorded systematically every nest he found.)

	% clutches started in:-					
	April	May	June	July	August	Total found
Gorse	21	47	25	6	1	291
Deciduous shrubs	1	31	41	23 —	4	132

Appendix 2. Measurements (mm. and gm.) of Parrot and Common Crossbills caught at Fair Isle. (From Davis 1963.)

	Adult cocks		Adult hens		Juveniles	
	Parrot	Common	Parrot	Common	Parrot	Common
Wing-length	100-105	91-101	96-103	89-99	92-97	90-100
Tail-length	61-67	51-62	58-65	52-61	56-60	53-62
Bill-length	19-22	19-23	19-21.5	18-23	18.5-21	18-22
Bill-depth	14-15.5	10.5-12	12-15	10-12	11-12.5	10.5-12
Weight	38.8-53.1	29.8-44.0	37.5-54.7	27.8-43.1	32.4-41.8	31.0-44.5
Number examined	13	24	14	40	9	40

Appendix 3. The hatching and fledging success of Chaffinches in different years, as shown by the records of the British Trust for Ornithology (from Newton 1964a).

Year	No. of nests	% clutches reaching hatching stage	% broods reaching fledging stage	% nests producing fledged young
1950	170	48	59	28
1951	399	37	68	25
1952	302	65	70	46
1953	187	64	74	47
1954	255	59	77	45
1955	272	54	57	31
1956	207	71	85	60
1957	202	60	77	46
1958	171	42	83	35
1959	111	72	50	36
1960	161	50	36	18

Appendix 4. The causes of nesting failure in the Chaffinch (from Newton 1964a).

| | Total number lost | Losses due to:- | | | |
		Predation	Desertion	Inclement weather	Other causes
Clutches	330	66%	27%	3%	2% 2%
Broods	126	60%	25%	14%	1% 1%

Appendix 5. Seasonal trends in the clutch-size of some finches. The figures show the average clutch in each month based on large samples (Hildén 1969), Monk (1954), Newton (1964c and unpublished), and Stokes (1950).

	April	May	June	July	August	September
Greenfinch (England)	4.7	4.8	4.9	4.8	-	-
Linnet (England)	4.7	4.8	5.0	4.7	4.0	-
Bullfinch (England)		4.8	4.6	4.3	3.8	-
Mealy Redpoll (Lapland)			5.4	4.6	-	-
American Goldfinch (Wisconsin)				5.3	4.4	3.6

Appendix 6. The normal incubation and nestling periods of the European
cardueline finches.

	Incubation period	Nestling period
A. Nest usually in low shrub		
Linnet	11-12	11-12
Twite	11-13	11-12
Redpoll	10-11	11-12
Scarlet Rosefinch	11-12	10-11
B. Nest usually in tall shrub		
Greenfinch	12-14	13-16
Serin	12-14	14-16
Bullfinch	12-14	15-17
Pine Grosbeak	13-14	13-14*
C. Nest usually in tree		
Hawfinch	11-13	13-14
Goldfinch	11-13	13-16
Siskin	11-13	13-17
Citril Finch	13-14	17-18
Common Crossbill	13-16	16-25
Scottish Crossbill	13-15	17-20
Parrot Crossbill	14-16	15-25

Note: Information is lacking for the Two-barred Crossbill.
 * One brood in captivity.

Appendix 7. The percentage (by volume) of animal-matter in the food of nestling Greenfinches, according to age and time of year. All broods
in farmland. (From Newton 1967b.)

	Number of broods	Number of examinations	Nestling day 1-3	4-6	7-9	10-12
Young hatched in May and June	22	520	11	9	3	+
Young hatched in July and August	12	484	3	2	0	0

Note: One inspection of one nestling = one examination. There were usually
4-6 nestlings per brood.

Appendix 8. The percentage (by volume) of animal-matter in the food of nestling Bullfinches, according to age and habitat. (From Newton 1967d.)

	Number of broods	*Number of examinations*	*1-5*	*6*	*7*	*8*	*9*	*10*	*11*	*12*
						Nestling day				
Woodland	16	598	38	25	34	29	29	21	23	10
Farmland	24	824	20	22	17	27	25	14	4	1

Note: One inspection of one nestling = one examination. There were usually 4-6 nestlings per brood.

Appendix 9. Comparison of the development of young Bullfinches and young Common Crossbills. The figures show the age (in days) at which various events occur.

	Eyes begin to open	*Feathers emerge*	*Young leave nest*	*Young begin to feed*	*Young become independent*
Bullfinch	3	5	15-17	20	35
Crossbill	5	7	18-22	38	>45

Appendix 10. The extent of predation on finch nests. The figures show the percentage of nests which were lost to predators in different months in southern England, several years combined (from Monk 1954, Newton 1964c and unpublished).

	April/May	*June*	*July/August*
Greenfinch	37%	36%	22%
Linnet	68%	50%	46%
Bullfinch (woodland)	85%	50%	30%
Bullfinch (farmland)	56%	33%	16%

Appendix 11. The timing and duration of moult in various finches.
All records are from southern England, except those for the Twite (Fair Isle), Siskin (captive birds) and Redpoll (Northumberland). Details from Evans (1966), Newton (1966a, 1968a and unpublished).

| | Mean duration of moult (weeks) | Dates of onset | |
		Median date	95% of birds start between
Chaffinch	10	23 June	27 May - 20 July
Greenfinch	12	5 August	25 June - 14 September
Goldfinch	11	29 July	2 July - 25 August
Siskin	10	?	?
Linnet	10	24 July	21 June - 25 August
Redpoll	8	6 August	16 July - 27 August
Twite	10	20 July	1 July - 10 August
Bullfinch	12	9 August	10 July - 9 August

Appendix 12. The growth periods (in days) of the flight feathers of four finches. Primaries and secondaries are numbered from the centre of the wing outwards, in the order in which they are moulted. In all cases the range of variation was up to two days on either side of the mean. Details from Newton (1967a, 1969b and unpublished).

| | Primaries | | | | | | | | | Secondaries | | | | | |
	9	8	7	6	5	4	3	2	1	1	2	3	4	5	6
Greenfinch	30	28	26	26	24	21	20	20	19	20	20	20	20	19	19
Bullfinch	28	26	26	23	22	22	21	21	20	21	21	20	20	19	19
Siskin	22	21	20	18	17	17	16	16	16	16	16	16	16	15	15
Lesser Redpoll	21	20	20	17	15	15	14	14	14	14	14	14	14	14	14

Appendix 13. The weights (in milligrams) of fresh and worn plumage of adult Bullfinches. The figures in brackets show the number of birds examined. (From Newton 1968c.)

	Large wing feathers	Large tail feathers	Body feathers
Fresh (36)	300	115	1,610
Worn (31)	296	106	1,050

Appendix 14. The weights (in grams) of finches at migration time.

		Usual weight before migration season	Usual weight during migration season	Maximum weight recorded in the migration season
Goldfinch	Cocks	15-18	16-19	22
	Hens	14-17	15-18	20
Siskin	Cocks	12-14	14-16	19
	Hens	11-13	13-15	17
Linnet	Cocks	18-21	19-23	24
	Hens	17-20	19-22	23
Twite	Cocks	15-18.5	16-20	21
	Hens	14.5-18	15-19	20
Mealy Redpoll	Cocks	12-14	13-15	19
	Hens	11.5-13.5	12.5-14.5	17
Lesser Redpoll	Cocks	10-12	11-14	16*
	Hens	10-11.5	10.5-13	15*
Northern Bullfinch	Cocks	26-30	28-34	?
	Hens·	26-30	28-34	?
Northern Chaffinch	Cocks	23-27	24-28	31
	Hens	22-25	23-26	28
Brambling	Cocks	24-27	25-30	33
	Hens	22-25	24-27	32

Note: Details from personal records, A. Frudd, C.J. Mead, R.S. Scott, Bullock (1967), Evans (1966, 1969), Evans, Elton & Sinclair (1967), Dolnik & Blyumental (1967), Musson (1968), Newton (1966b, 1969b).

* Captive birds only.

Appendix 15. The passage of Siskins over Oland, southern Sweden, 1947-1955. (From Svärdson 1957.)

			Percentage of season's total seen during:-				
Year	Birch-seed index	August 16-31st	September 1-15th	September 16-30th	October 1-15th	October 16-31st	Season's total (in thousands)
1955	1.1	-	31	49	13	7	4.0
1949	1.5	3	30	37	25	5	9.8
1947	2.0	-	2	16	75	7	2.7
1952	2.0	-	-	34	52	14	4.3
1953	2.0	-	-	76	18	6	6.5
1951	2.2	-	1	37	46	16	1.2
1950	2.5	-	-	14	75	11	0.7
1954	2.9	-	-	3	66	31	1.0
1948	3.1	-	1	8	23	68	4.0

Appendix 16. The dates of some recent invasions of Common Crossbills into southwest Europe

Year of invasion	Date of first reported arrivals in Britain	Intervals (years) between invasions
1901*	?	
		2
1903**	9 July	
		6
1909**	23 June	
		1
1910**	20 June	
		1
1911*	?	
		5
1916*	27 July	
		9
1925*	4 July	
		2
1927**	May	
		2
1929**	26 June	
		1
1930**	2 July	
		5
1935**	20 June	
		3
1938**	?	
		1
1939**	?	
		3
1942**	May	
		5
1947*	?	
		1
1948*	?	
		5
1953**	12 May	
		3
1956**	3 June	
		2
1958**	26 June	
		1
1959**	12 July	
		3
1962**	27 June	
		1
1963**	10 July	

Note: * Small invasion. ** Large invasion.

Appendix 17. The number of adult and young Crossbills caught or seen on migration in different years.

Location	Year	Adults (both sexes)	Number of:—			% of young in sample
			Adult cocks	Adult hens	Young	
North Sea	1927	9	2	7	72	88%
Fair Isle	1953	54	17	37	45	54%
Signilshar, Finland	1956	47	?	?	188	80%
Fair Isle	1958 1959 1962	9	4	5	8	47%
Heligoland	1962	46	19	27	23	33%
Heligoland	1963	141	63	78	9	6%
Britain (4 localities)	1963	150	85	65	14	8%
Col de Bretolet, Switzerland	1963	638	305	333	370	37%
Stavanger, Norway	1963	50	?	?	22	31%

Note: Details from Murray (1928), Hildén (1960), Davis (1964), Vauk (1964), and unpublished Swiss records.

Appendix 18. The usual weights (in grams) of finches at different times of year.

		January – February	March – April (migration in some species)	May – July (breeding)	August – September (moulting)	October (migration in some species)	November – December
Greenfinch	Cocks	28-36	27-35	26-32	26-33	27-33	27-35
	Hens	27-35	26-34	26-34	26-32	26-32	26-34
Goldfinch	Cocks	16.5-20.5	15-20	14-18	15-18.5	15-19	16-19
	Hens	15.5-20	15-19	14.5-19.5	14-17.5	13.5-18	15-18.5
Siskin	Cocks	12-15	11.5-15.5	10.5-12	11.5-13.5	12-16	11.5-14.5
	Hens	12-14	11-14.5	11-14.5	10.5-13	11-15	11-13.5
Linnet	Cocks	18.5-22	17.5-20.5	16.5-20	16.5-21	17.5-22.5	18.5-21.5
	Hens	18-21.5	16.5-20	17-22	15.5-20	17-22	18-21
Twite	Cocks	17-21	16-20	14-18	14.5-18.5	16-20	15.5-19
	Hens	16-20	14.5-19	14.5-19.5	14-18	14.5-19	15-18.5
Lesser Redpoll	Cocks	11.5-13	11-13.5	10:11.5	10-12.5	10.5-13	11.5-13
	Hens	11-12.5	10.5-13	10-13	10-1r.5	10-12.5	11-12
Bullfinch	Cocks	23.5-27	22.5-25.5	21-23.5	22-24.5	22-25	22-26.5
	Hens	23.5-27	22.5-25.5	22-27	22-24.5	22-25	22-26.5
British Chaffinch	Cocks	21-26	21-25	20-23	20-24	20-23.5	20.5-24.5
	Hens	20-24.5	20-24	20-25	19-23.5	19-23	20-24
Scandinavian Chaffinch	Cocks	24-29	24-29	?	23-27*	23.5-30	23.5-28.5
	Hens	23.5-26.5	22.5-27	?	22-25*	22.5-27	22-26.5
Brambling	Cocks	25-32	24-29	22-25*	24-27*	24-30	24-29
	Hens	24-30	23-28	23-29*	22-25*	23-27	23-28

Notes: Details from personal records, J. Cudworth, A. Frudd, C.J. Mead, T. Gladwin, Abs (1964), Bullock (1966), Creutz (1961), Evans (1966, 1969), Havlin (1957), Miles (1968), Musson (1968), Newton (1966b, 1968c, 1969a, 1969b). * From captive birds.

BIBLIOGRAPHY

ABS, M. 1964. Flügelmesswerte und Gewichte wandernder Erlenzeisige (*Carduelis spinus*). *Vogelwarte* 22: 173-6.

ANDREW, R. J. 1961. The displays given by passerines in courtship and reproductive fighting: a review. *Ibis* 103a: 315-48, 549-79.

ANDREW, R. J. & HINDE, R. A. 1956. The systematic position of *Fringilla* – some ethological evidence. *J. Orn. Lpz.* 97: 263-73.

ANVÉN, B. & ENEMAR, A. 1957. Homing and average expectation of life in the Chaffinch (*Fringilla coelebs*). *Vår Fågelvärld* 16: 161-77. (In Swedish, with English summary.)

ARMITAGE, J. 1937. Field notes on the Corsican Citril Finch. *Br. Birds* 31: 98-100.

AUSTIN, O. L. 1968. Life histories of North American Cardinals, Grosbeaks, Buntings, Towhees, Finches, Sparrows and allies. Part I. *U.S. Nat. Mus. Bull.* 237. Washington.

AXELL, H. E., LACK, D., PARSLOW, J. L. F. & WILCOCK, J. 1963. Migration at Minsmere seen and unseen. *Bird Notes* 30: 181-6.

BAILEY, A. M., NIEDRACH, R. J. & BAILY, A. L. 1953. The Red Crossbills of Colorado. *Publs. Denver mus. Nat. Hist.* 9: 1-64.

BAILEY, R. E. 1952. The incubation patch of passerine birds. *Condor* 54: 121-36.

BAKER, J. R. 1938. The evolution of breeding seasons. P. 161-77 in *Evolution*, ed. G. R. de Beer. London & New York: Oxford University Press.

BALDWIN, P. H. 1961. Distribution, overlap, and hybridisation of two species of Redpolls in Alaska. *Bull. Ecol. Soc. Amer.* 42: 152.

BANNERMAN, D. A. 1953. *The Birds of the British Isles*. Vol. 1. Edinburgh & London: Oliver & Boyd.

BARRETT, J. H. 1947. Some notes on the breeding habits of the Chaffinch. *Ibis* 89: 439-50.

BARTLESON, F. D. & JENSEN, O. F. 1955. A study of Purple Finch winter weights. *Wilson Bull.* 67: 55-9.

BATTEN, L. A. 1969. Bird population changes on farmland and in woodland for the years 1967-68. *Bird Study* 16:163-8.

BELL, B. D. 1968. The population ecology of the Reed Bunting, *Emberiza schoeniclus* (L.). Ph.D. thesis, Nottingham University.

BERGMAN, G. 1956. Zur Populationsdynamik des Buchfinken, *Fringilla coelebs*. *Ornis fenn.* 33: 61-71.

BERNHOFT-OSA, A. 1965. Om Bergiriksens *Carduelis flavirostris* trekk. *Stavanger Museums Arbok* 35: 109-18.

BERNHOFT-OSA, A. 1960. (Successful breeding of Pine Grosbeak (*Pinicola enucleator*) in captivity.) *Vår Fågelvärld* 19: 220-3. (In Swedish, with English summary.)

BIRCH, D. M. 1968. Success with Crossbills. *A.S.P.E.B.A., Occ. Publ.* 2: 5-8.

BLOK, A. X. & SPAANS, A. L. 1962. (On the occurrence of the Redpoll, *Carduelis flammea* (Linnaeus), as a breeding-bird in the Netherlands.) *Limosa* 35: 4-16.

266   BIBLIOGRAPHY

BOASE, H. 1948. Notes of the behaviour and nesting of some finches. *Scott. N. i*
60: 107–20.

BOYD, A. W. 1931. On some results of ringing Greenfinches. *Br. Birds* 24: 329–37.

BROOKS KING, M. 1949. A study of dialect in the song of the Chaffinch. *Devon Birds* 4: 35–9.

BROOKS, W. S. 1968. Comparative adaptations of the Alaskan Redpolls to the Arctic environment. *Wilson Bull.* 80: 253–80.

BRUCH, A., & LÖSCHAU, M. 1960. Berghänfling – Invasion in Berlin. *Orn. Mitt.* 12: 31.

BUB, H. 1969. Nahrungspflanzen des Berghänflings (*Carduelis fl. flavirostris*). *Vogelwarte* 25: 134–41.

BULLOCK, B. A. 1967. Siskin weights. *Surrey Bird Report* 1965.

COLLINGE, W. E. (1924–27). *The food of some British wild birds*. York.

CONDER, P. J. 1948. The breeding biology and behaviour of the Continental Goldfinch *Carduelis carduelis carduelis*. *Ibis* 90: 493–525.

CORNWALLIS, R. K. 1961. Four invasions of Waxwings during 1956–60. *Br. Birds* 54: 1–30.

COUTLEE, E. L. 1968. Comparative breeding behaviour of Lesser and Lawrence's Goldfinches. *Condor* 70: 228–42.

CRAMP, S. & TOMLINS, A. D. 1966. The birds of Inner London 1951–65. *Br. Birds* 59: 209–33.

CREUTZ, G. 1961. Einige Feststellungen an überwinternden Bergfinken (*Fringilla montifringilla*). *Vår Fågalvärld* 20: 302–18.

CROOK, J. H. 1960. Studies on the social behaviour of *Quelea q. quelea* (Linn.) in French West Africa. *Behaviour* 16: 1–55.

CROOK, J. H. 1962. The adaptive significance of pair formation types in weaver birds. *Symp. zool. Soc. Lond.* 8: 57–70.

CZARNECKI, Z. 1961. (Das Vorkommen vom Karmingimpel, *Erythrina erythrina erythrina* (Pall.) an der Warta.) *Acta orn. Warsz.* 6: 37–40. (In Polish, with German summary.)

CZARNECKI, Z. 1962. (Some biological observations on the Scarlet Grosbeak, *Carpodacus erythrinus erythrinus* (Pall.)). *Przeglad Zool.* 6: 171–6. (In Polish, with English summary.)

DAMSTÉ, P. H. 1947. Experimental modification of the sexual cycle of the Greenfinch. *J. exp. Biol.* 24: 20–35.

DARBY, H. C. 1956. The clearing of woodland in Europe. Pp. 183–216 in *Man's role in changing the face of the earth*, ed. W. L. Thomas. Chicago: University Press.

DARWIN, C. 1871. *The descent of man*. London: Murray.

DAVIS, P. 1963. The Parrot Crossbill irruption at Fair Isle. *Bird Migrat.* 2: 260–4.

DAVIS, P. 1964. Crossbills in Britain and Ireland in 1963. *Br. Birds* 57: 477–501.

DE CROUSAZ, G. & LEBRETON, P. 1963. Notes sur la migration du Venturon Montagnard (*Carduelis citrinella* L.) aux cols de Cou-Bretolet, et sur son hivernage en Suisee et en France. *Nos Oiseaux* 27: 46–61.

DEELDER, C. L. 1949. On the autumn migration of the Scandinavian Chaffinch (*Fringilla c. coelebs* L.). *Ardea* 37: 1–88.

DE KIRILINE, L. 1949. The Red Crossbill at Pimisi Bay, Ontario. *Can. Fld. Nat.* 63: 147–60.

DE KIRILINE, L. 1954. The voluble singer of the tree-tops. *Audubon Mag.* 56: 109–11.

DEMENTIEV, G. P. & GLADKOV, N. A. 1954. (*Birds of the Soviet Union*), Vol. 5. Moscow.

DICKINSON, B. H. B. & DOBINSON, H. M. 1969. A study of a Greenfinch roost. *Bird Study* 16: 135–46.

DIEN, J. 1965. Ornithologischer Jahresbericht 1964 für das Hamburger Berichtsgebiet. *Hamb. avifaun. Beitr., Hamburg* 2: 120–94.

DILGER, W. C. 1960. Agonistic and social behaviour of captive Redpolls. *Wilson Bull.* 72: 114–32.

DOERBECK, F. 1963. Zur Biologie des Gimpels (*Pyrrhula pyrrhula* (Sic)) in der Grossetatd. *Vogelwelt* 84: 97–114.

DOLNIK, V. R. 1963. (A quantitative study of vernal testicular growth in several species of finches (Fringillidae)). *Dokl. Akad. Nauk S.S.S.R.* 149: 370–2. (In Russian.)

DOLNIK, V. R. & BLYUMENTAL, T. I. 1967. Autumnal premigratory and migratory periods in the Chaffinch (*Fringilla coelebs coelebs*) and some other temperate-zone passerine birds. *Condor* 69: 435–68.

DURANGO, S. 1947. Till kännedomen om hämplingens, *Carduelis c. cannabina* (L.), förekomst under de senaste decennierna. *Svensk. Faun. Revy* 1: 3–17.

EBER, G. 1956. Vergleichende Untersuchungen über die Ernarhrung einige Finkenvögel. *Biol. Abh.* 13 & 14: 1–60.

ENEMAR, A. 1969. On the Redpoll *Carduelis flammea* in the Ammarnäs area, Swedish Lapland, in 1968. *Vår Fågelvärld* 28: 230–5.

ERARD, C. 1966. Note sur les *Carduelis flammea* migrateurs en France. *Alauda* 34: 102–19.

ERIKSSON, K. 1970a. Wintering and autumn migration ecology of the Brambling, *Fringilla montifringilla. Sterna* 9: 77–90.

ERIKSSON, K. 1970b. Wintering and migration ecology of Siskin and Redpoll. *Abstracts from the 15th Int. Orn. Congr. Hague.* 1970: 96–7.

ERKAMO, V. 1948. (On the winter nourishment and biology of the Bullfinch, *Pyrrhula p. pyrrhula* (L.).) *Arch. Soz. zool-bot. fenn. Vanamo* 1: 86–101.

EVANS, P. R. 1966. Autumn movements, moult and measurements of the Lesser Redpoll *Carduelis flammea cabaret. Ibis* 108: 183–216.

EVANS, P. R. 1969. Ecological aspects of migration, and pre-migratory fat deposition in the Lesser Redpoll, *Carduelis flammea cabaret. Condor:* 71: 316–30.

EVANS, P. R., ELTON, R. A. & SINCLAIR, G. R. 1967. Moult and weight changes of Redpolls, *Carduelis flammea*, in north Norway. *Orn. fenn.* 44: 33–41.

EVANS, W. 1911. Notes of the recent immigration of Mealy Redpolls (*Acanthis linaria*), including the form known as Holboll's Redpoll. *Proc. R. phys. Soc. Edinb.* 18: 192–203.

EYRE, S. R. 1968. *Vegetation and soils.* (2nd ed.) London: Edward Arnold.

FARNER, D. S. 1955. The annual stimulus for migration: experimental and physiological aspects. Pp. 198–237 in *Recent Studies in Avian Biology*, ed. A. Wolfson, Urbana.

FAXÉN, L. 1945. (Die Invasion des Hakengimpels (*Pinicola enucleator* L.) im

Winter 1942–43.) *Vår Fågelvärld* 4: 18–26. (In Swedish, with German summary.)

FERGUSON-LEES, I. J. 1956. Photographic studies of some less familiar birds. 74. Citril Finch. *Br. Birds* 49: 398–400.

FERGUSON-LEES, I. J. 1968. Serins breeding in southern England. *Br. Birds* 61: 87–8.

FLORENCE, L. 1912, 1914, 1915. The food of birds. *Trans. R. Highld. agric. Soc. Scotl.* 1912: 180–219; 1914: 1–74; 1915: 1–53.

FLOWER, W. U., WEIR, T., & SCOTT, D. 1955. Pine Grosbeak on the Isle of May. *Br. Birds* 58: 133–4.

FORMOSOV, A. N. 1960. La production de graines dans les forêts de conifères de la taiga de l'U.S.S.R. et l'envahissement de l'Europe occidentale par certaines espèces d'oiseaux. *Proc. 12th Int. Orn. Congr.* 1958: 216–29.

FRENCH, N. R. 1954. Notes on the breeding activities and on gular sacs in the Pine Grosbeak. *Condor* 56: 83–5.

FRENCH, N. R. 1959. Life history of the Black Rosy Finch. *Auk* 76: 159–80.

FRITH, H. J. 1957. Clutch size in the Goldfinch. *Emu* 57: 287–8.

FRY, C. H., ASH, J. S. & FERGUSON-LEES, I. J. 1970. Spring weights of some Palearctic migrants at Lake Chad. *Ibis* 112: 58–82.

GAUSE, G. F. 1934. *The struggle for existence.* Baltimore.

GLAS, P. 1960. Factors governing density in the Chaffinch (*Fringilla coelebs*) in different types of wood. *Arch. Néerl. Zool.* 13: 466–72.

GRENQUIST, P. 1947. (Über die Biologie des Hakengimpels, *Pinicola e. enucleator* L.). *Ornis fenn.* 24: 1–10. (In Finnish, with German summary.)

GRINNELL, L. I. 1943. Nesting habits of the Common Redpoll. *Wilson Bull.* 55: 155–63.

GRISCOM, L. 1937. A monographic study of the Red Crossbill. *Proc. Boston Soc. Nat. Hist.* 41: 77–210.

GROTE, H. 1937. Der sibirische Hakengimpel (*Pinicola enucleator stschur* Part.) in Deutschland. *Orn. Mber.* 45: 83–5.

GUENIAT, E. 1948. Beobachtungen en einem Massenschlafplatz von Bergfink in der Ajoie im Winter 1946/47. *Orn. Beob.* 45: 81–98.

HAAPANEN, A. 1965, 1966. Bird fauna of the Finnish forests in relation to forest succession. *Ann. Zool. fenn.* 2: 153–96; 3: 176–200.

HALD-MORTENSEN, P. 1970. (Lesser Redpoll as a breeding bird in Denmark.) *Dansk. Orn. For. Tids.* 64: 163-93. (In Danish, with English summary.)

HAMNER, W. M. 1963. Diurnal rhythm and photoperiodism in testicular recrudescence of the House Finch. *Science, N.Y.* 142: 1294–5.

HAMNER, W. M. 1964. Circadian control of photoperiodism in the House Finch demonstrated by interrupted-night experiments. *Nature, Lond.* 203: 1400–1.

HAMNER, W. M. 1966. Photoperiodic control of the annual testicular cycle in the House Finch *Carpodacus mexicanus*. *Gen. comp. Endocr.* 7: 224–33.

HARRIS, G. J. & SCOTT, R. E. 1964. The birds of Romney Marsh and their migrations, as recorded by the Dungeness Bird Observatory. *Dungeness Bird Observatory*, 1952–1962: 4–70.

HARRIS, M. P., NORMAN, F. I. & MCCOLL, R. H. S. 1965. A mixed population of redpolls in northern Norway. *Br. Birds* 58: 288–94.

HARRISON, C. J. O. 1970. The crop of the Chaffinch *Fringilla coelebs*. *Bull. Br. Orn. Club* 90: 15–16.

HAVLIN, J. 1957. Die Schwankungen des Körpergewichts der in der Tschechoslowakei überwinternden Bergfinken (*Fringilla montifringilla* L.). *Zool. Listy* 6(20): 247–56. (In Czech, with German summary.)

HELMS, E. B. & BOWER, C. W. 1968. Seasonal variation in fatty acids of the Slate-coloured Junco (*Junco hyemalis*). *Physiol. Zoöl.* 41: 157–68.

HILDÉN, O. 1960. (Über die Alterverhältnisse von wandernden Kreuzschnäbeln.) *Ornis fenn.* 37: 51–5. (In Finnish, with German summary.)

HILDÉN, O. 1964. Habitat selection in birds. *Ann. Zool. fenn.* 2: 53–75.

HILDÉN, O. 1969. Über Vorkommen und Brutbiologie des Birkenzeisigs (*Carduelis flammea*) in Finnisch-Lappland im Sommer 1968. *Orn. fenn.* 46: 93–112.

HILPRECHT, A. 1964. Ein Punkthaus in Magdeburg, Schlafplatz von 800 Berghänflingen (*Carduelis flavirostris*) im Winter 1963/64. *Beitr. Vogelk., Leipzig*, 10: 177–83.

HINDE, R. A. 1954. The courtship and copulation of the Greenfinch (*Chloris chloris*). *Behaviour* 7: 207–32.

HINDE, R. A. 1955–56. A comparative study of the courtship of certain finches (Fringillidae). *Ibis* 97: 706–45; 98: 1–23.

HINDE, R. A. 1958. Alternative motor patterns in Chaffinch song. *Anim. Behav.* 6: 211–28.

HINDE, R. A. 1959. Behaviour and speciation in birds and lower vertebrates. *Biol. Rev.* 34: 85-128.

HINDE, R. A. 1961. Behaviour. Pp. 373–411 in *Biology and Comparative Physiology of Birds*, ed. A. J. Marshall. Vol. 2: New York & London: Academic Press.

HINDE, R. A. 1967. Aspects of the control of avian reproductive development within the breeding season. *Proc. 14th Int. Orn. Congr.* 1966: 135–54.

HINDE, R. A. & FISHER, J. 1951. Further observations on the opening of milk bottles by birds. *Br. Birds* 44: 393–6.

HODGKIN, C. & HODGKIN, T. E. 1920. The breeding of the Brambling in Scotland. *Scot. Nat.* 98: 181–2.

HOGSTAD, O. 1969. Breeding bird populations in two subalpine habitats in the middle of Norway during the years 1966–68. *Nytt. Mag. Zool.* 17: 81–91.

HOLCOMB, L. C. 1968. Growth of nestling Goldfinches compared to adult size and differential development rate of structures in relation to their function. *Nebraska Bird Rev., Nebraska.* 36: 22-32.

HOLLOM, P. A. D. 1940. Crossbills with brood building second nest in Surrey. *Br. Birds* 34: 86–7.

HOMES, R. C. (ed.) 1964. *Birds of the London area*. London: Rupert Hart-Davis.

HUSS, E. 1967. Kottillgången 1966–67. *Meddn. från skogs Högsk.*

JOHNSON, O. W. 1969. Red Crossbill breeding in Minnesota. *Auk* 86: 352–3.

KALELA, O. 1938. Über die regionale Verbreitung der Brutvogel-fauna im Flussgebiet des Kokemäenjoki. *Ann. Zool. Soc. 'Vánamo'* 5, 9; 1–291.

KALELA, O. 1949. Changes in geographical ranges in the avifauna of northern and central Europe in relation to recent changes in climate. *Bird-banding* 20: 77–103.

KALELA, O. 1952. Changes in the geographical distribution of Finnish birds and mammals in relation to recent changes in climate. *Fennia* 75: 38–51.

KARVIK, N.-G., BROBERG, L., ANDERSSON, S.-O., SWANBERG, P. O. & CURRY-LINDAHL, K. 1953. En invasion av tallbit (*Pinicola enucleator*) vintern 1952–53. *Vår Fågelvärld* 12: 139–40.

KEAR, J. 1962. Food selection in finches with special reference to interspecific differences. *Proc. zool. Soc. Lond.* 138: 163–204.

KEMPER, T. 1959. Notes on the breeding cycle of the Red Crossbill (*Loxia curvirostra*) in Montana. *Auk* 76: 181–9.

KING, J. R. 1967. Adipose tissue composition in experimentally induced fat deposition in the White-crowned Sparrow. *Comp. Biochem. Physiol.* 21: 393–403.

KING, J. R. & FARNER, D. S. 1965. Studies of fat deposition in migratory birds. *Ann. N.Y. Acad. Sci.* 131: 422–40.

KING, J. R. & FARNER, D. S. 1966. The adaptive role of winter fattening in the White-crowned Sparrow with comments on its regulation. *Amer. Nat.* 100: 403–18.

KING, J. R. & WALES, E. E. 1965. Photoperiodic regulation of testicular metamorphosis and fat deposition in three taxa of Rosy Finches. *Physiol. Zoöl.* 38: 49–68.

KIRIKOV, S. W. 1952. (Birds and mammals in the environment of the southern Urals.) *Publ. Acad. Sci. U.S.S.R., Moscow.* (In Russian.)

KLOPFER, P. H. 1963. Behavioural aspects of habitat selection: the role of early experience. *Wilson Bull.* 75: 15–22.

KOCH, H. J. & DE BONT, A. F. 1944. Influence de la mue sur l'intensité du métabolism chez le Pinson *Fringilla coelebs coelebs* L. *Ann. Soc. Roy. Zool. Belg.* 75: 81–6.

KOCH, H. J. & DE BONT, A. F. 1952. Standard metabolic rate, weight changes and food consumption of *Fringilla c. coelebs* L., during sexual maturation. *Ann. Soc. Roy. Zool. Belg.* 82: 1–12.

LACK, D. 1944. Correlation between beak and food in the Crossbill, *Loxia curvirostra* Linnaeus. *Ibis* 86: 552–3.

LACK, D. 1947. *Darwin's Finches*. Cambridge: University Press.

LACK, D. & E. 1952. Visible migration at Land's End. *Br. Birds* 45: 81–96.

LACK, D. & E. 1953. Visible migration through the Pyrenees: an autumn reconnaissance. *Ibis* 95: 271–309.

LACK, D. 1954. *The Natural Regulation of Animal Numbers*. Oxford: University Press.

LACK, D. 1957. The Chaffinch migration in north Devon. *Br. Birds* 50: 10–19.

LACK, D. 1959. Migration across the sea. *Ibis* 101: 374–99.

LACK, D. 1960. The influence of weather on passerine migration. A review. *Auk* 77: 171–209.

LACK, D. 1962. Radar evidence on migratory orientation. *Br. Birds* 55: 139–58.

LACK, D. 1968. *Ecological adaptations for breeding in Birds*. London: Methuen.

LANG, E. M. 1948. Beobachtungen am Zitronenzeisig *Carduelis c. citrinella* (Pallas). *Orn. Beob.* 45: 197–205.

LANGE, G. 1960. Merkwürdiges Verhalten und Vorkommen des Berghänflings (*Carduelis flavirostris*) in Zentrum Berlins. *J. Orn., Lpz.* 101: 390.

LINSDALE, J. M. 1957. Goldfinches on the Hastings Natural History Reservation, *Amer. Midl. Nat.* 57: 1-119.

LLOYD-EVANS, L. & NAU, B. S. 1965. A ringing study of Greenfinch weights. *Ann. Rep. Rye Meads Ringing Group* 3: 23–39.

LOFTS, B. & MARSHALL, A. J. 1960. The experimental regulation of *Zugunruhe* and the sexual cycle in the Brambling *Fringilla montifringilla*. *Ibis* 102: 209–14.

LOFTS, B. & MARSHALL, A. J. 1961. *Zugunruhe* activity in castrated Bramblings *Fringilla montifringilla*. *Ibis* 103a: 189–94.

LOFTS, B. & MURTON, R. K. 1968. Photoperiodic and physiological adaptations regulating avian breeding cycles and their ecological significance. *J. Zool. Lond.* 155: 327–94.

MACDONALD, D. 1968. Notes on the Siskin around Inverness. *Scot. Birds.* 5: 177-78.

MALMBERG, T. 1949. (The Pine Grosbeak, *Pinicola enucleator* (L.), in Skania and reflections on its wanderings.) *Vår Fågelvärld* 8: 121–31. (In Swedish, with English summary.)

MARKGREN, G. 1955. (An irruption of the Pine Grosbeak (*Pinicola enucleator*) in the winter of 1954–55.) *Vår Fågelvärld* 14: 168–77. (In Swedish, with English summary.)

MARKGREN, G. & LUNDBERG, S. 1959. (Irruptions of Pine Grosbeak (*Pinicola enucleator*) and Two-barred Crossbill (*Loxia leucoptera*) in Sweden 1956–57. *Vår Fågelvärld* 18: 185–205. (In Swedish, with English summary.)

MARLER, P. 1952. Variation in the song of the Chaffinch, *Fringilla coelebs*. *Ibis* 94: 458–72.

MARLER, P. 1956a. Behaviour of the Chaffinch *Fringilla coelebs*. *Behaviour*, Suppl. 5: 1–184.

MARLER, P. 1956b. The voice of the Chaffinch and its function as a language. *Ibis* 98: 231–61.

MARLER, P. 1956c. The voice of the Chaffinch. *New Biology* 20: 70–87. Harmondsworth: Penguin Books.

MARSHALL, A. J. 1959. Internal and environmental control of breeding. *Ibis* 101: 456–78.

MATTHEWS, G. V. T. 1968. *Bird Navigation*. (2nd ed.) Cambridge: University Press.

MAYR, E. 1926. Die Ausbreitung des Gerlitz *Serinus canaria serinus* L. Ein Beitrag zur Tiergeographie. *J. Orn., Lpz.* 74: 571–671.

MAYR, E. 1956. Die systematische Stellung der Gattung *Fringilla*. *J. Orn., Lpz.* 97: 258–63.

MCCABE, T. T. & MCCABE, E. 1933. Notes on the anatomy and breeding habits of Crossbills. *Condor* 35: 136–47.

MERIKALLIO, E. 1951. Der Einfluss der letzten Wärmeperiode (1930–49) auf die Vogelfauna Nordfinnlands. *Proc. 10th Int. Orn. Congr.* 1950: 484–93.

MERIKALLIO, E. 1958. Finnish Birds, their distribution and numbers. *Soc. Fauna et Flora Fennica* 5: 1–181.

MICHENER, H. & MICHENER, J. R. 1940. The molt of House Finches of the Pasadena region, California. *Condor* 42: 140–53.

MIDDLETON, A. L. A. 1969. The moult of the European Goldfinch near Melbourne, Victoria. *Emu* 69: 145–54.

MIDDLETON, A. L. A. 1970. Foods and feeding habits of the European Goldfinch near Melbourne. *Emu* 70:12–16.

MILES, P. 1968. (Variabilität des Korpergewichtes des Grünlings (*Chloris chloris* L.) in Jahresverlauf.) *Opera Corcontica* 5: 201–11. (In Czech, with German summary.)

MILLER, A. H. 1941. The buccal food-carrying pouches of the Rosy Finch. *Condor* 43: 72–3.

MOHR, R. 1967. Zum Vorkommen von *Acanthis flammea cabaret* im Rhein-Main-Nahe-Gebiet. *J. Orn., Lpz.* 108: 484–98.

MONK, J. F. 1954. The breeding biology of the Greenfinch. *Bird Study* 1: 2–14.

MOREAU, R. E. 1953. Migration in the Mediterranean area. *Ibis* 95: 329–64.

MOREAU, R. E. & DOLP, R. 1970. Fat, water, weights and wing-lengths of autumn migrants in transit on the northwest coast of Egypt. *Ibis* 112: 209–28.

MOUNTFORT, G. 1956. The territorial behaviour of the Hawfinch *Coccothraustes coccothraustes*. *Ibis* 98: 490–5.

MOUNTFORT, G. 1957. *The Hawfinch*. London: Collins.

MÜHLETHALER, F. 1952. Beobachtungen am Bergfinken – Schlafplatz bei Thun 1950/51. *Orn. Beof.* 49: 173–82.

MURRAY, D. R. W. 1928. The 1927 irruption of the Crossbill. *Br. Birds* 21: 227–8.

MURTON, R. K. 1965. *The Wood-pigeon*. London: Collins.

MURTON, R. K. 1971. *Man and Birds*. London: Collins.

MURTON, R. K., LOFTS, B. & WESTWOOD, N. J. 1970. The circadian basis of photo-periodically controlled spermatogenesis in the Greenfinch *Chloris chloris*. *J. Zool., Lond.* 161: 125–36.

MUSSON, D. F. 1968. Winter Chaffinch roost in Cornwall. *Cornwall Bird-watching and Preservation Society, 38th Ann. Rep*: 78–81.

NEKRASOV, B. W. 1958. (Functional morphological notes on the jaws of some finches.) *Reports of the Kazan Branch of the Academy of Science of the Soviet Union*. Biological Series, No. 6. (In Russian.)

NEWSTEAD, R. 1908. The food of some British Birds. *J. Bd. Agric. Fish.* Suppl. 9: 45–6.

NEWTON, I. 1964a. The breeding biology of the Chaffinch. *Bird Study* 11: 47–68.

NEWTON, I. 1964b. Bud-eating by Bullfinches in relation to the natural food-supply. *J. appl. Ecol.* 1: 265–79.

NEWTON, I. 1964c. The ecology and moult of the Bullfinch. D.Phil. thesis, Oxford University.

NEWTON, I. 1966a. The moult of the Bullfinch *Pyrrhula pyrrhula*. *Ibis* 108: 41–67.

NEWTON, I. 1966b. Fluctuations in the weights of Bullfinches. *Br. Birds* 59: 89–100.

NEWTON, I. 1966c. The Bullfinch problem. *Birds* 1: 74–77.

NEWTON, I. 1967a. Feather growth and moult in some captive finches. *Bird Study* 14: 10–24.

NEWTON, I. 1967b. The adaptive radiation and feeding ecology of some British finches. *Ibis* 109: 33–98.

NEWTON, I. 1967c. Attacks on fruit buds by Redpolls *Carduelis flammea*. *Ibis* 109: 440–1.

NEWTON, I. 1967d. The feeding ecology of the Bullfinch (*Pyrrhula pyrrhula* L.) in southern England. *J. Anim. Ecol.* 36: 721–44.

NEWTON, I. 1967e. The Bullfinch problem. *Oxford Research* 1: 13–16.

NEWTON, I. 1968a. The moulting seasons of some finches and buntings. *Bird Study* 15: 84–92.

NEWTON, I. 1968b. Bullfinches and fruit buds. Pp. 199–209 in 'The Problems of Birds as Pests'. *Inst. Biol. Symp.* No. 17, ed. R. K. Murton and E. N. Wright. London: Academic Press.

NEWTON, I. 1968c. The temperatures, weights and body composition of molting Bullfinches. *Condor* 70: 323–32.

NEWTON, I. 1969a. Winter fattening in the Bullfinch. *Physiol. Zoöl.* 42: 96–107.

NEWTON, I. 1969b. Moults and weights of captive Redpolls. *J. Orn., Lpz.* 110: 53–61.

NEWTON, I. 1970a. Crossbill irruptions. *Birds* 3: 32–5.

NEWTON, I. 1970b. Irruptions of Crossbills in Europe. Pp. 337–57 in *Animal Populations in relation to their Food Resources*, ed. A. Watson. Oxford: Blackwells Scientific Publications.

NEWTON, I. & EVANS, P. R. 1966. Weights of birds in winter. *Bird Study* 13: 96–8.

NICKELL, W. P. 1951. Studies of habitats, territory, and nests of the Eastern Goldfinch. *Auk* 68: 447–70.

NICOLAI, J. 1956. Zur Biologie und Ethologie des Gimpels (*Pyrrhula pyrrhula* L.). *Z. Tierpsychol.* 13: 93–132.

NICOLAI, J. 1957. Die systematische Stellung des Zitronenzeisigs ('*Carduelis' citrinella*). *J. Orn., Lpz.* 98: 363–71.

NIETHAMMER, G. 1966. Über die Kehltaschen des Rotflügelgimpels, *Rhopdoechys sanguinea*. *J. Orn., Lpz.* 107: 278–82.

OAKES, C. 1952. *The Birds of Lancashire*. London & Edinburgh: Oliver & Boyd.

OLSSON, V. 1960. (Observations at a nest of the Parrot Crossbill (*Loxia pytyopsittacus*).) *Vår Fågelvärld* 19: 1–19. (In Swedish, with English summary.)

OLSSON, V. 1964. Studies of less familiar birds. 126. Parrot Crossbill. *Br. Birds* 57: 118–23.

PALMGREN, P. 1930. Quantitative Untersuchungen über die Vogelfauna in den Wäldern Südfinnlands. *Acta Zool. Fenn.* 7: 1–219.

PARSLOW, J. L. F. 1968. Changes in status among breeding birds in Britain and Ireland. *Br. Birds* 61: 51–9.

PEIPONEN, V. 1957. Wechselt der Birkenzeisig, *Carduelis flammea* (L.), sein Brutgebiet während des Sommers? *Ornis fenn.* 34: 41–64.

PEIPONEN, V. A. 1962. Über Brutbiologie Nahrung und geographische Verbreitung des Birkenzeisigs (*Carduelis flammea*). *Ornis fenn.* 39: 37–60.

PEIPONEN, V. A. 1967. Südliche Fortpflanzung und Zug von *Carduelis flammea* (L.) in Jahre 1965. *Ann. Zool. fenn.* 4: 547–59.

PERDECK, A. C. 1961. Jaarverslag van het Vogeltrekstation over 1960. *Limosa* 34: 169–85.

PERRINS, C. M. 1966. The effect of beech crops on Great Tit populations and movements. *Br. Birds* 59: 419–32.

PETTERSSON, M. L. R. 1956. Diffusion of a new habit among Greenfinches. *Nature, Lond.* 77: 709–10.

PETTERSSON, M. 1961. The nature and spread of Daphne-eating in the Green-finch and the spread of some other habits. *Anim. Behav.* 9: 114.

POLUNIN, N. 1960. *Introduction to Plant Geography and some Related Sciences.* London: Longmans.

POULSEN, H. 1951. Inheritance and learning in the song of the Chaffinch. *Behaviour* 3: 216–27.

PRESTON, F. W. 1966. The mathematical representation of migration. *Ecology* 47: 375–92.

PROMPTOFF, A. 1930. Die geographische Variabilität des Buchfinkenschlags (*Fringilla coelebs* L.) in Zusammenhang mit etlichen allgameinen Fragen der Saisonvögelzuge. *Biol. Zbl.* 50: 478–503.

PTUSENKO, E. C. & INOZEMTZEV, A. A. 1968. (*The biology and rural economy of birds of the Moscow district and neighbouring territories.*) Moscow. (In Russian.)

REINIKAINEN, A. 1937. The irregular migrations of the Crossbill, *Loxia c. curvirostra*, and their relation to the cone-crop of the conifers. *Ornis fenn.* 14: 55–64.

REINIKAINEN, A. 1939. (Zur Brutbiologie des Karmingimpels *Carpodacus e. erythrinus* (Pallas).) *Ornis fenn.* 16: 73–95. (In Finnish, with German summary.)

RETZ, M. 1966. Ringfunde des Hänflings (*Carduelis cannabina*). *Auspicium* 2: 231–47.

RETZ, M. 1968. Ringfunde des Hänflings (*Carduelis cannabina*). *Auspicium* 2: 412–46.

RICHTERS, W. 1952. Sammebericht über Bergfinken – Beobachtungen (*Fringilla montifringilla*) in Deutschland 1946–51. *Orn. Mitt.* 4: 193–9.

RISBERG, E. L. 1970. (Immigration of the Scarlet Grosbeak *Carpodacus erythrinus* into Sweden and studies of its breeding biology.) *Vår Fågelvärld* 29: 77–89.

ROBERTSON, A. W. P. 1954. *Bird Pageant.* London: Batchworth Press.

ROSS, W. M. 1948. Notes on the Crossbill. *Scott. Nat.* 60: 147–56.

ROWAN, W. 1926. On photoperiodism, reproductive periodicity, and the annual migrations of birds and certain fishes. *Proc. Bost. Soc. Nat. Hist.* 38: 147–89.

ROWAN, W. 1929. Experiments in bird migration. I. Manipulation of the reproductive cycle: seasonal histological changes in the gonads. *Proc. Bost. Soc. Nat. Hist.* 29: 151–208.

ROWAN, W. 1932. Experiments in bird migration. III. The effects of artificial light, castration and certain extracts on the autumn movements of the American Crow (*Corvus brachyrhynchos*). *Proc. Nat. Acad. Sci.* 18: 639–54.

RUTTLEDGE, W. 1965. Goldfinch roost in Inner London. *Br. Birds* 58: 442–3.

SALOMONSEN, F. 1928. Bemerkungen über die Verbreitung der *Carduelis linaria* Gruppe und Ihre Variationen Vidensk. *Medd. fra Dansk Naturhist. Forens. Copenhagen* 86: 123–202.

SALOMONSEN, F. 1951. *The Birds of Greenland.* Part 3. Copenhagen.

SAXBY, H. L. 1874. *The Birds of Shetland.* London: Simpkin, Marshall & Co.

SCHIFFERLI, A. 1953. Der Bergfinken – Masseneinfall (*Fringilla montifringilla*) 1950/51 in der Schweiz. *Orn. Beol.* 50: 65–89. (In German.)

SHOEMAKER, H. H. 1939. Social hierarchy in flocks of the Canary. *Auk* 56: 381–406.

SICH, H. 1939. Ueber die Dialektbildung beim 'Regenruf' des Buchfinken. *J. Orn., Lpz.* 87: 568–92.

SIMS, R. W. 1955. The morphology of the head of the Hawfinch. *Bull. Br. Mus. nat. Hist.* 2: 369–93.

SKEAD, C. J. 1960. *The Canaries, Seedeaters and Buntings of Southern Africa.* Johannesburg: Central News Agency.

SNOW, D. W. 1953. Two pairs of Bullfinches nesting together in the same bush. *Br. Birds* 46: 379–80.

SNOW, D. W. 1967. A guide to moult in British Birds. *British Trust for Ornithology Field Guide no. 11.*

SNYDER, D. P. & CASSEL, J. F. 1951. A late summer nest of the Red Crossbill in Colorado. *Wilson Bull.* 63: 177–80.

SOKOLOWSKI, J. 1958. *Birds of Poland,* Vol. 1. Warsaw. (In Polish.)

SOKOLOWSKI, J. 1962. (Studies on the individual variation and biology of the Goldfinch *Carduelis carduelis* (L.) in Poland.) *Acta orn. Warsz.* 7: 33–67. (In Polish, with English summary.)

SOKOLOWSKI, J. 1969. (*The Chaffinch.*) Warsaw. (In Polish.)

STEINFATT, O. 1938. Das Brutleben des Weidenlaubsanger. *Ber. Schles. Ornith. Ver.* 23: 20.

STENHOUSE, D. 1960. The Redpoll in New Zealand. *Agric. Bull.* 366. Canterbury Chamber of Commerce.

STENHOUSE, D. 1962. A new habit of the Redpoll *Carduelis flammea* in New Zealand. *Ibis* 104: 250-2.

STOKES, A. W. 1950. Breeding behaviour of the Goldfinch. *Wilson Bull.* 62: 107–27.

STRESEMANN, E. & STRESEMANN, V. 1966. Die Mauser der Vögel. *J. Orn., Lpz.* 107. Suppl.

SULKAVA, S. 1969. On small birds spending the night in the snow. *Aquilo* 7: 33–7.

SUORMALA, 1938. Zur Brutbiologie von *Loxia c. curvirostra* L. *Orn. fenn.* 15: 16-20.

SUTTER, E. 1948. Der Bergfinken – Masseneinfall im Winter 1946/47 in der Schweiz und in Südwestdeutschland. *Orn. Beob.* 45: 98–106.

SVÄRDSON, G. 1953. Visible migration within Fenno-Scandia. *Ibis* 95: 181–211.

SVÄRDSON, G. 1955. Crossbills in Sweden in 1953. *Br. Birds* 48: 425–8.

SVÄRDSON, G. 1957. The 'invasion' type of bird migration. *Br. Birds* 50: 314–43.

SWANBERG, P. O. 1936. *Fjällfåglarnas paradis.* Stockholm.

SWENK, M. H. 1929. The Pine Siskin in Nebraska: its seasonal abundance and nesting. *Wilson Bull.* 41: 77–92.

TANSLEY, A. G. 1949. *Britain's Green Mantle.* London: Allen & Unwin Ltd.

TAST, J. 1968. Changes in the distribution, habitat requirements and nest-sites of the Linnet, *Carduelis cannabina* (L.), in Finland. *Ann. Zool. fenn.* 5: 159–78.

TAST, J. 1970. Group nesting and the breeding season of the Linnet *Carduelis cannabina* in Finland. *Ornis fenn.* 47: 74–82.

TAYLOR, R. J. F. 1954. Notes on the Birds of Finmark. *Sterna* 10: 3–36.

TERNOVSKIJ, D. V. 1954. (The winter breeding of crossbills.) *Bjullet. M. O-va Isp. Prirody, Otd. Biol.* 59: 37–40. (In Russian, English abstract in *Ibis* 97: 596.)

THOMPSON, W. C. 1960. Agonistic behavior in the House Finch. Part I: Annual cycle and display patterns. *Condor* 62: 245–71.

THORPE, W. H. 1956. *Learning and Instinct in Animals.* London: Methuen.

THORPE, W. H. 1958. The learning of song pattern by birds, with especial reference to the song of the Chaffinch, *Fringilla coelebs. Ibis* 100: 535–70.

THORPE, W. H. 1961. *Bird-song*. Cambridge: University Press.

TICEHURST, C. B. 1915. On the plumages of the male Crossbill (*Loxia curvirostra*). *Ibis* 10(3): 662–9.

TOMIALOJC, L. 1967. (The Twite, *Carduelis flavirostris* (L.) in Poland and adjacent territories.) *Acta orn., Warsz.* 10: 109–56. (In Polish, with English summary.)

TORDOFF, H. B. 1952. Notes on plumages, molts, and age variation of the Red Crossbill. *Condor* 54: 200–3.

TORDOFF, H. B. 1954. Social organisation and behaviour in a flock of captive, nonbreeding Red Crossbills. *Condor* 56: 346–58.

TORDOFF, H. B. & DAWSON, W. R. 1965. The influence of daylength on reproductive timing in the Red Crossbill. *Condor* 67: 416–22.

UDVARDY, M. D. F. 1956. Observations on the habitat and territory of the Chaffinch, *Fringilla c. coelebs* L., in Swedish Lapland. *Ark. Zool. Ser.* 2, 9: 499–505.

ULFSTRAND, S. 1963. Ecological aspects of irruptive bird migration in north-western Europe. *Proc. 13th Int. Orn. Congr.* 1962: 780–94.

VAN DOBBEN, W. H. 1953. Bird migration in the Netherlands. *Ibis* 95: 212–34.

VAUK, G. 1964. Invasionen von Kreuzschnäbeln (*Loxia*) und Buntspechten (*Dendrocopus major*). *Vogelwelt* 84: 113–20.

VAURIE, C. 1959. *The Birds of the Palaearctic Fauna*, Vol. 1. London: Witherby.

VERHEYEN, R. 1955a. Les Linottes, *Carduelis cannabina* (L.), nicheurs et visiteurs d'hiver en Belgique. *Gerfaut* 45: 5–25.

VERHEYEN, R. 1955b. Over de trek van de Groenvink, *Chloris chloris* (L.) in en door België. *Gerfaut* 45: 173–84. (In Flemish, with French summary.)

VERHEYEN, R. 1960. La migration du Pinson Chanteur, *Fringilla coelebs* L., en Belgique. *Gerfaut* 50: 101–53.

VINCE, M. A. 1958. 'String-pulling' in birds. (2) Differences related to age in Greenfinches, Chaffinches and Canaries. *J. Anim. Behav.* 6: 53–9.

VOITKEVICH, A. A. 1966. *The feathers and plumage of birds*. London: Sidgwick & Jackson.

VÖLKER, O. 1957. Die experimentalle Rotfärbung des Gefieders beim Fichten-kreuzschnabel (*Loxia curvirostra*). *J. Orn., Lpz.* 98: 210–14.

VOOUS, K. H. 1951. Geographical variation of the Greenfinch, *Chloris chloris*. *Limosa* 24: 81–91.

VOOUS, K. H. 1960. *Atlas of European Birds*. London & Amsterdam: Nelson.

VOROBLEV, K. A. 1955. (Winter breeding of the Crossbill.) *Priroda* 6: 107–8. (In Russian.)

WALKINSHAW, L. H. 1938, 1939. Life-history studies of the eastern Goldfinch. Parts *1 & 2*. *Jack-pine Warbler* 16: 3–11 & 14–15; 17: 3–12.

WALLIN, L. 1966. (Some observations on the behaviour of the Hawfinch (*Coccothraustes coccothraustes*) during the early part of the breeding season.) *Vår Fågelvärld* 25: 327–45. (In Swedish, with English summary.)

WARD, P. 1965. Feeding ecology of the Black-faced Dioch *Quelea Quelea* in Nigeria. *Ibis* 107: 173–214.

WATSON, A. 1957. Birds in Cumberland Peninsula, Baffin Island. *Can. Fld. Nat.* 71: 87–109.

WEAVER, R. L. & WEST, F. H. 1943. Notes on the breeding of the Pine Siskin. *Auk.* 60: 492–504.

WEBER, H. 1953. Bewirkung des Farbwechsels bei männlichen Kreuzschäbeln. *J. Orn., Lpz.* 94: 342–46.

WEISE, C. M. 1967. Castration and spring migration in the White-throated Sparrow. *Condor* 69: 49–68.

WEST, G. C. & MENG, M. S. 1968. The effect of diet and captivity on the fatty acid composition of Redpoll (*Acanthis flammea*) depot fats. *Comp. Biochem. Physiol.* 25: 535–40.

WHISTLER, H. 1941. *Popular Handbook of Indian Birds.* 3rd ed. London & Edinburgh: Gurney & Jackson.

WHITE, C. M. 1966. The annual lipid cycle and feeding behavior in Redpolls, *Acanthis* spp. Unpublished Master's thesis, University of Alaska.

WILLIAMS, G. R. 1953. The dispersal from New Zealand and Australia of some introduced European passerines. *Ibis* 95: 676–92.

WILLIAMSON, K. 1963. Movements as an indicator of population changes. *Bird Migrat.* 2: 207-23.

WILLIAMSON, K. 1965. *Fair Isle and its Birds.* Edinburgh: Oliver & Boyd.

WILLIAMSON, K. & SPENCER, R. 1960. Ringing recoveries and the interpretation of bird-movements. *Bird Migrat.* 1: 176–81.

WITHERBY, H. F., JOURDAIN, F. C. R., TUCKER, B. W. & TICEHURST, N. F. 1938. *The Handbook of British Birds.* Vol. 1. London:Witherby.

WITT-STRÖMER, B., INGRITZ, G. & MAGNUSSON, L. 1956. Tidiga och sydliga häckningar av gråsiska (*Carduelis flammea*) våren 1955. *Vår Fågelvärld* 15: 56–8.

WRIGHT, E. N. & SUMMERS, D. D. B. 1960. The biology and economic importance of the Bullfinch. *Ann. appl. Biol.* 48: 415–18.

WYNNE-EDWARDS, V. C. 1952. Zoology of the Baird Expedition (1950). 1. The birds observed in central and south-east Baffin Island. *Auk* 69: 353–91.

WYNNE-EDWARDS, V. C. 1962. *Animal Dispersion in relation to Social Behaviour.* Edinburgh: Oliver & Boyd.

YARRELL, W. 1876–82. *A History of British Birds.* Vol. 2. (Revised ed. by A. Newton.) London: van Voorst.

ZISWILER, V. 1965. Zur Kenntnis des Samenöffnens und der Struktur des hörneren Gaumens bei kornerfressenden Oscines. *J. Orn., Lpz.* 106: 1–48.

AUTHOR INDEX

GENERAL INDEX